Modern Trigonometry

Modern Trigonometry

Timothy D. Cavanagh

Colorado State College

Wadsworth Publishing Company, Inc.
Belmont, California

Preface

Trigonometry, once an almost exclusive science for navigators and surveyors, has expanded into virtually all fields of science and engineering. As its uses have become less specific, trigonometry has increasingly become an analytic subject. Therefore, Modern Trigonometry, as its name implies, gives primary consideration to the analytic aspects of the field, although the computational aspects are not overlooked.

This book is a concise coverage of the subject designed for students who have studied college algebra or its equivalent. It will fit nicely into a one-semester course meeting three times a week, or a quarter course that meets daily. To cover the book in a shorter time would necessitate the omission of some topics. A teacher's manual that includes solutions for all exercises also gives suggestions for pacing courses of different lengths.

The function concept is emphasized through the text. Periodic functions are discussed in Chapter 0, and trigonometric functions are introduced in Chapter 1. The concept of trigonometric functions of real numbers is discussed in terms of "wrapping" the real number line around the unit circle. Inverse trigonometric functions are the subject of Chapter 4. Chapter 5, on the solutions of triangles, also relates the definitions of the trigonometric functions of real numbers to the ratios of different sides of a right triangle.

Chapter 6 explores complex numbers through De Moivre's theorem. The rectangular and polar forms for the representation of a complex number are compared.

Color is used throughout to stress basic concepts introduced in the text and to focus attention on parts of graphs being emphasized.

Chapter 0, as its number implies, will be review material for many students and, as such, may be covered very quickly in some classes. However, all classes should cover the last two sections, which discuss the idea of periodic functions.

The answer section for Chapter 2 contains proofs of some of the identities in the exercises. There are many carefully worked identities included as examples in the chapter. The emphasis in Chapter 3 is on the general solution of trigonometric equations, but in a way that principal solutions could be emphasized readily by the teacher who prefers to do so.

An abundance of exercises is provided in each chapter—more than could be assigned to one class—to give teachers the opportunity to vary assignments from class to class. Each chapter ends with a set of exercises for review.

I am indebted to Professors Rex Schweers and Forest Fisch of Colorado State College for their help in class testing the material in this book and the helpful suggestions that resulted from the testing. Thanks also go to James L. Jackson, College of San Mateo, and Raymond C. Strauss, De Anza College, who reviewed the manuscript, and Joseph Teeters, a graduate student at Colorado State College who helped prepare the selected answers. Finally, I thank Berniece Zimmerman and Susan Phelps for the many long hours they spent in typing the manuscript.

Contents

0

Sets, relations, and functions

0.1   Introduction

The science of trigonometry was originally concerned with computing the unknown sides and angles of triangles. As such, trigonometry was an important subject in colleges and universities during the early days of our country, for many students later applied their mathematics to surveying and navigation. So, even then, trigonometry, unlike some mathematical studies, had very practical applications. As science and mathematics have developed, trigonometric concepts have been broadened, and trigonometry now is usually treated from an analytic viewpoint. Trigonometric analysis today is an important tool in most branches of science and engineering. Therefore, this book gives primary consideration to the analytic aspects of the subject, but the computational aspects are also considered.

0.2   Sets

One of the unifying ideas in mathematics is the idea of **set.** Basically, we think of a set as being **a collection of objects.** We shall assume that there is some way to tell whether a particular object is in the set under consideration. The objects in sets are called **elements.**

Here, lowercase letters, such as a, b, and x, and other symbols, will represent the elements in sets. Uppercase letters, such as A, C, and Q, will represent sets. The symbol $\in$, derived from the Greek letter ϵ, is used to indicate that a particular element is in a set. Thus $x \in A$ means that the element x is in the set A; and $x \in A$ may be read as *x is in A* or *x belongs to A.* If the set A consists of several elements, such as a, $*$, and 6, we can indicate it by $a \in A$, $* \in A$, $6 \in A$. Since this could become quite cumbersome, we use braces to indicate the same idea and write $A = \{a, *, 6\}$ which states that A consists of a, $*$, and 6.

It is important to consider the relationships between sets. One of these is that of one set being a **subset** of another set.

*A set A is a **subset** of a set B if and only if every element in the set A is also in the set B. This is designated by $A \subseteq B$, and is read "A is a subset of B."*

There is a special kind of subset called a **proper subset.**

*A is a **proper subset** of B if and only if $A \subseteq B$ and there exists at least one element in B which is not in A. This is designated by $A \subset B$*

Thus, every subset of B except B itself is a proper subset of B.

A diagonal slash, $/$, drawn through certain symbols expressing relationships, is used to indicate that these relationships do not hold. Thus, $A \not\subseteq B$ is read *A is not a subset of B*, and $x \notin A$ is read *x does not belong to A.*

$$\{\star, 0\} \subset \{\star, 0, \square\} \qquad \{\star, 0\} = \{0, \star\}$$
$$\{\star, 0, \square\} \not\subseteq \{\star, 0\} \qquad \{\star, 0, \square\} \subseteq \{0, \square, \star\}$$
$$0 \in \{\star, 0\} \qquad \square \notin \{\star, 0\} \qquad 0 \neq \{0\}$$

Figure 0.1

The idea of **equality**, important in all of mathematics, also expresses an important relationship between sets. *Two sets, A and B, could be said to be equal if and only if they consist of exactly the same elements.* This would be a satisfactory definition of equality of sets, and it is a definition which is often used. However, we shall use a different definition of equality of sets, although it will carry the same meaning.

*Two sets A and B are **equal** if and only if $A \subseteq B$ and $B \subseteq A$. Equality is designated by $A = B$.*

We will observe that $\{*, \circ\} = \{\circ, *\}$. We also use $A \neq B$ to indicate that *A is not equal to B.* Thus, $\{*, \circ\} \neq \{*, \square, \circ\}$, since $\{*, \square, \circ\} \not\subseteq \{*, \circ\}$. Examples of the symbols used to express relationships between sets are shown in Figure 0.1.

A very special set in mathematics is called the **empty set.**

*The **empty set** is the set which does not contain any elements. It is designated by ∅, which is read "the empty set" or "the null set."*

The empty set is considered to be a subset of every set and a proper subset of every set except itself.

Sometimes we refer to a relationship between two sets by saying that the two sets are in **one-to-one correspondence.** Intuitively, this means that the two sets have exactly the same number of elements. This idea is only appropriate for finite sets, so we define one-to-one correspondence in a different way.

*Two sets are in **one-to-one correspondence** if and only if the elements of the two sets can be matched so that each element of one set corresponds to exactly one element in the other set.*

We can demonstrate that two sets are in one-to-one correspondence by showing how the elements of the two sets are matched. This is illustrated in Figure 0.2 with the sets $A = \{*, \circ, \triangle, \square\}$ and $B = \{a, e, i, u\}$. Two different ways of matching the elements in sets A and B are shown in the Figure. One such matching would be sufficient to demonstrate a one-to-one correspondence between the two sets. You can probably illustrate several other similar matchings between the two sets.

Figure 0.2

Another useful way of discussing sets is illustrated by $\{x \mid x$ **is a whole number between 2 and 6**$\}$, which is read *the set of all x such that x is a whole number between 2 and 6*. This collection of symbols, called **set-builder notation,** is used extensively in this book. It names a variable (x in this case) and states a condition which the variable must satisfy (in this case, x is a whole number between 2 and 6) in order to belong to the particular set under consideration. We note that

$$\{x \mid x \text{ is a whole number between 2 and 6}\} = \{3, 4, 5\}.$$

Another example of the set-builder notation is

$$\{1, 3, 5, 7\} = \{y \mid y \text{ is one of the first four odd natural numbers}\}.$$

The set-builder notation is particularly useful when one is dealing with large finite sets or with infinite sets.

Exercises 0.1

1. Let $A = \{1, 2\}$.

    a. List all the subsets of A that contain 0 elements.
    b. List all the subsets of A that contain 1 element.
    c. List all the subsets of A that contain 2 elements.
    d. How many subsets does A have?
    e. List all the proper subsets of A.

2. Let $B = \{\#, \$, \circ\}$.

    a. List all the subsets of B that contain 0 elements.
    b. List all the subsets of B that contain 1 element.
    c. List all the subsets of B that contain 2 elements.
    d. List all the subsets of B that contain 3 elements.
    e. How many subsets does B have?
    f. List all the proper subsets of B.

3. Let $C = \{4, 5, 6, 7\}$.

    a. List all the subsets of C that contain 0 elements.
    b. List all the subsets of C that contain 1 element.
    c. List all the subsets of C that contain 2 elements.
    d. List all the subsets of C that contain 3 elements.
    e. List all the subsets of C that contain 4 elements.
    f. How many subsets does C have?
    g. List all the proper subsets of C.

4. Some of the information in the table below comes from Exercises 1–3. Fill in the rest of the table, if you can.

number of elements in set	0	1	2	3	4	5	6	n
number of subsets			4	8	16			

5. Consider the following sets: $A = \{1, 2, 3\}$, $B = \{1, 3\}$, $C = \{1, 2, 4\}$, $\emptyset$.

    a. Indicate, with the appropriate symbols, all the subset relationships among the four sets.
    b. Indicate, with the appropriate symbols, all the proper subset relationships among the four sets.
    c. Indicate, with the appropriate symbols, all cases in which one set is *not* a subset of another set.

In Exercises 6–9, indicate, with the appropriate symbols, whether or not the two given sets are equal.

6. $A = \{5\}$, $B = \{9\}$.
7. $A = \{5, 7, 11\}$, $B = \{11, 7, 5\}$.
8. $A = \{4, 5, 6, 7\}$, $B = \{x \mid x$ is a natural number between 3 and 8$\}$.
9. $A = \{0\}$, $\emptyset$.

Indicate whether a one-to-one correspondence exists between the two given sets.

10. $A = \{5\}$, $B = \{9\}$.
11. $A = \{2, 3, 4\}$, $B = \{2, 4\}$.
12. $A = \{1, 3, 15\}$, $B = \{x \mid x$ is an odd natural number less than 6$\}$.
13. $A = \{1, 2, 3\}$, $B = \emptyset$.

In Problems 14–17, replace the comma between set symbols with either $\in$ or $\notin$ so as to form a true statement.

14. $\emptyset$, $\{1, 2, 3\}$
15. $\{7\}$, $\{4, 5, 6, 7\}$
16. 6, $\{6, 7, 8\}$
17. 5, $\{x \mid x$ is an odd natural number$\}$

Designate each of the sets by using braces and listing the members.

Example

$\{x \mid x$ is a natural number between 3 and 7$\}$

Solution

$\{4, 5, 6\}$

18. $\{x \mid x$ is a day in the week$\}$
19. $\{x \mid x$ is a natural number between 15 and 21$\}$
20. $\{z \mid z$ is a digit in your home address$\}$
21. $\{y \mid y$ is a month in the year$\}$
22. $\{t \mid t$ is a digit in your age in years$\}$
23. $\{w \mid w$ is a natural number less than 7$\}$

Designate each set by using the set-builder notation.

Example

$\{1, 2, 3\}$

Solution

$\{x \mid x$ is one of the first three natural numbers$\}$

24. $\{2, 4, 6, 8\}$
25. $\{5, 6, 7, 8, 9, 10\}$

26. $\{2, 4, 8, 16\}$
27. {April, June, September, November}

0.3 Operations on sets

There are several operations on sets which are used frequently. One of these is the **union** of two sets.

> The **union** of sets A and B is the set of all the elements which are in set A, in set B, or in both sets A and B. This is designated by $A \cup B$ and is read "the union of A and B" or sometimes "A cup B."

Thus, if $A = \{1, 3\}$, $B = \{3, *, \circ\}$, and $C = \{g, h\}$, then $A \cup B = \{1, 3, *, \circ\}$ and $A \cup C = \{1, 3, g, h\}$. If A is any set, $A \cup A = A$ and $A \cup \emptyset = A$. Why? A second important set operation is the **intersection** of two sets.

> The **intersection** of sets A and B is the set of all the elements which are in both set A and set B. This is designated by $A \cap B$ and is read "the intersection of A and B" or, sometimes, "A cap B."

Thus, if $A = \{1, 3\}$, $B = \{3, *, \circ\}$, and $C = \{g, h\}$, then $A \cap B = \{3\}$ and $A \cap C = \emptyset$. If A is any set, $A \cap \emptyset = \emptyset$ and $A \cap A = A$. Why?

> Two nonempty sets A and B are said to be **disjoint** if and only if $A \cap B = \emptyset$.

Thus, in the above example, A and C are disjoint sets and B and C are disjoint sets, but A and B are not disjoint sets.

In many cases we consider only subsets of some particular set. This particular set under consideration is called **the universal set** or, sometimes, **the universe.** The universal set is usually designated by U. Let A be any subset of a universal set U. There is another subset of U which is closely related to A. This set is called the **complement of A.**

> If A is a subset of U, the set of all the elements in U which are not in A is called **the complement of A.** The complement of A is designated by A'.

For example, if $U = \{1, 2, 3, 4, 5\}$, $A = \{1, 5\}$, and $B = \{3\}$, then $A' = \{2, 3, 4\}$ and $B' = \{1, 2, 4, 5\}$.

Closely related to the complement of a set A is the idea of the **difference** of two sets.

> For any two sets A and B, the **difference** of A and B is the set of all the elements which are in A and not in B. This is designated by $A - B$.

If $C = \{a, e, o\}$, $D = \{o, u\}$ and $E = \{a, e\}$, then $C - D = \{a, e\}$, $D - C$ $= \{u\}$, and $D - E = \{o, u\}$. Note that it is not necessary for B to be a subset of A to discuss the difference of A and B. If A and B are subsets of a universal set U, then $A - B = A \cap B'$. *Why?*

Exercises 0.2

Let $U = \{1, 2, 3, 4, 5, 6, 7, 8\}$, $A = \{1, 3, 5, 7\}$, $B = \{2, 4, 6\}$, $C = \{1, 2, 4, 8\}$, and $D = \{1, 2, 3\}$. Perform the following set operations.

1. A'	2. B'	3. C'
4. D'	5. $A \cup B$	6. $A \cap B$
7. $A - B$	8. $(A \cup B)'$	9. $(A \cap B)'$
10. $A' \cup B'$	11. $A' \cap B'$	12. $A \cap B'$
13. $A \cap C$	14. $A - C$	15. $C - A$
16. $C \cap B$	17. $C - B$	18. $A - D$
19. $C - U$	20. $D - U$	21. $B - U$
22. $A \cup B'$	23. $C' \cap D'$	24. $D - C$
25. $A' - C'$	26. $C \cap A'$	27. $(D')'$
28. $(B')'$	29. $(A \cap B) \cup C$	30. $(D' - B) \cap C$
31. $(A \cup C) \cap (B \cup C)$	32. $A - (B \cup C)'$	33. $(B \cup C) \cap D$
34. $(B \cap D) \cup (C \cap D)$	35. $(A - B)' \cup D'$	36. $(A \cup B) \cap C$

For problems 37–42, let A, B, and C be any sets.

37. Is $A \cup B = B \cup A$? Why?
38. Is $A \cap B = B \cap A$? Why?
39. Is $A - B = B - A$? Why?
40. Can $A - B = B - A$? Why?
41. Is $(A \cup B) \cup C = A \cup (B \cup C)$? Why?
42. Is $(A \cap B) \cap C = A \cap (B \cap C)$? Why?

0.4   Our number system

You are familiar with real numbers from studying arithmetic and algebra. Some real numbers are called **natural numbers.** Other subsets of the real numbers are called **integers, rational numbers,** and **irrational numbers.** In this section we shall briefly consider some of the different sets of numbers involved in the development of the real-number system.

1.   The **set of natural numbers,** denoted by N, whose elements are the familiar "counting" numbers.

$$N = \{1, 2, 3, \dots\}.$$

2.   The **set of whole numbers,** denoted by W, which consists of the set of natural numbers and 0.

$$W = \{0\} \cup N = \{0, 1, 2, 3, \dots\}.$$

3.   The **set of integers,** denoted by J, whose elements are the natural numbers, their additive inverses, and 0.

$$J = \{\dots, -3, -2, -1, 0, 1, 2, 3, \dots\}.$$

4.   The **set of rational numbers,** denoted by Q, which consists of all those numbers that can be represented as the quotient of two integers where the divisor is not 0. Among the elements of Q are such numbers as $-\frac{2}{3}, \frac{18}{24}, \frac{7}{3}, -\frac{5}{1}$, and $\frac{0}{5}$. Thus,

$$Q = \left\{ x \mid x = \frac{a}{b}, a \in J, b \in J, b \neq 0 \right\}.$$

It can be proved, although we shall not do so here, that all rational numbers can be expressed as **terminating decimals** or as **repeating decimals.** Examples of these are $1/4 = .25$, a terminating decimal, and $1/11 = .09090\overline{9}$, a repeating decimal. Conversely, every number that is a terminating decimal or a repeating decimal is a rational number.

5.   The **set of irrational numbers,** denoted by H, which consists of all numbers with decimal expansions which are nonrepeating and nonterminating. Among the elements of this set are such numbers as $\sqrt{2}, -\sqrt{3}$, and π.

$$H = \{x \mid x \text{ is an irrational number}\}.$$

6.   The **set of real numbers,** denoted by R, which is the union of the set of rational numbers and the set of irrational numbers.

$$R = Q \cup H.$$

7.   The **set of complex numbers,** denoted by C, which consists of all numbers that can be represented in the form $x + yi$, where x and y are real numbers and $i = \sqrt{-1}$. Thus,

$$C = \{z \mid z = x + yi, x \in R, y \in R, i = \sqrt{-1}\}.$$

Complex numbers with $x = 0$, which may be represented in the form yi, are called **pure imaginary numbers.**

In a course in modern algebra or the structure of numbers, distinctions would be made among the sets of numbers that have not been made here. This is intended only as a quick review of material with which you should be familiar, not as a thorough development of our number system.

A **real-number line** can be drawn as follows. Draw any line and pick

two points on the line. Call the point on the left 0 and the point on the right 1.
The natural numbers can be assigned to the points *at unit intervals past one*,
and their additive inverses can be assigned to points *at unit intervals to the
left of* 0. It is easy to determine the point half-way between 0 and 1 and call that
point 1/2. In a similar fashion the other rational and irrational numbers can be
assigned to points on the line. It can be proved that there is a one-to-one correspondence between the set of points on the line and the set of real numbers,
but we shall not do so here.

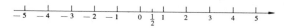

Figure 0.3

Exercises 0.3

Express the following fractions as decimals.

1. $\dfrac{1}{5}$　　　　2. $\dfrac{3}{4}$　　　　3. $\dfrac{2}{3}$　　　　4. $\dfrac{5}{6}$　　　　5. $\dfrac{3}{11}$

6. $\dfrac{4}{15}$　　　　7. $\dfrac{5}{7}$　　　　8. $\dfrac{7}{8}$　　　　9. $\dfrac{29}{11}$　　　　10. $\dfrac{13}{6}$

In Exercises 11–22, express the decimals as fractions. Reduce to lowest terms.

Examples

a.　.375　　　　　　b.　.23$\overline{23}$　　　　　　c.　2.354$\overline{354}$

Solutions

a.　$.375 = \dfrac{375}{1000}$

$= \dfrac{3(125)}{8(125)}$

$= \dfrac{3}{8}.$

b.　Let $x = .23\overline{23}$.

$100x = 23.23\overline{23},$

$100x - x = 23.00\overline{00},$

$99x = 23,$

$x = \dfrac{23}{99}.$

c.　Let $x = 2.354\overline{354}$.

then $1000x = 2354.354\overline{354},$

$1000x - x = 2352,$

$x = \dfrac{2352}{999},$

$= \dfrac{3(784)}{3(333)}$

$= \dfrac{784}{333}.$

11.　.235　　　　　　　12.　.3125　　　　　　13.　16.1
14.　5.472　　　　　　　15.　.45$\overline{45}$　　　　　　16.　.29$\overline{29}$

17. .896$\overline{896}$ 18. .2345$\overline{2345}$ 19. 4.37$\overline{37}$
20. 5.291$\overline{291}$ 21. 6.382$\overline{382}$ 22. 21.12$\overline{12}$
23. Let P be the set of pure imaginary numbers. Does $C = R \cup P$? Why?

0.5   Intervals

There are times when we want to talk about certain portions, or **intervals,** of the real-number line. We might want to talk about all the points between 0 and 1, for example. In order to facilitate this, we shall review some familiar notation. If a and b are numbers and a is less than b, we indicate this by writing $a < b$. To indicate that b *is greater than a*, write $b > a$. If a is less than or equal to b, we write $a \leq b$. If a is greater than or equal to b, we write $a \geq b$.

If $a < b$ and c is between a and b, then we know that $a < c$ and $c < b$. This can be written in one expression as $a < c < b$. So, if we wish to discuss all the points between 0 and 1, we might call this set S and write

$$S = \{x \mid 0 < x < 1\}.$$

A more common way to express S is what we might call the interval notation:

$$S = (0, 1).$$

We can read this as S *is the* **open interval** *from* 0 *to* 1. When we refer to S as an open interval, we mean that the interval does not include either of its end points.

Let us consider the set T consisting of all the points between 0 and 1 and the two end points of the interval. We might express T as

$$T = \{x \mid 0 \leq x \leq 1\}.$$

A second way to write T is

$$T = [0, 1].$$

This would be read T *is the* **closed interval** *from* 0 *to* 1. T is called a closed interval, since T includes both of its end points. Note that parentheses are used for open intervals, when the end points are *not* included in the interval, and brackets are used for closed intervals, when the end points are included in the interval.

So far we have discussed two types of bounded intervals, those for which both end points are included in the interval and those for which both are excluded from the interval. There are two other types of bounded intervals. Each includes one of the end points, but not the other. These are called **half-open** or **half-closed** intervals.

The ways of expressing the four different intervals for which a and b are the end points are listed next.

$\{x \mid a < x < b\}$ (a, b) *open interval from a to b*
$\{x \mid a \leq x \leq b\}$ $[a, b]$ *closed interval from a to b*

$$\{x \mid a < x \le b\} \qquad (a, b] \qquad \text{\textit{half-open or half-closed interval}}$$
from a to b

$$\{x \mid a \le x < b\} \qquad [a, b) \qquad \text{\textit{half-open or half-closed interval}}$$
from a to b.

Graphical methods of representing these intervals are shown in Figure 0.4. Note that an open circle indicates that the end point is not included in the interval, and a filled-in circle indicates that the end point is included in the interval.

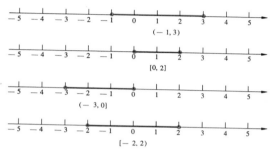

Figure 0.4

The intervals we have considered so far are called *finite intervals* or *bounded intervals,* since they are bounded on both ends. We also have *infinite intervals* to consider—intervals that are bounded on just one end or not bounded at all.

The set of all real numbers greater than a is an example of an infinite interval. We might write this in either of the two ways indicated below.

$$\{x \mid x > a\} \quad \text{or} \quad (a, \infty)$$

The symbol ∞ represents *infinity,* which is not a real number. We use infinity here to indicate that this set has no upper bound—that is, it contains numbers larger than any number we could pick.

The interval (a, ∞) is called *the open interval from a to infinity.* We use the parenthesis on the right since the set has *no* upper bound. In similar fashion, we can represent the set of all real numbers greater than or equal to a in this way:

$$\{x \mid x \ge a\} = [a, \infty).$$

This is called the *closed interval from a to infinity.* We will note that infinite intervals are open or closed depending on whether the one endpoint which is a real number is included in the interval.

We use similar notation when considering the set of all real numbers less than some real number a. This set may be represented thus:

$$\{x \mid x < a\} = (-\infty, a).$$

This interval is called the *open interval from negative infinity to a*. **Negative infinity** is used to mean that the set does not have any lower bound. We must remember here that every negative number is less than every positive number.

In a similar fashion, the *closed interval from negative infinity to a* is given by

$$(-\infty, a] \quad \text{or} \quad \{x \mid x \le a\}.$$

These infinite intervals may be represented graphically as shown in Figure 0.5. Note that we still use the *open circle* to indicate that the end point which

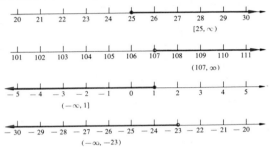

Figure 0.5

is a real number is not included in the set and the *closed circle* to indicate that it is included in the set. When we consider the entire set of real numbers, we realize that this set is not bounded on either end. Thus, we sometimes write

$$R = (-\infty, \infty).$$

All of these intervals are subsets of the set of real numbers. If we consider R to be the universal set, we can apply to intervals the set operations considered in the last section. When applying set operations to intervals, it is helpful to sketch the graph of the intervals before performing the set operations. Observe in Figure 0.6 that the **union** of the intervals **(2, 5]** and **[3, 7]** must be the interval **(2, 7]**, and the **intersection** of these two intervals must be **[3, 5]**. In Figure 0.7 we consider the interval (2, 5]; the complement of this interval must be all remaining real numbers.

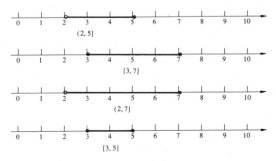

Figure 0.6

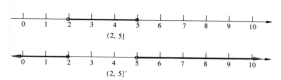

Figure 0.7

Exercises 0.4

Represent the following intervals graphically.

1. $(-3, 2)$ 2. $[-2, 3)$ 3. $[1, 4]$
4. $(0, 3]$ 5. $[-2, \infty)$ 6. $[-2, 5]$
7. $(6, \infty)$ 8. $(-\infty, -3]$ 9. $(-\infty, 2)$
10. $(-6, -2)$ 11. $\left(\dfrac{3}{2}, 2\right)$ 12. $\left[-\dfrac{1}{4}, \dfrac{1}{3}\right]$

Perform the following set operations. Remember that R is the universal set. Represent your answers graphically.

13. $(-1, 2] \cup (0, 3)$ 14. $(0, 4) \cap [1, 12)$
15. $(3, 5) \cup (4, \infty)$ 16. $(3, 5) \cap (-\infty, 4]$
17. $(-1, 0) \cap [0, 2)$ 18. $(-1, 0) \cup [0, 2)$
19. $(0, 3]'$ 20. $(-4, 2)'$
21. $[3, 6]'$ 22. $(3, \infty)'$
23. $(-2, 1) \cup (0, 3]'$ 24. $((-2, 1) \cup (0, 3])'$
25. $(-2, 1) \cap (0, 3]'$ 26. $(-\infty, 2)' \cap (-1, \infty)'$

0.6 Cartesian products

We have used the notation (a, b) to refer to the set of all the numbers which are between a and b. This same notation is used to refer to an **ordered pair** of elements in which *a is the first element or the first component* and *b is the second element or the second component*. It is usually clear from the context which of the two meanings is intended. As you probably remember from your study of algebra, the ordered pairs (a, b) and (c, d) are **equal** if and only if $a = c$ and $b = d$. Thus, $(2, 3) = (2, 3)$, but $(2, 3) \neq (3, 2)$.

The concept of an ordered pair is important in defining a new operation on sets: **the Cartesian product.**

*The **Cartesian products** of two sets A and B is $\{(x, y) \mid x \in A, y \in B\}$. We denote the Cartesian product of A and B as $A \times B$.*

Thus, if

$$A = \{1, 2, 3\}, \quad B = \{a, e\}, \quad \text{and} \quad C = \{\$, \&\},$$

we have

$$A \times B = \{(1, a), (1, e), (2, a), (2, e), (3, a), (3, e)\},$$
$$B \times A = \{(a, 1), (a, 2), (a, 3), (e, 1), (e, 2), (e, 3)\},$$

and

$$C \times B = \{(\$, a), (\$, e), (\&, a), (\&, e)\}.$$

We note that the elements in the Cartesian product of two sets are ordered pairs. We also note in the example that $A \times B \neq B \times A$, since not one of the ordered pairs of $A \times B$ occurs as an element of $B \times A$, and vice versa. It would be enough to have one ordered pair in either $A \times B$ or $B \times A$ which is not an element of the other to make $A \times B \neq B \times A$.

In general, $A \times B \neq B \times A$. There are two exceptions. One of them is illustrated in Problem 10 of the exercises following this section. The other occurs when $A = B$. For example, if $A = \{1, 2\}$ and $B = \{1, 2\}$, then

$$A \times B = \{(1, 1), (1, 2), (2, 1) (2, 2)\} = B \times A.$$

Even though it is usually not true that $A \times B = B \times A$, the two sets $A \times B$ and $B \times A$ are very closely related. If A and B are any nonempty sets, a one-to-one correspondence exists between the elements of $A \times B$ and $B \times A$.

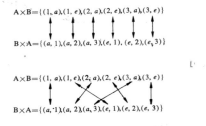

Figure 0.8

Earlier we considered an example in which $A = \{1, 2, 3\}$ and $B = \{a, e\}$. Figure 0.8 illustrates two different ways in which one-to-one correspondences could be established between the two sets $A \times B$ and $B \times A$. This will be explored further in the exercises.

Exercises 0.5

Let $A = \{7, 8, 9\}$, $B = \{3, 6\}$, and $C = \{\$, \&\}$. Find the following Cartesian products.

1. $C \times B$ 2. $B \times A$ 3. $C \times C$

4. $C \times A$ 5. $A \times A$ 6. $B \times C$

7. $A \times C$ 8. $B \times B$ 9. $A \times B$

10. Let $A = \{1, 2\}$.

     a. Are there any elements in the set $\{(x, y) \mid x \in A, y \in \emptyset\}$?

     b. What is $A \times \emptyset$?

     c. Are there any elements in the set $\{(x, y) \mid x \in \emptyset, y \in A\}$?

     d. What is $\emptyset \times A$?

     e. Let B be any set. What is $B \times \emptyset$?

     f. Let B be any set. What is $\emptyset \times B$?

     g. Let B be any set. Is $B \times \emptyset = \emptyset \times B$?

11. a. If A contains 2 elements and B contains 3 elements, how many elements are in $A \times B$?   in $B \times A$?

     b. If A contains 2 elements and B contains 4 elements, how many elements are in $A \times B$?   in $B \times A$?

     c. If A contains 5 elements and B contains 3 elements, how many elements are in $A \times B$?   in $B \times A$?

     d. If A contains 9 elements and B contains 6 elements, how many elements are in $A \times B$?   in $B \times A$?

     e. If A contains m elements and B contains n elements, how many elements are in $A \times B$?   in $B \times A$?

     f. If A and B are nonempty sets, do $A \times B$ and $B \times A$ have the same number of elements?

12. a. If $(x, y) \in A \times B$, must we have $(y, x) \in B \times A$? Why?

     b. If $(y, x) \in B \times A$, must we have $(x, y) \in A \times B$? Why?

     c. Let $(x, y) \in A \times B$ and $(c, d) \in B \times A$. Define a correspondence between $A \times B$ and $B \times A$ as follows: (x, y) corresponds to (c, d) if and only if $(c, d) = (y, x)$. Is this a one-to-one correspondence?

0.7 The Cartesian coordinate system

We have already discussed the set of real numbers. The Cartesian product of this set with itself could be denoted by $R \times R$. For the sake of convenience we shall usually use R^2 instead.

The trigonometric functions which we shall consider in Chapter 1 will all be subsets of R^2. When we look at the graphs of the trigonometric functions, we will be using a graphical representation of R^2 to assist us. This graphical representation is called **the Cartesian coordinate system.**

In order to have a coordinate system we need two real-number lines that intersect, and we need a unit distance defined on each of these real-number lines. We could use a coordinate system like the one in Figure 0.9. However,

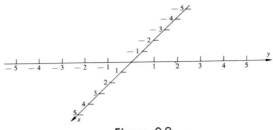

Figure 0.9

for the sake of convenience we shall put restrictions on the real-number lines that we use. We shall use two perpendicular lines, one drawn *horizontally* and the other, *vertically*. The point of intersection is called the **origin,** and we usually use 0 to refer to it, because the origin is the point corresponding to 0 on both lines. We shall use the *same unit distance* on both of these lines. The **positive directions** will be as indicated in Figure 0.10. The two lines divide the plane into four **quadrants.** These quadrants are labeled as illustrated in Figure 0.10.

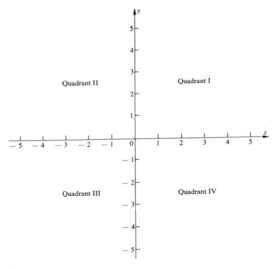

Figure 0.10

We refer to a point by using either an uppercase letter or an ordered pair of real numbers. The elements of this ordered pair are often referred to as coordinates. The **first coordinate** is the **abscissa** and the **second coordinate** is the **ordinate.**

*The **abscissa** is the real number corresponding to the point at which the perpendicular from the point to the x-axis intersects the x-axis. The **ordinate*** *is the real number corresponding to the point at which the perpendicular from the point to the y-axis intersects the y-axis.*

In Figure 0.11, the point P corresponds to the ordered pair $(3, 2)$; Q corresponds to the point $(1, -4)$, and S corresponds to the point $(0, -3)$.

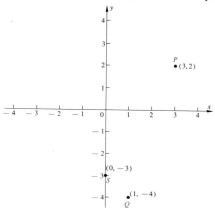

Figure 0.11

Since there is only one perpendicular from a point to each axis, there is exactly one ordered pair which corresponds to a point in the plane. Similarly, there is exactly one point corresponding to each ordered pair. This may be established with the assistance of a property of the real-number line stated in Section 0.4. Let (a, b) be any ordered pair of real numbers. Since the x-axis is a real-number line, there is *exactly one point* on the x-axis corresponding to a. Draw the perpendicular to the x-axis at this point. The y-axis, also a real-number line, contains *exactly one point* corresponding to b. Draw the perpendicular to the y-axis at this point. The point of intersection of these two perpendiculars is the point corresponding to (a, b). The location of this point is illustrated in Figure 0.12.

Since there is exactly one perpendicular to the x-axis at the point corresponding to a and exactly one perpendicular to the y-axis at the point corresponding to b, and since two distinct lines which intersect have exactly one point of intersection, there is exactly one point which corresponds to (a, b). Thus, *we have a one-to-one correspondence between the points on the plane and R^2.* We frequently refer to the point (x, y) instead of the point corresponding to (x, y). This will be done for the sake of convenience.

If A and B are subsets of R, then $A \times B$ is a subset of R^2, and we can represent $A \times B$ graphically. For example, if $A = \{1, 2\}$ and $B = \{-1, 0, 1, 2,\}$, then

$A \times B = \{(1, -1), (1, 0), (1, 1), (1, 2), (2, -1), (2, 0), (2, 1), (2, 2)\}.$

$A \times B$ is represented graphically in Figure 0.13.

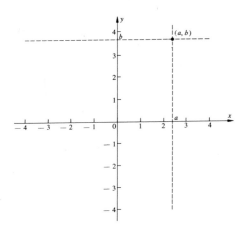

Figure 0.12

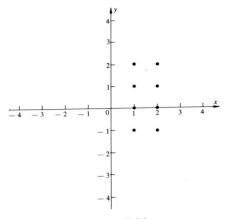

Figure 0.13

We shall use the results of the Pythagorean theorem to define the distance between two points. We will use the notation $d(P, Q)$ to refer to the distance between the two points P and Q. If P has coordinates (x_1, y_1) and Q has coordinates (x_2, y_2), the distance between the points P and Q is given by the formula

$$d(P, Q) = \sqrt{(x_2 - x_1)^2 + (y_2 - y_1)^2}.$$

Thus, the distance between the two points $(2, 5)$ and $(5, 1)$ is

$$\sqrt{(5 - 2)^2 + (1 - 5)^2} = \sqrt{3^2 + (-4)^2} = \sqrt{9 + 16} = \sqrt{25} = 5.$$

Any two points P and Q determine a line. Part of this line is called the **segment** determined by P and Q.

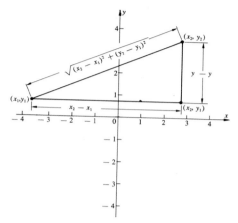

Figure 0.14

The **segment** *determined by the two points P and Q consists of the points P and Q and all the points on the line which are between P and Q. This segment is denoted by $\overline{PQ}$.*

There is a point on the segment $\overline{PQ}$ which is *half-way* between P and Q. This point is called the **midpoint** of the segment $\overline{PQ}$. If P has coordinates (x_1, y_1) and Q has coordinates (x_2, y_2), the midpoint of the segment $\overline{PQ}$ has coordinates given by

$$\left(\frac{x_1 + x_2}{2}, \frac{y_1 + y_2}{2}\right).$$

If P is the point $(3, 7)$ and Q is the point $(1, -15)$, the midpoint of $\overline{PQ}$ is

$$\left(\frac{3 + 1}{2}, \frac{7 + (-15)}{2}\right) = \left(\frac{4}{2}, \frac{-8}{2}\right) = (2, -4).$$

Let P be (x_1, y_1), Q be (x_2, y_2), and M be the midpoint of $\overline{PQ}$. Then M has coordinates

$$\left(\frac{x_1 + x_2}{2}, \frac{y_1 + y_2}{2}\right).$$

(1) $d(M, Q) = d\left(\left(\dfrac{x_1 + x_2}{2}, \dfrac{y_1 + y_2}{2}\right), (x_2, y_2)\right)$

(2) $= \sqrt{\left(x_2 - \dfrac{x_1 + x_2}{2}\right)^2 + \left(y_2 - \dfrac{y_1 + y_2}{2}\right)^2}$

(3) $= \sqrt{\left(\dfrac{2x_2 - x_1 - x_2}{2}\right)^2 + \left(\dfrac{2y_2 - y_1 - y_2}{2}\right)^2}$

(4) $= \sqrt{\left(\dfrac{x_2 - x_1}{2}\right)^2 + \left(\dfrac{y_2 - y_1}{2}\right)^2}$

$$(5) \qquad = \sqrt{\frac{1}{4}[(x_2 - x_1)^2 + (y_2 - y_1)^2]}$$

$$(6) \qquad = \frac{1}{2}\sqrt{(x_2 - x_1)^2 + (y_2 - y_1)^2}$$

$$(7) \qquad = \frac{1}{2}d(P, Q).$$

It is also true that

$$d(P, M) = \frac{1}{2}d(P, Q).$$

You will have an opportunity to show this in the exercises.

If (x, y) is any point in the plane, there are three points closely related to (x, y) which we shall consider now. The relationships involved here deal with **symmetry.** Before we look at these points related to (x, y), we need to define what we mean by the statement that two points are **symmetric** with respect to a line.

> Let P and Q be any two points. P and Q are **symmetric with respect to a line** *l if and only if the two following conditions are met:*
> (i) $\overline{PQ}$ *is perpendicular to l, and*
> (ii) *the midpoint of* $\overline{PQ}$ *is on the line l.*

With this definition of symmetry to guide us, we can see that the point $(x, -y)$ is symmetric to the point (x, y) with respect to the x-axis and that the point $(-x, y)$ is symmetric to the point (x, y) with respect to the y-axis. Figure 0.15 helps us to see that the segment connecting (x, y) and $(x, -y)$ is perpendicular to the x-axis and that the segment connecting (x, y) and $(-x, y)$ is perpendicular to the y-axis. In the exercises we shall see whether the midpoints of these segments do lie on the appropriate lines.

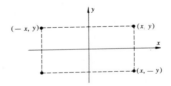

Figure 0.15

> Two points P and Q are **symmetric with respect to the origin** *if and only if the midpoint of* $\overline{PQ}$ *is the origin.*

The point $(-x, -y)$ is symmetric to the point (x, y) with respect to the origin. This will also be shown in the exercises.

If P is the point $(-2, 3)$, the three points related to P in the ways described above are identified next.

Symmetric to $(-2, 3)$ with respect to the x-axis: $(-2, -3)$.
Symmetric to $(-2, 3)$ with respect to the y-axis: $(-(-2), 3) = (2, 3)$.
Symmetric to $(-2, 3)$ with respect to the origin: $(-(-2), -3) = (2, -3)$.

Exercises 0.6

1. Graph the following points on the Cartesian coordinate plane.

   a. $(3, -5)$ b. $(-5, 3)$ c. $(-1, -4)$ d. $(2, 3)$
   e. $(5, 0)$ f. $(0, -6)$ g. $(-4, -1)$ h. $(-6, 0)$

2. Without graphing, indicate in which quadrant each of the following points is located. (*Note:* If a point is on one of the coordinate axes, then it is not in a quadrant.)

   a. $(-4, 2)$ b. $(4, -2)$ c. $(3, 0)$ d. $(-1, -6)$
   e. $(5, -1)$ f. $(0, -4)$ g. $(1, 5)$ h. $(-6, -943)$

3. Let $A = \{1, 2, 4\}$ and $B = \{1, 2\}$. Represent the following sets graphically.

   a. $A \times B$ b. $B \times A$ c. $A \times A$ d. $B \times B$

4. Let P be the point (x_1, y_1) and Q be the point (x_2, y_2). Then

$$d(P, Q) = \sqrt{(x_2 - x_1)^2 + (y_2 - y_1)^2} \quad \text{and} \quad d(Q, P) = \sqrt{(x_1 - x_2)^2 + (y_1 - y_2)^2}.$$

Is $d(P, Q) = d(Q, P)$? Why?

5. Find the distances between the following pairs of points and the midpoints of the segments connecting the pairs of points. Find the distance from the midpoint to each of the given points.

   a. $(-4, 2)$ and $(2, -6)$ b. $(4, 0)$ and $(-1, 12)$
   c. $(6, 1)$ and $(3, -3)$ d. $(-5, -2)$ and $(-7, 7)$

6. Show that if $P = (x_1, y_1)$, $Q = (x_2, y_2)$, and M is the midpoint of $\overline{PQ}$, then $d(M, P) = \frac{1}{2}d(P, Q)$.

7. Find the midpoints of the segments connecting the following pairs of points.

   a. (x, y) and $(x, -y)$ b. (x, y) and $(-x, y)$
   c. (x, y) and $(-x, -y)$ d. $(x, -y)$ and $(-x, y)$

Give the points which are symmetric to the following points (a) with respect to the x-axis, (b) with respect to the y-axis, and (c) with respect to the origin.

8. $(-5, 17)$ 9. $(14, 123)$ 10. $(-9, -8)$

Three points which are not collinear determine a triangle. Plot each of the following sets of points. Find the lengths of the sides of each triangle. Indicate which of the following sets of points determine (a) an isosceles triangle, (b) an equilateral triangle, and (c) a right triangle.

11. $(-4, 6)$, $(4, 6)$ and $(0, 2)$
12. $(5, 2)$, $(7, -4)$ and $(-1, 3)$
13. $(1, 2)$, $(-2, 5)$ and $(2, 6)$
14. $(-1, 3)$, $(3, -1)$ and $(1 + 2\sqrt{3}, 1 + 2\sqrt{3})$
15. $(-4, -2)$, $(-1, 7)$ and $(3, 5)$
16. $(0, 6)$, $(9, -6)$ and $(-3, 0)$

0.8 Relations and functions

Basically, any set of ordered pairs is a **relation.** This idea, though, is so general that it will be of relatively little use to us here. We will be concerned with a relation in a particular set.

*Let U be any set. A **relation in U** is any subset of $U \times U$.*

Once the set U is specified, there are two ways in which a relation might be defined. One way is to list all the ordered pairs in the relation. This method can be very cumbersome, and sometimes even impossible, so it appears that a second method might be preferable. The second method of defining a relation is to give a rule. Then the relation is the set of all the ordered pairs in $U \times U$ which satisfy the rule.

Let the universal set be $U = \{1, 2, 3, 4\}$. Define R_1 to be the subset of $U \times U$ given by the equation

$$R_1 = \{(x, y) \,|\, y = x + 1\}.$$

In this case, we could also define R_1 by listing the ordered pairs in R_1:

$$R_1 = \{(1, 2), (2, 3), (3, 4)\}.$$

A graphical representation of R_1 is shown in Figure 0.16.

We define R_2 to be a second relation in U, so that

$$R_2 = \{(x, y) \,|\, y \le x + 1\}.$$

A graphical representation of R_2 is given in Figure 0.17.

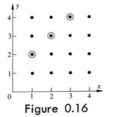

Figure 0.16

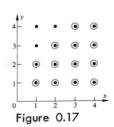

Figure 0.17

Let us define a relation R_3 to be a relation in R. This means that R_3 will be a subset of R^2, so that

$$R_3 = \{(x, y) \mid y = x + 1\}.$$

The graph of the relation R_3 is shown in Figure 0.18.

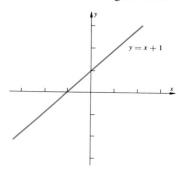

Figure 0.18

You will notice that the graphs of relations R_1 and R_3 are quite different even though these two relations have the same defining equation. This is because R_1 was defined to be a relation in the set $U = \{1, 2, 3, 4\}$, while R_3 was defined to be a relation in R. Since these relations are defined in different sets, they consist of different sets of ordered pairs.

There are two important sets connected with a relation. These are the **domain** and the **range** of the relation.

*Let S be any relation. The **domain** of the relation S is the set of all the first components in the ordered pairs which constitute S. The **range** of the relation S is the set of all the second components in the ordered pairs which constitute S.*

You should be able to see that if S is a relation in a set U, the domain and the range of S must both be subsets of the set U. The domains and ranges for the three relations which we have considered are given below.

relation	domain	range
R_1	$\{1, 2, 3\}$	$\{2, 3, 4\}$
R_2	$\{1, 2, 3, 4\}$	$\{1, 2, 3, 4\}$
R_3	R	R

Many times we do not specify the set in which a relation is defined. In these instances, *we assume that the relation is defined in R* and that *the relation consists of all the ordered pairs in R^2 which satisfy the rule.*

A special kind of relation of great importance in mathematics is a **function.**

A function is a relation in which each element in the domain of the relation occurs in exactly one ordered pair in the relation.

In the examples considered earlier, R_2 is not a function, since (2, 2) and (2, 3) both belong to R_2. These are distinct ordered pairs with the same first component. R_1 and R_3 are both functions.

If we look at the graph of a relation with the elements of the domain appearing on the horizontal axis and the elements of the range appearing on the vertical axis, we can tell whether or not the relation is a function in the following way. If no vertical line contains more than one point of the graph of the relation, then the relation is a function. If some vertical line contains more than one point of the graph of the relation, then the relation is *not* a function, since the two points represent different ordered pairs with the same first element. Consider the graphs of the relations

$$T = \{(x, y) \mid y = x^2\} \quad \text{and} \quad W = \{(x, y) \mid y^2 = x\},$$

which appear in Figures 0.19 and 0.20, respectively. We can see from these graphs that T is a function and W is *not* a function. Since the set in which the relations T and W are defined is not specified, both relations are defined in R.

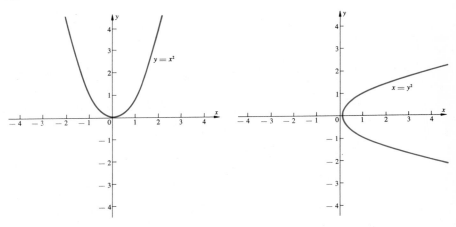

Figure 0.19   Figure 0.20

We said earlier in this section that when a relation is defined by a rule, the relation consists of all ordered pairs in the appropriate set which satisfy the rule. Thus, T consists of all ordered pairs (x, y) in $R \times R$ which satisfy the rule $y = x^2$. We can see that the **domain of** T is $R = (-\infty, \infty)$ and the **range of** T is the interval $[0, \infty)$. The relation W consists of all ordered pairs (x, y) in $R \times R$ which satisfy the rule $y^2 = x$. The **domain of** W is the interval $[0, \infty)$, and the **range of** W is $R = (-\infty, \infty)$.

It is fairly common practice to use letters like f, g, and h to represent functions. Thus, we might write

$$f = \{(x, y) \mid y = 3x - 2\}.$$

Since there is a *unique* y corresponding to each x, f is a function. Frequently, the same function will be indicated by

$$f(x) = 3x - 2,$$

it being understood that this is one way of defining the function. Since you will encounter the notation "$f(x) = \cdots$" frequently, you should become accustomed to it. $f(x)$ is read "f of x," or "f at x," or "the value of the function f at x."

In the example above, we observe that

$$f(2) = 3(2) - 2 = 6 - 2 = 4,$$
$$f(-1) = 3(-1) - 2 = -3 - 2 = -5,$$
$$f\left(\frac{2}{3}\right) = 3\left(\frac{2}{3}\right) - 2 = 2 - 2 = 0.$$

Exercises 0.7

Give the domain and the range of each of the following relations. Indicate whether each relation is a function.

1. $\{(2, 5), (4, 6), (6, 2), (2, 3), (5, 7)\}$
2. $\{(f, a), (r, t), (k, r), (l, j), (w, p), (f, r), (n, f), (t, c)\}$
3. $\{(1, 7), (2, 6), (9, 3), (4, 6), (5, 4)\}$
4. $\left\{(\pi, -1), \left(\frac{\pi}{2}, 0\right), (0, 1), (2\pi, 1), \left(-\frac{\pi}{2}, 0\right)\right\}$
5. $\{(1, 4), (3, 4), (5, 4), (7, 4), (1, 4)\}$
6. $\{(3, 2), (4, 1), (7, -2), (2, 3), (-3, 2), (3, -2), (-4, 5)\}$

State whether or not the following graphs represent functions.

7.   8.   9.

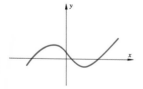 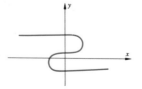 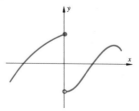

10.
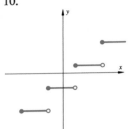

11.
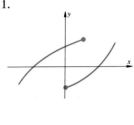

12.
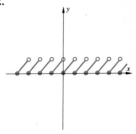

If $f(x) = 2x + 5$, evaluate the following.

13. $f(0)$ 14. $f(-7)$ 15. $f(3)$ 16. $f\left(\frac{7}{2}\right)$

17. $f(-\sqrt{2})$ 18. $f(\pi)$ 19. $f(a)$ 20. $f(f(-1))$

If $h(x) = x^2 - 4x + 6$, evaluate the following.

21. $h(5)$ 22. $h(-1)$ 23. $h(k-1)$ 24. $h(m+n)$

If $f(x) = x - 2$ and $g(x) = 2x + 3$, evaluate the following.

Example

$f(g(0))$

Solution

$g(0) = 2(0) + 3 = 0 + 3 = 3$
$f(g(0)) = f(3) = 3 - 2 = 1$

25. $f(5)$ 26. $g(1)$ 27. $f(g(1))$ 28. $f(g(x))$
29. $f(g(-1))$ 30. $g(f(4))$ 31. $g(f(x))$ 32. $g(f(-1))$

State whether or not the given equation defines a function.

Examples

(a) $x^2 y = 3$ (b) $x^2 + y^2 = 36$

Solutions

Solve explicitly for y.

(a) $y = \dfrac{3}{x^2}$

   Yes. There is only one value
   of y for each value of x ($x \neq 0$).

(b) $y^2 = 36 - x^2$

   $y = \pm\sqrt{36 - x^2}$

   No. If $-6 < x < 6$, there are
   two possible values of y. For
   example, if $x = \sqrt{20}$, $y = 4$ or
   $y = -4$.

33. $x - y = 5$ 34. $y = \sqrt{x^2 + 1}$ 35. $y^2 = x^2$
36. $y^2 = x^3$ 37. $y^3 = x^2$ 38. $y = x^2 - 5x + 2$
39. $x = y^2 - 4y + 6$ 40. $y = \sqrt[3]{x}$ 41. $x^2 - y^2 = 4$

0.9   Some special functions

There are many functions in mathematics that have their own special symbols. In this section, we shall discuss the **absolute-value function** and the **greatest-integer function.** The absolute-value function is defined next.

> ***absolute-value function*** $= \{(x, y) \mid \text{if } x \geq 0, \ y = x; \ \text{if } x < 0, \ y = -x\}$. *The absolute value of a number x is denoted by $|x|$.*

For example,

$$|3| = 3, \quad \left|-\frac{3}{2}\right| = -\left(-\frac{3}{2}\right) = \frac{3}{2}, \quad |-4| = -(-4) = 4, \quad |\pi| = \pi,$$

$$|-\sqrt{2}| = -(-\sqrt{2}) = \sqrt{2}, \quad \text{and} \quad |0| = 0.$$

Thus, we observe from the definition of the absolute-value function and the examples above that the absolute value of a real number is always non-negative. The **domain** of the absolute-value function is **the entire set of real numbers,** and the **range** of the absolute-value function is **the interval** $[0, \infty)$. The graph of the absolute-value function is shown in Figure 0.21.

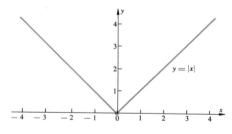

Figure 0.21

The second special function, the greatest-integer function, is often called the **bracket function,** because of the notation used to designate it.

> ***greatest-integer function***
> $= \{(x, y) \mid y \text{ is the greatest integer not greater than } x\}$.
> *The greatest integer of a real number x is denoted by $[x]$, often read "the greatest integer in x."*

As examples of some of the function values of the greatest-integer function, we have

$$\left[\frac{3}{2}\right] = 1, \quad \left[-\frac{5}{4}\right] = -2, \quad [\pi] = 3, \quad [-\pi] = -4,$$

$$[\sqrt{3}] = 1, \quad [-\sqrt{3}] = -2.$$

The graph of the greatest-integer function appears in Figure 0.22. The **domain** of the greatest-integer function is **R** and the **range** is **J**.

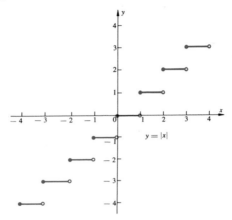

Figure 0.22

These functions can be used to define other interesting functions. Let us consider the function

$$g(x) = x - [x].$$

Table 1 helps us to graph the function g by giving some of the function values.

Table 1

x	0	1	−1	2	$\frac{1}{2}$	$\frac{1}{3}$	$\frac{3}{4}$	$\frac{9}{10}$	$\frac{5}{4}$	$\frac{3}{2}$	$\frac{5}{3}$	$\frac{13}{7}$
$[x]$	0	1	−1	2	0	0	0	0	1	1	1	1
$x - [x]$	0	0	0	0	$\frac{1}{2}$	$\frac{1}{3}$	$\frac{3}{4}$	$\frac{9}{10}$	$\frac{1}{4}$	$\frac{1}{2}$	$\frac{2}{3}$	$\frac{6}{7}$

The points (x, y) where $y = g(x)$ are plotted in Figure 0.23, which also shows what the graph of g looks like. Since the table gives only a finite number of points of the graph, the following analysis could be used to help us graph g: If $0 \le x < 1$, then

$$[x] = 0, \quad \text{and} \quad g(x) = x - 0 = x.$$

Thus, in the interval [0, 1), the graph of g is the same as the graph of $y = x$.

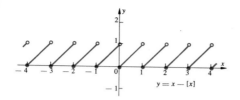

Figure 0.23

If $1 \leq x < 2$, then $[x] = 1$, and $g(x) = x - 1$. Thus, in the interval $[1, 2)$, the graph of g is the same as the graph of $y = x - 1$.

If $2 \leq x < 3$, then $[x] = 2$, $g(x) = x - 2$. Thus, in the interval $[2, 3)$, the graph of g is the same as the graph of $y = x - 2$.

If $-1 \leq x < 0$, then $[x] = -1$, and $g(x) = x - (-1) = x + 1$. Thus, in the interval $[-1, 0)$, the graph of g is the same as the graph of $y = x + 1$.

A careful consideration of Figure 0.23 will show that in the intervals $[-1, 0)$, $[0, 1)$, $[1, 2)$, and $[2, 3)$ the graph of g is exactly as stated in the paragraphs above. This particular function will be discussed further in the next section.

Exercises 0.8

1. Evaluate the following.

    a. $|2|$ b. $\left|-\dfrac{5}{2}\right|$ c. $[2]$ d. $\left[-\dfrac{5}{2}\right]$

    e. $\left[\left|-\dfrac{5}{2}\right|\right]$ f. $\left|\left[-\dfrac{5}{2}\right]\right|$ g. $|3 - 5|$ h. $|3| - |5|$

    i. $\left[\dfrac{5}{4} - \dfrac{1}{2}\right]$ j. $\left[\dfrac{5}{4}\right] - \left[\dfrac{1}{2}\right]$ k. $\left[\left(\dfrac{3}{2}\right)^2\right]$ l. $\left[\dfrac{3}{2}\right]^2$

2. Does $[x + 1] = [x] + 1$?

3. Let $n \in J$. Does $[x + n] = [x] + n$?

4. Let $g(x) = x - [x]$.

    a.   Let x be any real number. Does $g(x + 1) = g(x)$?

    b.   Let x be any real number and $n \in J$. Does $g(x + n) = g(x)$?

Sketch the graph of each of the following functions.

Example

$f(x) = [2x]$.

Solution

The following table gives us some points on the graph.

x	0	1	$\frac{1}{2}$	$\frac{1}{4}$	$\frac{1}{3}$	$\frac{2}{3}$	$\frac{3}{4}$
$2x$	0	2	1	$\frac{1}{2}$	$\frac{2}{3}$	$\frac{4}{3}$	$\frac{3}{2}$
$[2x]$	0	2	1	0	0	1	1

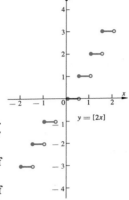

$y = [2x]$

The following analysis should help you more in the graph.
If $0 \le 2x < 1$, then $[2x] = 0$. But $0 \le 2x < 1$ if and only
if $0 \le x < 1/2$. Thus, if $0 \le x < 1/2$, then $[2x] = 0$.
If $1 \le 2x < 2$, then $[2x] = 1$. But $1 \le 2x < 2$ if and only if
$1/2 \le x < 1$. Thus, if $1/2 \le x < 1$, then $[2x] = 1$.
If $-1 \le 2x < 0$, then $[x] = -1$. But $-1 \le 2x < 0$ if
and only if $-1/2 \le x < 0$. Thus, if $-1/2 \le x < 0$, then
$[2x] = -1$.

5. $g(x) = |2x|$.
6. $h(x) = |x + 2|$.
7. $f(x) = [x - 2]$.
8. $f(x) = [|x|]$.
9. $g(x) = |[x]|$.
10. $h(x) = |x| - x$.
11. $h(x) = x + [x]$.
12. $f(x) = 2x - [2x]$.
13. $g(x) = |[2x] - 2x|$.
14. $h(x) = \left[\dfrac{x}{3}\right]$.

0.10   Periodic functions

In the last section we considered the function $g(x) = x - [x]$, the graph
of which appears in Figure 0.24. Note that any horizontal line which intersects
this graph intersects it at regular intervals. In Exercise 4 of the previous section,
we saw that for any real number x,

$$g(x + 1) = g(x),$$

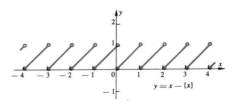

$y = x - [x]$

Figure 0.24

and also that for any real number x and for any integer n,

$$g(x + n) = g(x).$$

This is an example of what we call a **periodic function,** defined more formally below.

> *A function f is said to be a **periodic function** if and only if there exists some positive number p such that every time x and $x + p$ are both in the domain of f,*
>
> $$f(x + p) = f(x).$$
>
> *p is called a **period** of f. The **smallest positive period** of f, if such a period exists, is called the **fundamental period** of f.*

The function $g(x) = x - [x]$ is a periodic function and has a period of 1. You can probably observe from Figure 0.24 that the fundamental period of g is 1.

Another problem in the last section asked you to graph the function $f(x) = 2x - [2x]$. The graph of this function appears in Figure 0.25. We observe that

$$\begin{aligned}
f(x + 1) &= 2(x + 1) - [2(x + 1)] \\
&= 2x + 2 - [2x + 2] \\
&= 2x + 2 - ([2x] + 2) \\
&= 2x - [2x] \\
&= f(x).
\end{aligned}$$

Since $f(x + 1) = f(x)$, for any real number x, f is a periodic function with period 1.

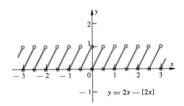

$$y = 2x - [2x]$$

Figure 0.25

The fundamental period of f is 1 if and only if 1 is the smallest positive period of f. You can probably see from Figure 0.25 that the fundamental period of f is 1/2. We can demonstrate that 1/2 is a period of f thus:

$$f\left(x + \frac{1}{2}\right) = 2\left(x + \frac{1}{2}\right) - \left[2\left(x + \frac{1}{2}\right)\right]$$
$$= 2x + 1 - [2x + 1]$$
$$= 2x + 1 - ([2x] + 1)$$
$$= 2x - [2x]$$
$$= f(x).$$

It would be difficult to demonstrate algebraically that 1/2 is the fundamental period of f. It is much easier to observe this from the graph of f.

The two examples considered so far are related, in that $f(x) = g(2x)$. The fundamental period of $g(x)$ is 1. The fundamental period of $g(2x)$ is 1/2. This illustrates a property of periodic functions which we shall not prove here. *If f is any periodic function with fundamental period m and if k is any real number such that $k \neq 0$, then $f(kx)$ is a periodic function with fundamental period $m/|k|$.* This property of periodic functions will be discussed further when we consider the trigonometric functions.

For example, if $h(x) = 6x - [6x]$, we see that $h(x) = g(6x)$. Since g is a periodic function with fundamental period 1, h is a periodic function and the fundamental period of h is $1/|6| = 1/6$. If $j(x) = -x/3 - [-x/3]$, then $j(x) = g(-1/3x)$. Thus, j is a periodic function, and the fundamental period of j is

$$\frac{1}{\left|-\frac{1}{3}\right|} = \frac{1}{\left(\frac{1}{3}\right)} = 3.$$

Exercises 0.9

1. Assume that $f(x)$ defines a periodic function with a fundamental period of 5. Determine the fundamental period of the following.

    a. $f\left(\frac{x}{2}\right)$ b. $f(-2x)$ c. $f(-x)$

    d. $f\left(-\frac{x}{2}\right)$ e. $f\left(\frac{x}{10}\right)$ f. $f(-10x)$

2. Let $h(x)$ be a function with the domain the interval $[0, \infty)$ such that $h(x) = $ the remainder when x is divided by 3. For example,

$$h(5) = 2, \quad \text{since } 5 = 1 \cdot 3 + 2,$$
$$h\left(7\frac{1}{2}\right) = 1\frac{1}{2}, \quad \text{since } 7\frac{1}{2} = 2 \cdot 3 + 1\frac{1}{2},$$

and

$$h(1) = 1, \quad \text{since } 1 = 0 \cdot 3 + 1.$$

Graph $h(x)$.

3. What is the range of h?

4. Is h a periodic function? If so, what is the fundamental period of h?

5. What is the fundamental period of

    a. $h(3x)$?   b. $h\left(\frac{x}{2}\right)$?   c. $h\left(-\frac{6x}{17}\right)$?   d. $h\left(\frac{mx}{b}\right)$?

Review Exercises

1. Let $U = \{1, 2, 3, 4, 5, 6, 7, 8\}$, $A = \{1, 5, 6\}$, $B = \{2, 3, 4, 6\}$, $C = \{5, 6, 7, 8\}$. Find the indicated sets.

    a. $A \cup B'$ b. $C' - A'$ c. $(B \cup C)'$
    d. $B' \cap C'$ e. $\emptyset - C$ f. $\emptyset'$
    g. $A \cup (B \cap C)$ h. $A \cap (B \cup C)$ i. $A' \cap (B \cup C)$

2. Evaluate the following expressions.

    a. $\left[-\frac{7}{3} \right]$ b. $\left| -\frac{7}{3} \right|$ c. $||-2| - |4||$

    d. $\left| \left[-\frac{11}{5} \right] \right|$ e. $\left[\left| -\frac{11}{5} \right| \right]$ f. $\left[-\frac{2}{3} - \frac{2}{3} \right]$

3. Let $A = \{1, 2, 3, 4\}$, $B = \{1, 2, 3\}$. Graph the following sets.

    a. $A \times B$
    b. $\{(x, y) \mid x \in A, y \in B, x < 2y\}$
    c. $\{(x, y) \mid x \in A, y \in B, y = 2x\}$
    d. $\{(x, y) \mid x \in A, y \in B, x + y = 3\}$
    e. $\{(x, y) \mid x \in A, y \in B, x^2 + y^2 = 10\}$

4. Which of the sets in Problem 3 are functions?

5. Graph the following intervals.

    a. $(-2, 4]$ b. $(-\infty, -3] \cap (-4, 2)$
    c. $(6, 8] \cup (3, 6)$ d. $(2, \infty)'$
    e. $[3, 6] \cap (2, 5]$ f. $(-\infty, 1] \cup (0, \infty)$

6. Which of the following graphs are graphs of functions?

a.

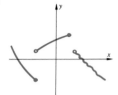

b.

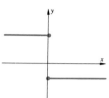

c.

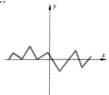

d.

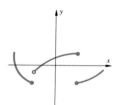

e.

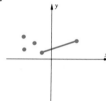

f.

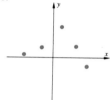

7. Let $g(x) = x - 1$, $h(x) = 2x + 3$. Evaluate the following.

a. $g(2)$ b. $h(3)$ c. $g(h(1))$
d. $h(g(1))$ e. $g(g(1))$ f. $h(h(1))$

8. Give the following sets by listing.

a. $\{x \mid x$ is an even prime$\}$
b. $\{y \mid y$ is an odd natural number less than 10$\}$
c. $\{z \mid z$ is a perfect square less than 10$\}$
d. $\{x \mid x$ is a prime less than 10$\}$
e. $\{y \mid y$ is both a prime and a perfect square$\}$

The trigonometric functions and their properties

1.1 Introduction

As you probably remember from your geometry, a **circle** is the set of all the points which are the same distance from a given point. The given point is called the **center** of the circle and the distance is called the **radius.** If that distance is 1 unit, the circle is called a **unit circle.** If the center of a unit circle is at the origin of a coordinate system, the circle is often referred to as *the* unit circle.

At this point we shall use "u" and "v" as our coordinates for convenience. If (u, v) are the coordinates of a point on the unit circle, then we know that $\sqrt{u^2 + v^2} = 1$, or that $u^2 + v^2 = 1$, by applying the distance formula to the point (u, v) and to the origin, which has coordinates $(0, 0)$. See Figure 1.1.

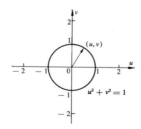

Figure 1.1

Now let us consider a real-number line tangent to the unit circle at the point (1, 0). The origin of this real-number line is located at the point of tangency. This real-number line will have the same unit distance as does the coordinate system. We shall define a function for which the domain will be the set of points on the real-number line and the range will be the set of points on the unit circle. See Figure 1.2.

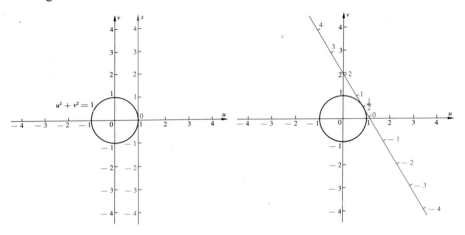

Figure 1.2   Figure 1.3

To determine the point on the circle which corresponds to a given point on the real-number line, the real-number line is "wrapped" around the circle until the desired point on the real-number line lies at the point of tangency. This wrapping is in a **counterclockwise** direction if we are working with a **positive** number; it is in a **clockwise** direction if we are working with a **negative** number. The point of tangency on the circle will be the desired point in the range. We assume that there is no slippage during this process. See Figure 1.3.

Since there is a one-to-one correspondence between the points on the real-number line and the set of real numbers, this wrapping process also establishes a correspondence between the set of real numbers and the set of points on the unit circle. However, this correspondence between the set of real numbers and the set of points on the unit circle is not a one-to-one correspondence. For the sake of convenience, we shall often refer to *the point x* rather than to *the point on the unit circle corresponding to the real number x.*

Since the circumference of a circle is 2π times the radius, the circumference of the unit circle is 2π. Thus, 2π will correspond to the point (1, 0), and from this we can determine that π corresponds to $(-1, 0)$, $\pi/2$ corresponds to (0, 1), and so forth. Some of these correspondences are illustrated in Figure 1.4.

We can also draw other conclusions. If x corresponds to a point (u, v), then $x + 2\pi$ also corresponds to the point (u, v) since one counterclockwise

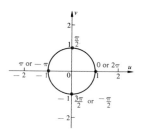

Figure 1.4

wind of the line about the circle puts the point $x + 2\pi$ where the point x was. Similarly, one clockwise wind puts $x - 2\pi$ where the point x was; so $x - 2\pi$ also corresponds to (u, v). In fact, $x, x \pm 2\pi, x \pm 4\pi, x \pm 6\pi, \ldots$ all correspond to the same point on the circle. Thus, any point of the form $x + 2n\pi$, $n \in J$, corresponds to the same point on the circle as does x.

If x corresponds to a point (u, v) on the circle, it can be seen that $-x$ corresponds to the point $(u, -v)$. Thus, x and $-x$ *are symmetric with respect to the u-axis.*

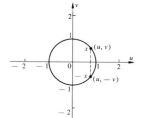 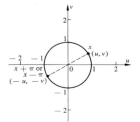

Figure 1.5   Figure 1.6

If x corresponds to a point (u, v) on the circle, it can be seen that $x + \pi$ corresponds to the point $(-u, -v)$, since π is exactly one-half the circumference of the unit circle. Thus, x and $x + \pi$ *are symmetric with respect to the origin.* Since $x + \pi$ and $x - \pi$ differ by 2π, $x - \pi$ also corresponds to the point $(-u, -v)$, and $x - \pi$ is also symmetric to the point x with respect to the origin.

If x corresponds to the point (u, v), $-x$ corresponds to the point $(u, -v)$. Thus, $-x + \pi$ must correspond to the point $(-u, -(-v)) = (-u, v)$. Thus, the points x and $-x + \pi$ *are symmetric with respect to the v-axis.* We frequently refer to $\pi - x$ instead of $-x + \pi$. Thus, the points x and $\pi - x$ are symmetric with respect to the v-axis.

The symmetry of the points x and $\pi - x$ are illustrated in Figure 1.7. The three facts about symmetry just discussed are summarized in Figure 1.8.

From the information we have so far, we know that $0, \pm 2\pi, \pm 4\pi, \ldots$ all correspond to the point $(1, 0)$. We can conclude that $\pm \pi, \pm 3\pi, \pm 5\pi, \ldots$ all correspond to the point $(-1, 0)$; that $\ldots, -5\pi/2, -\pi/2, 3\pi/2, 7\pi/2, \ldots$

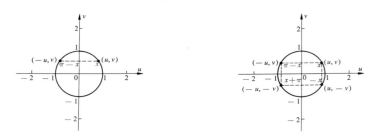

Figure 1.7   Figure 1.8

all correspond to the point $(0, -1)$; and that $-7\pi/2, -3\pi/2, \pi/2, 5\pi/2, \ldots$ all correspond to the point $(0, 1)$. From this we can determine the quadrants in which other points lie. For example, since $2\pi/3$ is in the interval $(\pi/2, \pi)$, we can see that $2\pi/3$ must lie in the **second** quadrant. This tells us immediately that $-2\pi/3$ must lie in the **third** quadrant (since $2\pi/3$ and $-2\pi/3$ are symmetric with respect to the u-axis). These facts and other considerations of symmetry can also be used to help us determine where other points, such as $5\pi/3$, must be located.

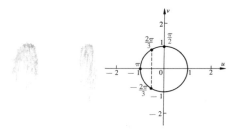

Figure 1.9

This relationship between the points on the real-number line and the points on the unit circle could be established in a second way. We must assume that an arc has measurable length.

We will also use the idea of a **free** point, by which we mean a point without a fixed location, one that can move about. However, the movement of this free point will be restricted to the circular path determined by the unit circle. The initial location of the fixed point would be at $(1, 0)$ so the real number 0 corresponds to the point $(1, 0)$.

To find the point on the unit circle corresponding to a *positive* real number x, we shall move the free point in a *counterclockwise* direction around the unit circle until it has covered exactly x units. The point on the unit circle where the free point stops will be the point corresponding to the positive real number x. If $x > 2\pi$, the free point would have to make more than one complete revolution, since the circumference of the unit circle is 2π. The points corresponding to *negative* real numbers could be obtained by having the free point move in a *clockwise* direction around the unit circle from $(1, 0)$.

Exercises 1.1

1. In which quadrant does the given point lie?

    a. $\dfrac{3\pi}{4}$ b. $-\dfrac{9\pi}{7}$ c. $\dfrac{11\pi}{3}$ d. $\dfrac{7\pi}{6}$

    e. $-\dfrac{7\pi}{4}$ f. $-\dfrac{7\pi}{6}$ g. $-\dfrac{\pi}{3}$ h. $\dfrac{13\pi}{6}$

2. Give four other real numbers which correspond to the same point on the unit circle as the given number.

    a. $\dfrac{\pi}{3}$ b. $\dfrac{\pi}{6}$ c. $\dfrac{3\pi}{4}$ d. $\dfrac{4\pi}{3}$ e. $-\dfrac{5\pi}{6}$ f. $-\dfrac{\pi}{4}$

Name a point which is symmetric to the given point with respect to (a) the *u*-axis; (b) the *v*-axis; (c) the origin.

3. $\dfrac{\pi}{6}$ 4. $\dfrac{\pi}{3}$ 5. $\dfrac{3\pi}{4}$ 6. $\dfrac{5\pi}{8}$

7. $\dfrac{3\pi}{7}$ 8. $\dfrac{5\pi}{9}$ 9. $-\dfrac{\pi}{12}$ 10. $-\dfrac{\pi}{10}$

1.2   The sine and cosine functions

In Section 1.1 we established a relationship between the set of real numbers and the set of points on the unit circle. This relationship may be used to define two very important functions. They are the **sine function** and the **cosine function.**

sine function
$\doteq \{(x, v) \mid x \in R, (u, v) \text{ is the point on the unit circle corresponding to } x\}$. *We frequently* $\sin x = v$ *to indicate that the ordered pair* (x, v) *belongs to the sine function.*

cosine function
$= \{(x, u) \mid x \in R, (u, v) \text{ is the point on the unit circle corresponding to } x\}$. *We frequently write* $\cos x = u$ *indicate that the ordered pair* (x, u) *belongs to the cosine function.*

Since the unit circle is used in the definitions of both functions, we frequently refer to the sine function and the cosine function as **circular functions.** They are also called **trigonometric functions,** since they are two of the basic functions studied in trigonometry.

Let x be any real number and let (u, v) be the point on the unit circle corresponding to x. Then

$$\cos x = u \quad \text{and} \quad \sin x = v.$$

Since u and v are on the unit circle, $u^2 + v^2 = 1$. Thus,

$$(\cos x)^2 + (\sin x)^2 = 1.$$

For the sake of convenience, we usually write $\cos^2 x$ instead of $(\cos x)^2$. In general, if $n \in R$ and $n \neq -1$, $(\cos x)^n$ is usually written $\cos^n x$, and similarly for $(\sin x)^n$. Thus, the expression above could have been written as

$$\cos^2 x + \sin^2 x = 1.$$

This is true for every real number x. This is our first example of an identity in trigonometry. Identities will be studied in detail in Chapter 2.

Since the real numbers 0, $\pi/2$, π, $3\pi/2$, and 2π correspond to the points $(1, 0)$, $(0, 1)$, $(-1, 0)$, $(0, -1)$, and $(1, 0)$, respectively, we can determine the values of the sine and the cosine of each of these numbers. These values of the cosine and sine functions are given in the Table 1. To indicate these function values we can write $\sin \pi/2 = 1$, $\cos \pi = -1$, and so forth.

Table 1

x	$\cos x$	$\sin x$
0	1	0
$\dfrac{\pi}{2}$	0	1
π	-1	0
$\dfrac{3\pi}{2}$	0	-1
2π	1	0

There are four points at which the unit circle intersects the coordinate axes, two on each axis, and there are some real numbers that correspond to each of these four points. However, most real numbers do not correspond to any one of these four points of intersection; they correspond to points on the unit circle which lie in one of the four quadrants. If a real number corresponds to a point in a given quadrant, certain conclusions may be drawn about the sine and the cosine of that real number. The numbers in the interval $(0, 2\pi)$ are used for illustration, in Figure 1.10.

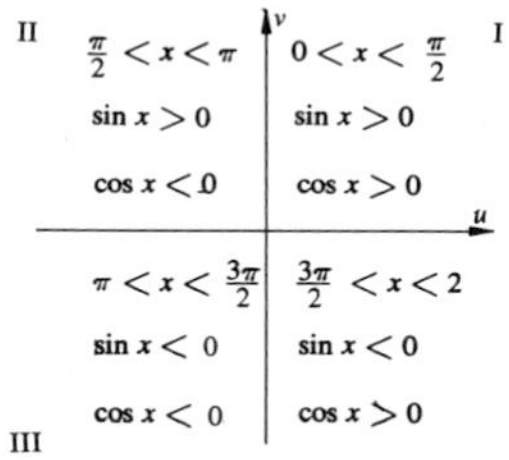

II $\frac{\pi}{2} < x < \pi$ | $0 < x < \frac{\pi}{2}$ I

$\sin x > 0$ | $\sin x > 0$

$\cos x < 0$ | $\cos x > 0$

$\pi < x < \frac{3\pi}{2}$ | $\frac{3\pi}{2} < x < 2$

$\sin x < 0$ | $\sin x < 0$

$\cos x < 0$ | $\cos x > 0$

III

Figure 1.10

We can use our knowledge of the geometry of circles and the relationship $u^2 + v^2 = 1$ to determine the cosine and the sine of some special values of x.

Example

Find $\cos \dfrac{\pi}{4}$ and $\sin \dfrac{\pi}{4}$.

Solution

Let P, Q, and R be located as in Figure 1.11. We observe that

$$\cos \frac{\pi}{4} = a \quad \text{and} \quad \sin \frac{\pi}{4} = b.$$

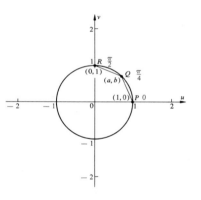

The lengths of the arcs $\widehat{PQ}$ and $\widehat{QR}$ are each $\pi/4$. Since arcs of equal length are subtended by chords of equal length, $d(P, Q) = d(Q, R)$. Thus, we have

$$\sqrt{(a-1)^2 + (b-0)^2} = \sqrt{(0-a)^2 + (1-b)^2},$$
$$(a-1)^2 + b^2 = a^2 + (1-b)^2,$$
$$a^2 - 2a + 1 + b^2 = a^2 + 1 - 2b + b^2,$$
$$-2a = -2b,$$
$$a = b.$$

Figure 1.11

Thus, we find that $a = b$. We also know that $a^2 + b^2 = 1$, since (a, b) is on the unit circle. Solving, we get

$$a^2 + b^2 = 1,$$
$$2a^2 = 1,$$
$$a^2 = \frac{1}{2} = \frac{2}{4},$$
$$a = \sqrt{\frac{2}{4}} = \frac{\sqrt{2}}{2},$$

since (a, b) is in the first quadrant. Since $a = b$, we also have $b = \sqrt{2}/2$. This enables us to conclude that

$$\cos \frac{\pi}{4} = \frac{\sqrt{2}}{2} \quad \text{and} \quad \sin \frac{\pi}{4} = \frac{\sqrt{2}}{2}.$$

Example

Find $\sin \dfrac{\pi}{6}$ and $\cos \dfrac{\pi}{6}$.

Solution

Let the points S, T, and U be located as in Figure 1.12. We see that

$$\cos \frac{\pi}{6} = c \quad \text{and} \quad \sin \frac{\pi}{6} = e.$$

If T has coordinates (c, e), then S has coordinates $(c, -e)$. Why? And $d(S, T) = 2e$. Why?

The arcs $\overset{\frown}{ST}$ and $\overset{\frown}{TU}$ both have the same length, $\pi/3$. Since arcs of equal length are subtended by chords of equal length,

$$d(T, U) = d(S, T) = 2e.$$

This tells us that

$$\sqrt{(0 - c)^2 + (1 - e)^2} = 2e,$$
$$c^2 + (1 - e)^2 = 4e^2,$$
$$c^2 + 1 - 2e + e^2 = 4e^2,$$
$$1 - 2e + 1 = 4e^2 \qquad (c^2 + e^2 = 1, \text{ since } (c, e) \text{ is on the unit circle}),$$
$$4e^2 + 2e - 2 = 0,$$
$$2e^2 + e - 1 = 0,$$
$$(2e - 1)(e + 1) = 0,$$
$$e = \frac{1}{2} \quad \text{or} \quad e = -1.$$

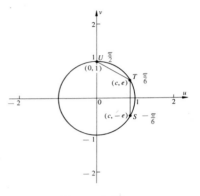

Figure 1.12

Since the point (c, e) is in the first quadrant, e must be positive. This enables us to conclude that $e = 1/2$. Since (c, e) is both in the first quadrant and on the unit circle,

$$c^2 + e^2 = 1,$$
$$c^2 = 1 - e^2,$$
$$c^2 = 1 - \frac{1}{4} = \frac{3}{4},$$
$$c = \sqrt{\frac{3}{4}} = \frac{\sqrt{3}}{2}.$$

Thus, we conclude that

$$\cos \frac{\pi}{6} = \frac{\sqrt{3}}{2} \quad \text{and} \quad \sin \frac{\pi}{6} = \frac{1}{2}.$$

By using Figure 1.13, the fact that arcs of equal length are subtended by chords of equal length, and the material in the previous example, you should be able to derive that

$$\cos \frac{\pi}{3} = \frac{1}{2} \quad \text{and} \quad \sin \frac{\pi}{3} = \frac{\sqrt{3}}{2}.$$

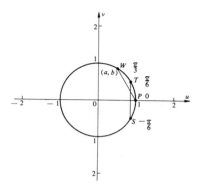

Figure 1.13

The preceding examples enable us to complete the table that follows.

Table 2

x	$\cos x$	$\sin x$
0	1	0
$\dfrac{\pi}{6}$	$\dfrac{\sqrt{3}}{2}$	$\dfrac{1}{2}$
$\dfrac{\pi}{4}$	$\dfrac{\sqrt{2}}{2}$	$\dfrac{\sqrt{2}}{2}$
$\dfrac{\pi}{3}$	$\dfrac{1}{2}$	$\dfrac{\sqrt{3}}{2}$
$\dfrac{\pi}{2}$	0	1

These are important function values for the student to remember.

Exercises 1.2

1. a. If x has coordinates (u, v), what coordinates does $-x$ have?
    b. $\cos x = u$. What is $\cos (-x)$?
    c. $\sin x = v$. What is $\sin (-x)$?

2. Find the following function values.

   a. $\cos\left(-\dfrac{\pi}{3}\right)$ b. $\cos\left(-\dfrac{\pi}{4}\right)$ c. $\cos\left(-\dfrac{\pi}{6}\right)$

   d. $\sin\left(-\dfrac{\pi}{3}\right)$ e. $\sin\left(-\dfrac{\pi}{4}\right)$ f. $\sin\left(-\dfrac{\pi}{6}\right)$

3. a. If x has coordinates (u, v), what coordinates does $x + \pi$ have?
   b. What is $\cos(x + \pi)$?
   c. What is $\sin(x + \pi)$?

4. Find the following function values.

   a. $\cos \dfrac{7\pi}{6}$ b. $\cos \dfrac{5\pi}{4}$ c. $\cos \dfrac{4\pi}{3}$

   d. $\sin \dfrac{7\pi}{6}$ e. $\sin \dfrac{5\pi}{4}$ f. $\sin \dfrac{4\pi}{3}$

5. a. If x has coordinates (u, v), what coordinates does $\pi - x$ have?
   b. What is $\cos(\pi - x)$?
   c. What is $\sin(\pi - x)$?

6. Find the following function values.

   a. $\cos \dfrac{3\pi}{4}$ b. $\cos \dfrac{2\pi}{3}$ c. $\cos \dfrac{5\pi}{6}$

   d. $\sin \dfrac{3\pi}{4}$ e. $\sin \dfrac{2\pi}{3}$ f. $\sin \dfrac{5\pi}{6}$

7. If x has coordinates (u, v), what coordinates does $x \pm 2\pi$ have?

   a. What is $\cos(x + 2\pi)$?   b. What is $\sin(x + 2\pi)$?
   c. What is $\cos(x - 2\pi)$?   d. What is $\sin(x - 2\pi)$?

8. Use the results of exercises 1–7 to find the following function values.

   a. $\cos\left(\dfrac{7\pi}{4}\right)$ $\dfrac{\sqrt{2}}{2}$ b. $\cos\left(-\dfrac{7\pi}{6}\right)$ $-\dfrac{\sqrt{3}}{2}$ c. $\cos\left(\dfrac{10\pi}{3}\right)$ $-\dfrac{1}{2}$

   d. $\sin\left(-\dfrac{5\pi}{4}\right)$ $\dfrac{\sqrt{2}}{2}$ e. $\sin\left(\dfrac{11\pi}{6}\right)$ $-\dfrac{1}{2}$ f. $\sin\left(-\dfrac{4\pi}{3}\right)$ $\dfrac{\sqrt{3}}{2}$

   g. $\sin\left(-\dfrac{5\pi}{6}\right)$ $-\dfrac{1}{2}$ h. $\sin\left(\dfrac{8\pi}{3}\right)$ $\dfrac{\sqrt{3}}{2}$ i. $\sin\left(-\dfrac{9\pi}{4}\right)$ $-\dfrac{\sqrt{2}}{2}$

   j. $\cos\left(\dfrac{5\pi}{6}\right)$ $-\dfrac{\sqrt{3}}{2}$ k. $\cos\left(-\dfrac{11\pi}{6}\right)$ $\dfrac{\sqrt{3}}{2}$ l. $\cos\left(\dfrac{13\pi}{4}\right)$ $-\dfrac{\sqrt{2}}{2}$

Use the fact that $\sin^2 x + \cos^2 x = 1$ and the given quadrant to find the function value indicated.

Example

x is in the third quadrant, $\sin x = -\dfrac{12}{13}$. Find $\cos x$.

Solution

Since x is in the third quadrant, $\cos x$ is negative.

$$\sin^2 x + \cos^2 x = 1 \qquad \left[\dfrac{12}{13}\right]^2 + \cos^2 x = 1$$

$$\frac{144}{169} + \cos^2 x = 1 \qquad \cos^2 x = \frac{25}{169}$$

$$\cos^2 x = 1 - \frac{144}{169} \qquad \cos x = -\frac{5}{13} \text{ (since } \cos x \text{ is negative)}$$

9. x is in the second quadrant, $\cos x = -\frac{15}{17}$. Find $\sin x$.

10. x is in the fourth quadrant, $\cos x = \frac{3}{5}$. Find $\sin x$.

11. x is in the fourth quadrant, $\sin x = -\frac{1}{3}$. Find $\cos x$.

12. x is in the second quadrant, $\sin x = \frac{\sqrt{5}}{5}$. Find $\cos x$.

13. z is in the first quadrant, $\sin z = \frac{8}{17}$. Find $\cos z$.

14. z is in the third quadrant, $\sin z = -\frac{3}{4}$. Find $\cos z$.

15. y is in the third quadrant, $\cos y = -\frac{2}{5}$. Find $\sin y$.

16. t is in the first quadrant, $\cos t = \frac{5}{13}$. Find $\sin t$.

17. w is in the fourth quadrant, $\sin w = -\frac{2}{3}$. Find $\cos w$.

18. θ is in the second quadrant, $\cos \theta = -\frac{2}{7}$. Find $\sin \theta$.

1.3   The graphs of the sine function and the cosine function

In Section 1.1 we established a correspondence under which, if x is any real number, there is a point (u, v) on the unit circle which corresponds to x. In Section 1.2 we defined the sine function and the cosine function on the basis of this correspondence, so that $\cos x = u$ and $\sin x = v$. Thus, if x is any real number, the cosine function and the sine function are both defined at x. This tells us that *the domain of the cosine function is the entire set of real numbers* and *the domain of the sine function is also the entire set of real numbers.*

Taken individually, u can be any number in the interval $[-1, 1]$ and v can be any number in the interval $[-1, 1]$. u and v are related, though, in that $u^2 + v^2 = 1$. Since $u = \cos x$, $\cos x$ can be any number in the interval $[-1, 1]$, and *the range for the cosine function is the interval* $[-1, 1]$. Similarly, *the range of the sine function is also the interval* $[-1, 1]$.

If we wish to sketch a graph of the function given by $\{(x, y) \,|\, y = \sin x\}$, we have information which will be helpful. Since, for any real number x,

$$-1 \le \sin x \le 1,$$

we know that each point of the graph of $y = \sin x$ will either be *between* the lines $y = -1$ and $y = 1$ or it will be on one of the lines.

In Problem 7 of the preceding section, it was shown that if x is any real number

$$\sin (x + 2\pi) = \sin x.$$

This means that the sine function is a **periodic** function with **period 2π**. In fact, the **fundamental period** of the sine function is **2π**. This means that if we graph the sine function for any interval of length 2π, the periodicity of the sine function can be used to extend its graph. We start by graphing the sine function on the interval $[-\pi, \pi]$.

From the material in Section 1.2, we can construct Table 3.

Table 3

x	0	$\dfrac{\pi}{6}$	$\dfrac{\pi}{4}$	$\dfrac{\pi}{3}$	$\dfrac{\pi}{2}$	π
$\sin x$	0	$\dfrac{1}{2}$	$\dfrac{\sqrt{2}}{2}$	$\dfrac{\sqrt{3}}{2}$	1	0

In Problem 5 of the preceding section, we discovered that $\sin (\pi - x) = \sin x$. In Problem 6 we developed the function values in Table 4.

Table 4

x	$\dfrac{2\pi}{3}$	$\dfrac{3\pi}{4}$	$\dfrac{5\pi}{6}$
$\sin x$	$\dfrac{\sqrt{3}}{2}$	$\dfrac{\sqrt{2}}{2}$	$\dfrac{1}{2}$

In Problem 1 of the preceding section we developed the equation $\sin (-x) = -\sin x$. This fact may be used in conjunction with the information above to construct Table 5.

Table 5

x	$-\dfrac{\pi}{6}$	$-\dfrac{\pi}{4}$	$-\dfrac{\pi}{3}$	$-\dfrac{\pi}{2}$	$-\dfrac{2\pi}{3}$	$-\dfrac{3\pi}{4}$	$-\dfrac{5\pi}{6}$	$-\pi$
$\sin x$	$-\dfrac{1}{2}$	$-\dfrac{\sqrt{2}}{2}$	$-\dfrac{\sqrt{3}}{2}$	-1	$-\dfrac{\sqrt{3}}{2}$	$-\dfrac{\sqrt{2}}{2}$	$-\dfrac{1}{2}$	0

We can plot the function values given in these three tables to get an idea of what the sine function looks like. This is done in Figure 1.14. In Figure 1.15, a smoothed curve through these points shows an approximation of the graph of the sine function on the interval $[-\pi, \pi]$. As indicated previously, we can extend the graph in each direction, since the sine function is a periodic function with period 2π. This gives us the graph of the sine function, shown in Figure 1.15.

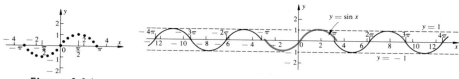

Figure 1.14   **Figure 1.15**

The sine and cosine functions have several properties in common, and their graphs show the corresponding similarities. The range of the cosine function is the same as the range of the sine function, the interval $[-1, 1]$. This means that the graph of the cosine function will also appear *between* the lines $y = -1$ and $y = 1$ and occasionally *on* one or the other of these lines.

We also discovered that

$$\cos (x + 2\pi) = \cos x,$$

so that the cosine function is also a periodic function with **period 2π**. In fact, the **fundamental period** of the cosine function is also 2π. Because of this, we first graph the cosine function for an interval of length 2π, and then use the periodicity of the cosine function to extend the graph.

From the material in Section 1.2 and in Problems 5 and 6 of the preceding section, we are able to obtain the function values to construct the following table:

Table 6

x	0	$\dfrac{\pi}{6}$	$\dfrac{\pi}{4}$	$\dfrac{\pi}{3}$	$\dfrac{\pi}{2}$	$\dfrac{2\pi}{3}$	$\dfrac{3\pi}{4}$	$\dfrac{5\pi}{6}$	π
$\cos x$	1	$\dfrac{\sqrt{3}}{2}$	$\dfrac{\sqrt{2}}{2}$	$\dfrac{1}{2}$	0	$-\dfrac{1}{2}$	$-\dfrac{\sqrt{2}}{2}$	$-\dfrac{\sqrt{3}}{2}$	-1

Problem 1 of the preceding section demonstrated that

$$\cos (-x) = \cos x.$$

This information allows us to obtain the following function values in Table 7. The function values from these two tables are the basis for Figure 1.16.

If these points are connected to form a smooth curve, we obtain the colored

Table 7

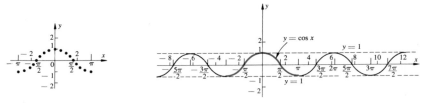

x	$-\dfrac{\pi}{6}$	$-\dfrac{\pi}{4}$	$-\dfrac{\pi}{3}$	$-\dfrac{\pi}{2}$	$-\dfrac{2\pi}{3}$	$-\dfrac{3\pi}{4}$	$-\dfrac{5\pi}{6}$	$-\pi$
$\cos x$	$\dfrac{\sqrt{3}}{2}$	$\dfrac{\sqrt{2}}{2}$	$\dfrac{1}{2}$	0	$-\dfrac{1}{2}$	$-\dfrac{\sqrt{2}}{2}$	$-\dfrac{\sqrt{3}}{2}$	-1

Figure 1.16   Figure 1.17

portion of the graph in Figure 1.17. The periodicity of the cosine function is used to extend the graph.

Exercises 1.3

1. a. Make a table of the values of the sine function between $-\pi$ and 4π, using values of x similar to those in the examples.
   b. Plot the corresponding values on a graph.
   c. Connect the points plotted with a smooth curve.
2. a. Make a table of values of the cosine function between $-\pi$ and 4π.
   b. Plot the corresponding function values on a graph.
   c. Connect the points plotted with a smooth curve.

Make a rough sketch of the graphs of the following functions.

Example

$\{(x, y) \mid y = 2 + \sin x\}$.

Solution

The graph of $y = 2 + \sin x$ is *between* the lines $y = 1$ and $y = 3$, or occasionally *on* one or the other of the lines. The student may wish to construct a table of function values.

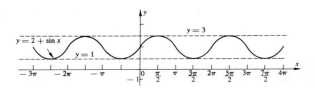

3. $\{(x, y) | y = 2 + \cos x\}$

4. $\{(x, y) | y = \sin x - 1\}$

5. $\{(x, y) | y = \cos x - 3\}$

6. $\{(x, y) | y = 1 + \sin x\}$

7. $\left\{(x, y) | y = \dfrac{1}{2} + \sin x\right\}$

8. $\left\{(x, y) | y = \cos x - \dfrac{1}{2}\right\}$

9. The fundamental period of the sine function $(y = \sin x)$ is 2π. What is the fundamental period of each of the following functions? '

    a. $\sin 3x$
             b. $\sin(-2x)$
             c. $\sin \dfrac{x}{2}$

    d. $\sin \dfrac{3x}{4}$
             e. $\sin\left(-\dfrac{z}{3}\right)$
             f. $\sin(-4z)$

10. The fundamental period of the cosine function $(y = \cos x)$ is 2π. What is the fundamental period of each of the following functions?

    a. $y = \cos 2x.$
             b. $y = \cos 5x.$
             c. $y = \cos\left(-\dfrac{x}{4}\right).$

    d. $y = \cos \dfrac{3x}{2}.$
             e. $y = \cos(-t).$
             f. $y = \cos(-3w).$

Attempt to sketch a graph of each of the following.

11. $\{(x, y) | y = 2 \sin x\}$
                      12. $\{(x, y) | y = -\cos x\}$

13. $\{(x, y) | y = \cos 2x\}$
                      14. $\left\{(x, y) | y = \sin \dfrac{x}{2}\right\}$

15. $\left\{(x, y) | y = \sin\left(x + \dfrac{\pi}{2}\right)\right\}$
           16. $\{(x, y) | y = \cos(x + \pi)\}$

1.4   Graphs of $y = a \sin bx$ and $y = a \cos bx$

     In Section 1.3 we developed the graphs of $y = \sin x$ and $y = \cos x$. The graph of $y = \sin x$ is called the **sine curve,** or sometimes the sine wave. Of the three basic ways to vary the sine curve, two will be discussed in this section. The sine curve, or wave, can be "stretched" or "shrunk" by increasing or decreasing the fundamental period of the function. We can increase or decrease the difference between the maximum function value.

     The sine curve can also be "moved" to the right or to the left. This involves what is known as **phase shift,** which will be discussed in Section 1.5. Different combinations of these three types of variation will be discussed at appropriate times.

     We have seen that the sine function and the cosine function are periodic functions. All variations of these functions to be studied in these sections are also periodic functions.

If p is the fundamental period of the sine or cosine function, the graph of that function over any interval of the horizontal axis of length p is called a cycle of the wave.

Another way of expressing the same idea is to say that if we are considering a function $f(x)$ which is a variation of the sine function or the cosine function and $f(x)$ has fundamental period p, the set of number pairs

$$\{(x, y) \mid y = f(x) \text{ and } c \le x \le c + p \text{ where } c \in R\}$$

is a **cycle of the function** *and the graph of that set of ordered pairs is a* **cycle of the wave.**

We indicated that one of the ways to vary the graph of the sine function or the cosine function is to vary the fundamental period of the function. Recall from Chapter 0 that if $f(x)$ is a periodic function with fundamental period p and if $k \ne 0$, then $f(kx)$ is a periodic function with fundamental period $p/|k|$.

Since the cosine function has fundamental period 2π, the function given by $y = \cos 2x$ has fundamental period $2\pi/2 = \pi$. We can construct a table of function values for $y = \cos 2x$ by letting $2x$ vary from 0 to 2π and letting x vary accordingly. It is probably easier to fill in the $2x$ row first, since we are graphing $y = \cos 2x$ and we know the numbers for which we know the basic function values. See Table 8.

Table 8

x	0	$\frac{\pi}{12}$	$\frac{\pi}{8}$	$\frac{\pi}{6}$	$\frac{\pi}{4}$	$\frac{\pi}{3}$	$\frac{3\pi}{8}$	$\frac{5\pi}{12}$	$\frac{\pi}{2}$
$2x$	0	$\frac{\pi}{6}$	$\frac{\pi}{4}$	$\frac{\pi}{3}$	$\frac{\pi}{2}$	$\frac{2\pi}{3}$	$\frac{3\pi}{4}$	$\frac{5\pi}{6}$	π
$\cos 2x$	1	$\frac{\sqrt{3}}{2}$	$\frac{\sqrt{2}}{2}$	$\frac{1}{2}$	0	$-\frac{1}{2}$	$-\frac{\sqrt{2}}{2}$	$-\frac{\sqrt{3}}{2}$	-1

x	$\frac{7\pi}{12}$	$\frac{5\pi}{8}$	$\frac{2\pi}{3}$	$\frac{3\pi}{4}$	$\frac{5\pi}{6}$	$\frac{7\pi}{8}$	$\frac{11\pi}{12}$	π
$2x$	$\frac{7\pi}{6}$	$\frac{5\pi}{4}$	$\frac{4\pi}{3}$	$\frac{3\pi}{2}$	$\frac{5\pi}{3}$	$\frac{7\pi}{4}$	$\frac{11\pi}{6}$	2π
$\cos 2x$	$-\frac{\sqrt{3}}{2}$	$-\frac{\sqrt{2}}{2}$	$-\frac{1}{2}$	0	$\frac{1}{2}$	$\frac{\sqrt{2}}{2}$	$\frac{\sqrt{3}}{2}$	1

The graph of $y = \cos 2x$ appears in Figure 1.18. The graph of the cycle of the function for which we constructed the table is in color, and the rest of the graph is obtained by using the periodicity of the function.

Figure 1.18

If we let

$$y = \sin \frac{x}{2} = \sin \left(\frac{1}{2}x\right),$$

we know that the fundamental period will be

$$\frac{2\pi}{\left(\frac{1}{2}\right)} = 4\pi.$$

A table for this function can be made in the same way that we made the table for $y = \cos 2x$. The graph of $y = \sin x/2$ appears in Figure 1.19. Once again, the graph of one fundamental period of the function is in color.

Figure 1.19

*One-half of the difference between the maximum function value and the minimum function value over any cycle of a function is called the **amplitude** of the function.*

For example, for any cycle of the function $y = \sin x$, the maximum function value is 1 and the minimum function value is -1. The amplitude of the sine function is

$$\frac{1}{2}[1 - (-1)] = 1.$$

The amplitude of the cosine function is also 1, and by now you should be able to show that both $y = \cos 2x$ and $y = \sin x/2$ also have an amplitude of 1.
    The function $g(x) = a \sin x$, where $a \in R$ and $a \neq 0$, can be graphed easily. For example, let us graph the function $g(x) = 2 \sin x$.

$$g(x + 2\pi) = 2 \sin (x + 2\pi)$$
$$= 2 \sin x$$
$$= g(x).$$

The function $g(x)$ has period 2π. In fact, the fundamental period of $g(x)$ is 2π.

Let us construct the table for $y = g(x)$ between 0 and 2π. See Table 9. The graph of $y = 2 \sin x$ appears in Figure 1.20. We have graphed one fundamental period of $y = 2 \sin x$ in color and used the periodicity of the function to extend the graph.

Table 9

x	0	$\frac{\pi}{6}$	$\frac{\pi}{4}$	$\frac{\pi}{3}$	$\frac{\pi}{2}$	$\frac{2\pi}{3}$	$\frac{3\pi}{4}$	$\frac{5\pi}{6}$	π
$\sin x$	0	$\frac{1}{2}$	$\frac{\sqrt{2}}{2}$	$\frac{\sqrt{3}}{2}$	1	$\frac{\sqrt{3}}{2}$	$\frac{\sqrt{2}}{2}$	$\frac{1}{2}$	0
$2 \sin x$	0	1	$\sqrt{2}$	$\sqrt{3}$	2	$\sqrt{3}$	$\sqrt{2}$	1	0

x	$\frac{7\pi}{6}$	$\frac{5\pi}{4}$	$\frac{4\pi}{3}$	$\frac{3\pi}{2}$	$\frac{5\pi}{3}$	$\frac{7\pi}{4}$	$\frac{11\pi}{6}$	2π
$\sin x$	$-\frac{1}{2}$	$-\frac{\sqrt{2}}{2}$	$-\frac{\sqrt{3}}{2}$	-1	$-\frac{\sqrt{3}}{2}$	$-\frac{\sqrt{2}}{2}$	$-\frac{1}{2}$	0
$2 \sin x$	-1	$-\sqrt{2}$	$-\sqrt{3}$	-2	$-\sqrt{3}$	$-\sqrt{2}$	-1	0

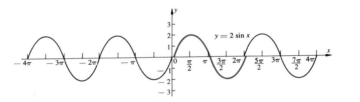

Figure 1.20

We note that several things are true about this graph. The function value for each x when $y = 2 \sin x$ is exactly two times the function value when $y = \sin x$. This means that the maximum function value in any cycle of the function is 2 and the minimum function value is -2. The amplitude of $y = 2 \sin x$ is

$$\frac{[2 - (-2)]}{2} = 2.$$

In general, the amplitude of $y = a \sin x$ is $|a|$. We can also say that the amplitude of $y = a \cos x$ is $|a|$. This means that the amplitude of $y = -3 \cos x$ is $|-3| = 3$.

The student should be able to construct a table of function values for $y = -3 \cos x$. The graph of $y = -3 \cos x$ is given in Figure 1.21. One fundamental period of the graph is in color.

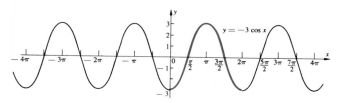

Figure 1.21

We can combine these two types of variation. This is done when we graph

$$y = -4 \cos 3x.$$

The amplitude and the fundamental period of this function are independent of each other. The amplitude of $y = -4 \cos 3x$ is $|-4| = 4$ and the fundamental period is $2\pi/3$.

We can construct a table for $y = -4 \cos 3x$ by letting $3x$ vary from 0 to 2π and then filling in the other rows accordingly. See Table 10. The graph of $y = -4 \cos 3x$ is given in Figure 1.22.

Table 10

x	0	$\dfrac{\pi}{18}$	$\dfrac{\pi}{12}$	$\dfrac{\pi}{9}$	$\dfrac{\pi}{6}$	$\dfrac{2\pi}{9}$	$\dfrac{\pi}{4}$	$\dfrac{5\pi}{18}$	$\dfrac{\pi}{3}$
$3x$	0	$\dfrac{\pi}{6}$	$\dfrac{\pi}{4}$	$\dfrac{\pi}{3}$	$\dfrac{\pi}{2}$	$\dfrac{2\pi}{3}$	$\dfrac{3\pi}{4}$	$\dfrac{5\pi}{6}$	π
$\cos 3x$	1	$\dfrac{\sqrt{3}}{2}$	$\dfrac{\sqrt{2}}{2}$	$\dfrac{1}{2}$	0	$-\dfrac{1}{2}$	$-\dfrac{\sqrt{2}}{2}$	$-\dfrac{\sqrt{3}}{2}$	-1
$-4\cos 3x$	-4	$-2\sqrt{3}$	$-2\sqrt{2}$	-2	0	2	$2\sqrt{2}$	$2\sqrt{3}$	4

x	$\dfrac{7\pi}{18}$	$\dfrac{5\pi}{12}$	$\dfrac{4\pi}{9}$	$\dfrac{\pi}{2}$	$\dfrac{5\pi}{9}$	$\dfrac{7\pi}{12}$	$\dfrac{11\pi}{18}$	$\dfrac{2\pi}{3}$
$3x$	$\dfrac{7\pi}{6}$	$\dfrac{5\pi}{4}$	$\dfrac{4\pi}{3}$	$\dfrac{3\pi}{2}$	$\dfrac{5\pi}{3}$	$\dfrac{7\pi}{4}$	$\dfrac{11\pi}{6}$	2π
$\cos 3x$	$-\dfrac{\sqrt{3}}{2}$	$-\dfrac{\sqrt{2}}{2}$	$-\dfrac{1}{2}$	0	$\dfrac{1}{2}$	$\dfrac{\sqrt{2}}{2}$	$\dfrac{\sqrt{3}}{2}$	1
$-4\cos 3x$	$2\sqrt{3}$	$2\sqrt{2}$	2	0	-2	$-2\sqrt{2}$	$-2\sqrt{3}$	-4

It is possible to sketch most graphs of functions of this type without constructing the extensive tables that we have seen in this section. For example, let us see how one might quickly sketch $y = 2 \sin (-3x)$.

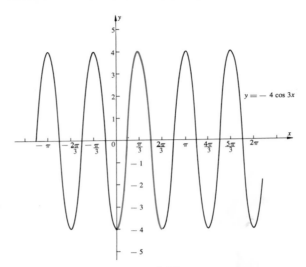

Figure 1.22

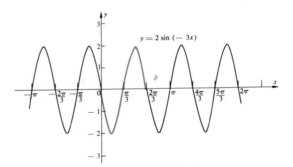

Figure 1.23

The fundamental period of $y = 2 \sin(-3x)$ is

$$\frac{2\pi}{|-3|} = \frac{2\pi}{3}.$$

As x varies from 0 to $2\pi/3$, $-3x$ varies from 0 to -2π. When

$$x = \frac{1}{2}\left(\frac{2\pi}{3}\right) = \frac{\pi}{3},$$

$-3x = -\pi$. Sin 0, sin $(-\pi)$, and sin (-2π) are all 0. The three points $(0, 0)$, $(\pi/3, 0)$, and $(2\pi/3, 0)$ are all plotted on the graph. When

$$x = \frac{1}{2}\left(\frac{\pi}{3}\right) = \frac{\pi}{6},$$

$-3x = -\pi/2$. Since $2 \sin(-\pi/2) = -2$, the point $(\pi/6, -2)$ is on the graph. When

$$x = \frac{3}{2}\left(\frac{\pi}{3}\right) = \frac{\pi}{2},$$

$-3x = -3\pi/2.$ Since

$$2 \sin\left(-\frac{3\pi}{2}\right) = -2 \sin\left(\frac{3\pi}{2}\right) = -(-2) = 2,$$

the point $(\pi/2, 2)$ is on the graph.

Since we know roughly what the sine curve looks like, we can make a rough sketch of one fundamental period of the function by using just these five points (see the portion of the graph in color). The remainder of the curve is obtained by using the periodicity of the function. If the x-intercepts, the maximum points, and the minimum points of the curve are located correctly, it is easy to sketch a good approximation of the curve.

Exercises 1.4

1. Give the amplitude of each of the following functions.

    a. $f(x) = \frac{1}{3} \cos x.$ b. $g(x) = 3 \cos x.$ c. $h(x) = -2 \sin x.$

    d. $f(x) = \frac{1}{2} \sin x.$ e. $g(x) = \frac{4}{3} \cos x.$ f. $h(x) = \frac{5}{9} \sin x.$

    g. $f(x) = \frac{-9}{5} \sin x.$ h. $g(x) = -17 \cos x.$ i. $h(x) = -6 \cos x.$

Graph the following functions.

2. $\{(x, y) \mid y = 3 \sin x\}$ 3. $\{(x, y) \mid y = -2 \cos x\}$

4. $\left\{(x, y) \mid y = \frac{3}{2} \cos x\right\}$ 5. $\left\{(x, y) \mid y = -\frac{1}{2} \sin x\right\}$

6. $\left\{(x, y) \mid y = \cos\left(-\frac{x}{4}\right)\right\}$ 7. $\left\{(x, y) \mid y = \sin \frac{x}{3}\right\}$

8. $\{(x, y) \mid y = \sin 4x\}$ 9. $\{(x, y) \mid y = \cos(-3x)\}$

10. $\left\{(x, y) \mid y = \frac{1}{2} \cos 3x\right\}$ 11. $\{(x, y) \mid y = 3 \sin 2x\}$

12. $\left\{(x, y) \mid y = 4 \cos \frac{x}{3}\right\}$ 13. $\left\{(x, y) \mid y = -\frac{3}{2} \sin \frac{x}{2}\right\}$

14. $\{(x, y) \mid y = -2 \cos 2\pi x\}$ 15. $\{(x, y) \mid y = 2 \sin \pi x\}$

1.5　Phase shift

In discussing variations of the sine function and the cosine function in Section 1.4, we worked with the fundamental period and with the amplitude. Here we shall work primarily with the concept of **phase shift**.

Let us begin by looking at the graph of

$$y = \sin\left(x - \frac{\pi}{4}\right).$$

If $x = \pi/4$, then $x - \pi/4 = 0$. If we let x vary from $\pi/4$ to $9\pi/4$, $x - \pi/4$ varies from 0 to 2π. Table 11 will help us to make a quick sketch of the graph of $y = \sin(x - \pi/4)$.

Table 11

x	$\dfrac{\pi}{4}$	$\dfrac{3\pi}{4}$	$\dfrac{5\pi}{4}$	$\dfrac{7\pi}{4}$	$\dfrac{9\pi}{4}$
$x - \dfrac{\pi}{4}$	0	$\dfrac{\pi}{2}$	π	$\dfrac{3\pi}{2}$	2π
$\sin\left(x - \dfrac{\pi}{4}\right)$	0	1	0	-1	0

Figure 1.24 shows the graph of $y = \sin(x - \pi/4)$. The five points obtained from the table are shown on the graph. The one fundamental period of the graph outlined by the five points given in the table is shown in color.

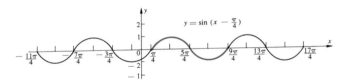

Figure 1.24

Observe that there is one basic difference between the graph in Figure 1.24 and that of $y = \sin x$. The graph of $y = \sin(x - \pi/4)$ appears to be "shifted" $\pi/4$ units to the right.

This is where we get the term phase shift. Basically, if $\alpha \in R$, the graph of $\sin(x - \alpha)$ appears to be shifted α units to the right. The phase shift of such a curve is said to be α. Note that if α is negative, the resulting shift is to the left. Basically, we are taking the sine of some quantity. The phase shift is the number the variable must be to make that quantity 0. $x - \pi/4 = 0$ if and only if $x = \pi/4$. Thus, the phase shift of $y = \sin(x - \pi/4)$ is $\pi/4$. In general, the phase shift of $y = \sin(x - \alpha)$ is α, and the curve is "shifted" α units to the right if α is positive.

The idea of phase shift is the same with the cosine function as it is with the sine function. As an example of this, the graph of $y = \cos(x + \pi/2)$ is shown in Figure 1.25. Note that the phase shift of $y = \cos(x + \pi/2)$ is $-\pi/2$.

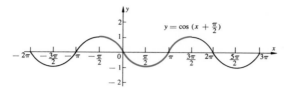

Figure 1.25

Let us consider the function given by

$$y = \sin (2x - \pi).$$

The phase shift of this function is $\pi/2$, since $2x - \pi = 0$ if and only if $x = \pi/2$. In this case, we have something to consider besides phase shift. The quantity $2x - \pi$ varies from 0 to 2π as x varies from $\pi/2$ to $3\pi/2$. This tells us that the fundamental period of $y = \sin (2x - \pi)$ is π. If we write $\sin (2x - \pi)$ as $\sin 2(x - \pi/2)$, we can see that the fundamental period should be $2\pi/2 = \pi$. The graph of $y = \sin (2x - \pi)$ is given in Figure 1.26. One fundamental period of the graph is in color.

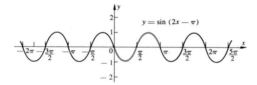

Figure 1.26

When we write $\sin (2x - \pi)$ as $\sin 2(x - \pi/2)$, it is easy to see that the phase shift is $\pi/2$ and the fundamental period is $2\pi/2 = \pi$. In general, if $y = \sin (ax - b)$, we can write this as $y = \sin a(x - b/a)$, and we see that the phase shift is b/a and the fundamental period is $2\pi/|a|$. The same is true for $\cos (ax - b)$.

Let us graph $y = \cos (\pi x - \pi)$. We can write this as $\cos \pi(x - 1)$. This tells us that the *phase shift is* 1 and the fundamental period is $2\pi/\pi = 2$. The graph of $y = \cos (\pi x - \pi)$ is given in Figure 1.27.

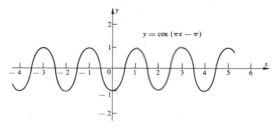

Figure 1.27

The consideration of amplitude is independent of the considerations of phase shift and fundamental period. The student should be able to combine different amplitudes with the other two variations of the sine curve at this point.

Exercises 1.5

Give the amplitude, phase shift, and fundamental period of each of the following.

1. $y = \sin\left(x + \frac{\pi}{2}\right)$.

2. $y = \cos\left(x - \frac{\pi}{2}\right)$.

3. $y = \cos(2x + \pi)$.

4. $y = \sin(3x - \pi)$.

5. $y = 2\sin(x + \pi)$.

6. $y = 3\cos(3x + 2\pi)$.

7. $y = -3\cos\left(2x - \frac{\pi}{2}\right)$.

8. $y = -2\sin\left(3x - \frac{\pi}{2}\right)$.

Graph each of the following.

9. $y = \sin\left(x + \frac{\pi}{2}\right)$.

10. $y = \cos\left(x - \frac{\pi}{2}\right)$.

11. $y = \cos(2x + \pi)$.

12. $y = \sin(3x - \pi)$.

13. $y = 2\sin(x + \pi)$.

✗14. $y = 3\cos(3x + 2\pi)$.

15. $y = -3\cos\left(2x - \frac{\pi}{2}\right)$.

16. $y = -2\sin\left(3x - \frac{\pi}{2}\right)$.

1.6   The other trigonometric functions

In addition to the sine function and the cosine function discussed in Section 1.2, there are four other trigonometric functions—**the tangent function, the cotangent function, the secant function, and the cosecant function.** These four functions are defined in terms of the sine function and the cosine function. All four are defined in this section.

The first to be considered is the tangent function, defined next.

> *tangent function* $= \{(x, y) \mid x \in R, \cos x \neq 0, \text{ and } y = \sin x/\cos x\}$.
> *We usually write* $\tan x = y$ *to indicate that the ordered pair* (x, y) *belongs to the tangent function.*

Recall that the domain for both the sine function and the cosine function is the entire set of real numbers. This is not the case, however, for the tangent function. The tangent function is not defined at a number x for which $\cos x = 0$. If we consider the graph of the cosine function (Figure 1.28), we see that

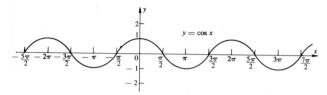

Figure 1.28

$\cos x = 0$ if $x = \pm\,\pi/2,\,\pm 3\pi/2,\,\pm 5\pi/2,\,\ldots$ We can summarize this by saying that $\cos x = 0$ if $x = \pi/2 + n\pi,\, n \in J$. This means that *the domain of the tangent function is the set given by*

$$\left\{x\,|\,x \in R,\, x \neq \frac{\pi}{2} + n\pi,\, n \in J\right\}.$$

The secant function is defined by
secant function $= \{(x, y)\,|\,x \in R,\, \cos x \neq 0,\, y = 1/\cos x\}.$
We usually write $\sec x = y$ *to indicate that the ordered pair* (x, y) *belongs to the secant function.*

We can observe that the secant function is not defined when $\cos x = 0$. In this sense, the secant function is quite similar to the tangent function. *The domain of the secant function is also the set given by*

$$\left\{x\,|\,x \in R,\, x \neq \frac{\pi}{2} + n\pi,\, n \in J\right\}.$$

The cotangent function is defined by
cotangent function $= \{(x, y)\,|\,x \in R,\, \sin x \neq 0,\, y = \cos x/\sin x\}.$
We usually write $\cot x = y$ *to indicate that the ordered pair* (x, y) *belongs to the cotangent function.*

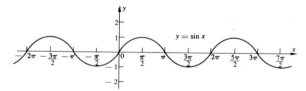

Figure 1.29

We can see that the cotangent function is not defined if $\sin x = 0$. By looking at the graph of the sine function (Figure 1.29), we see that $\sin x = 0$ if $x = 0,\,\pm\pi,\,\pm 2\pi,\,\ldots$ We can express this by saying that $\sin x = 0$ if $x = n\pi$, $n \in J$. This means that *the domain of the cotangent function is the set given by*

$$\{x\,|\,x \in R,\, x \neq n\pi,\, n \in J\}.$$

The cosecant function is defined by

cosecant function $= \{(x, y)\,|\,x \in R,\ \sin x \neq 0,\ y = 1/\sin x\}$.
We usually write $\csc x = y$ *to indicate that the ordered pair* (x, y) *belongs to the cosecant function.*

We can readily see that the domain for the cosecant function is the same as for the cotangent function. That is, *the domain for the cosecant function is the set*

$$\{x\,|\,x \in R,\ x \neq n\pi,\ n \in J\}.$$

We have already developed function values for $\sin x$ and $\cos x$ for some special real numbers, values you should know by now. These function values can be used to find the function values for $\tan x$, $\cot x$, $\sec x$, and $\csc x$ for some special real numbers.

We use the equations

$$\tan x = \frac{\sin x}{\cos x}, \quad \sec x = \frac{1}{\cos x}, \quad \cot x = \frac{\cos x}{\sin x}, \quad \text{and} \quad \csc x = \frac{1}{\sin x}$$

to find the function values given in Table 12. These are important function values that you should learn.

Table 12

x	$\tan x$	$\cot x$	$\sec x$	$\csc x$
0	0	undefined	1	undefined
$\dfrac{\pi}{6}$	$\dfrac{1}{\sqrt{3}}$ or $\dfrac{\sqrt{3}}{3}$	$\sqrt{3}$	$\dfrac{2}{\sqrt{3}}$ or $\dfrac{2\sqrt{3}}{3}$	2
$\dfrac{\pi}{4}$	1	1	$\dfrac{2}{\sqrt{2}}$ or $\sqrt{2}$	$\dfrac{2}{\sqrt{2}}$ or $\sqrt{2}$
$\dfrac{\pi}{3}$	$\sqrt{3}$	$\dfrac{1}{\sqrt{3}}$ or $\dfrac{\sqrt{3}}{3}$	2	$\dfrac{2}{\sqrt{3}}$ or $\dfrac{2\sqrt{3}}{3}$
$\dfrac{\pi}{2}$	undefined	0	undefined	1
π	0	undefined	-1	undefined
$\dfrac{3\pi}{2}$	undefined	0	undefined	-1
2π	0	undefined	1	undefined

In Section 1.2 you learned that $\sin x$ is positive in Quadrants I and II and that $\sin x$ is negative in Quadrants III and IV. You also learned that $\cos x$ is positive in Quadrants I and IV and negative in Quadrants II and III. This information can be used to determine the information contained in Figure 1.30.

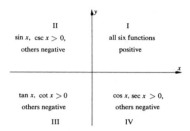

Figure 1.30

Recall from Section 1.2 that for every real number x, $\sin^2 x + \cos^2 x = 1$. If $x \neq \pi/2 + n\pi$, where $n \in J$, we can obtain

$$\frac{\sin^2 x}{\cos^2 x} + \frac{\cos^2 x}{\cos^2 x} = \frac{1}{\cos^2 x},$$

$$\left(\frac{\sin x}{\cos x}\right)^2 + 1 = \left(\frac{1}{\cos x}\right)^2,$$

$$\tan^2 x + 1 = \sec^2 x.$$

Thus, if $x \neq \pi/2 + n\pi$, where $n \in J$,

$$\tan^2 x + 1 = \sec^2 x.$$

In similar fashion, if $x \neq n\pi$, where $n \in J$, we have

$$\frac{\sin^2 x}{\sin^2 x} + \frac{\cos^2 x}{\sin^2 x} = \frac{1}{\sin^2 x},$$

$$1 + \left(\frac{\cos x}{\sin x}\right)^2 = \left(\frac{1}{\sin x}\right)^2,$$

$$1 + \cot^2 x = \csc^2 x.$$

Thus, if $x \neq n\pi$, where $n \in J$,

$$\cot^2 x + 1 = \csc^2 x.$$

These last two equations will be of use in the homework. Since they are basic identities that will be used frequently, the student should learn them.

Exercises 1.6

1. Recalling that $\sin(-x) = -\sin x$ and $\cos(-x) = \cos x$, develop expressions for

    a. $\tan(-x)$,   b. $\sec(-x)$,   c. $\cot(-x)$,   d. $\csc(-x)$.

2. Use the information acquired in Exercise 1 to evaluate

    a. $\tan\left(-\frac{\pi}{4}\right)$,   b. $\sec\left(-\frac{\pi}{6}\right)$,   c. $\csc\left(-\frac{\pi}{3}\right)$,

    d. $\cot\left(-\dfrac{\pi}{4}\right)$,   e. $\sec\left(-\dfrac{\pi}{3}\right)$,   f. $\tan\left(-\dfrac{\pi}{6}\right)$,

    g. $\cot\left(-\dfrac{\pi}{3}\right)$,   h. $\csc\left(-\dfrac{\pi}{4}\right)$,   i. $\cot\left(-\dfrac{\pi}{6}\right)$,

    j. $\csc\left(-\dfrac{\pi}{6}\right)$,   k. $\tan\left(-\dfrac{\pi}{3}\right)$,   l. $\sec\left(-\dfrac{\pi}{4}\right)$.

3. Using the fact that $\sin(\pi - x) = \sin x$ and $\cos(\pi - x) = -\cos x$, develop expressions for

    a. $\tan(\pi - x)$,   b. $\cot(\pi - x)$,

    c. $\sec(\pi - x)$,   d. $\csc(\pi - x)$.

4. Use the information acquired in Exercise 3 to evaluate

    a. $\tan\dfrac{3\pi}{4}$,   b. $\sec\dfrac{5\pi}{6}$,   c. $\csc\dfrac{2\pi}{3}$,

    d. $\cot\dfrac{3\pi}{4}$,   e. $\sec\dfrac{2\pi}{3}$,   f. $\tan\dfrac{5\pi}{6}$,

    g. $\cot\dfrac{2\pi}{3}$,   h. $\csc\dfrac{3\pi}{4}$,   i. $\cot\dfrac{5\pi}{6}$,

    j. $\tan\dfrac{2\pi}{3}$,   k. $\csc\dfrac{5\pi}{6}$,   l. $\sec\dfrac{3\pi}{4}$.

5. Use the fact that $\cos(x + \pi) = -\cos x$ and $\sin(x + \pi) = -\sin x$, to develop expressions for

    a. $\tan(x + \pi)$,   b. $\cot(x + \pi)$,

    c. $\sec(x + \pi)$,   d. $\csc(x + \pi)$.

6. Use the information acquired in Exercise 5 to evaluate

    a. $\sec\dfrac{5\pi}{4}$,   b. $\csc\dfrac{7\pi}{6}$,   c. $\tan\dfrac{4\pi}{3}$,

    d. $\cot\dfrac{7\pi}{6}$,   e. $\csc\dfrac{5\pi}{4}$,   f. $\cot\dfrac{4\pi}{3}$,

    g. $\tan\dfrac{7\pi}{6}$,   h. $\sec\dfrac{4\pi}{3}$,   i. $\cot\dfrac{5\pi}{4}$,

    j. $\csc\dfrac{4\pi}{3}$,   k. $\sec\dfrac{7\pi}{6}$,   l. $\tan\dfrac{5\pi}{4}$.

In each of the following exercises, use the given information to evaluate all the remaining trigonometric functions.

Example

$\cos x = \dfrac{15}{17}$, $\sin x < 0$.

Solution

Since $\cos x > 0$ and $\sin x < 0$, x is in the fourth quadrant. $\sec x > 0$; the others are negative.

$$\sec x = \frac{1}{\cos x} = \frac{17}{15},$$

$$\sin x = -\sqrt{1 - \cos^2 x} = -\sqrt{1 - \frac{225}{289}} = -\sqrt{\frac{64}{289}} = -\frac{8}{17},$$

$$\tan x = \frac{\sin x}{\cos x} = -\frac{8}{15},$$

$$\cot x = \frac{1}{\tan x} = -\frac{15}{8},$$

$$\csc x = \frac{1}{\sin x} = -\frac{17}{8}.$$

Example

$\tan x = -\dfrac{3}{4}$, $\sin x > 0$.

Solution

Since $\tan x < 0$, $\sin x > 0$, x is in the second quadrant. $\csc x > 0$; the others are negative.

$$\sec^2 x = \tan^2 x + 1 = \frac{9}{16} + 1 = \frac{25}{16},$$

$$\sec x = -\frac{5}{4}, \quad \text{since } \sec x < 0,$$

$$\cos x = -\frac{4}{5},$$

$$\cot x = -\frac{4}{3}.$$

Since $\dfrac{\sin x}{\cos x} = \tan x,$

$$\sin x = \cos x \tan x = \left(-\frac{4}{5}\right)\left(-\frac{3}{4}\right) = \frac{3}{5},$$

$$\csc x = \frac{1}{\sin x} = \frac{5}{3}.$$

7. $\sec x = -\dfrac{13}{5}$, $\tan x > 0$.

8. $\csc x = \dfrac{2\sqrt{3}}{3}$, $\sec x > 0$.

9. $\tan x = \dfrac{1}{2}$, $\cos x > 0$.

10. $\sin x = \dfrac{5}{13}$, $\cot x < 0$.

11. $\cos x = \dfrac{2}{\sqrt{13}}$, $\tan x < 0$.

12. $\csc x = -\dfrac{17}{15}$, $\cos x < 0$.

13. $\cot x = \dfrac{1}{3}$, $\csc x < 0$.

14. $\sec x = \dfrac{5}{3}$, $\sin x > 0$.

1.7 Graphs of the other trigonometric functions

The secant function was defined so that $\sec x = 1/\cos x$. From this definition, we determined that the domain of the secant function is $\{x \mid x \in R$ and $x \neq \pi/2 + n\pi$, where $n \in J\}$. There is other information about the secant function which we can obtain from the definition. Since $\cos (x + 2\pi) = \cos x$, we have

$$\sec (x + 2\pi) = \frac{1}{\cos (x + 2\pi)}$$

$$= \frac{1}{\cos x}$$

$$= \sec x.$$

This leads us to the conclusion that the secant function is also a periodic function with period 2π. In fact, the fundamental period of the secant function is 2π.

We shall discuss the range of the secant function after we graph it. Our graph will be for one fundamental period, between $-\pi$ and π; we can then use the periodicity of the function to extend its graph.

Since the secant function is not defined when $x = \pi/2 + n\pi$, $n \in J$, we use vertical dotted lines on the graph for values of x equal to $\pi/2 + n\pi$, $n \in J$. The graph of $y = \sec x$ does not intersect these vertical lines. We can easily obtain the function values for Table 13 from the material and exercises in the preceding section. The function values in the table are plotted in Figure 1.31.

Table 13

x	0	$\dfrac{\pi}{6}$	$\dfrac{\pi}{4}$	$\dfrac{\pi}{3}$	$\dfrac{\pi}{2}$	$\dfrac{2\pi}{3}$	$\dfrac{3\pi}{4}$	$\dfrac{5\pi}{6}$	π
$\sec x$	1	$\dfrac{2\sqrt{3}}{3}$	$\sqrt{2}$	2	undefined	-2	$-\sqrt{2}$	$-\dfrac{2\sqrt{3}}{3}$	-1

x	$-\dfrac{\pi}{6}$	$-\dfrac{\pi}{4}$	$-\dfrac{\pi}{3}$	$-\dfrac{\pi}{2}$	$-\dfrac{2\pi}{3}$	$-\dfrac{3\pi}{4}$	$-\dfrac{5\pi}{6}$	$-\pi$
$\sec x$	$\dfrac{2\sqrt{3}}{3}$	$\sqrt{2}$	2	undefined	-2	$-\sqrt{2}$	$-\dfrac{2\sqrt{3}}{3}$	-1

As x approaches $\pi/2$, $\cos x$ approaches 0, and $1/\cos x$ gets very large. Furthermore, $1/\cos x$ will have the same sign as $\cos x$. Using these ideas, we can approximate the graph of $y = \sec x$ by making smooth curves that go through the points graphed but do not intersect the dotted lines. This is done in color

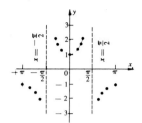

Figure 1.31

in Figure 1.32. The periodicity of the secant function is used to extend the graph beyond the interval $[-\pi, \pi]$.

From the graph in Figure 1.32, it appears that the range of the secant function is $(-\infty, -1] \cup [1, \infty)$. And this actually is the range of the secant function, although we shall not formally develop the fact here.

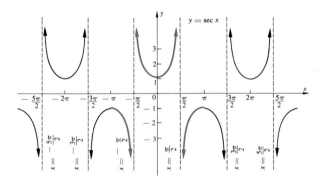

Figure 1.32

The tangent function is defined in terms of both the sine function and the cosine function. As we remember,

$$\tan x = \frac{\sin x}{\cos x}$$

if $x \neq \pi/2 + n\pi$, $n \in J$. Since both the sine function and the cosine function are periodic functions, with fundamental period 2π, we have

$$\tan (x + 2\pi) = \frac{\sin (x + 2\pi)}{\cos (x + 2\pi)}$$

$$= \frac{\sin x}{\cos x}$$

$$= \tan x.$$

Thus, the tangent function is a periodic function with period 2π, However, we shall see after graphing the tangent function that its fundamental period is not 2π.

Our graph of the tangent function will be on the closed interval from $-\pi$ to π, except where $x = \pi/2 + n\pi$, $n \in J$. Dotted lines are used at $x = \pi/2 + n\pi$, as in the graph of the secant function. It is easy to determine the function values in Table 14 from the material and exercises in the preceding section. These function values are graphed in Figure 1.33.

Table 14

x	0	$\dfrac{\pi}{6}$	$\dfrac{\pi}{4}$	$\dfrac{\pi}{3}$	$\dfrac{\pi}{2}$	$\dfrac{2\pi}{3}$	$\dfrac{3\pi}{4}$	$\dfrac{5\pi}{6}$	π
$\tan x$	0	$\dfrac{1}{\sqrt{3}}$	1	$\sqrt{3}$	undefined	$-\sqrt{3}$	-1	$-\dfrac{1}{\sqrt{3}}$	0

x	$-\dfrac{\pi}{6}$	$-\dfrac{\pi}{4}$	$-\dfrac{\pi}{3}$	$-\dfrac{\pi}{2}$	$-\dfrac{2\pi}{3}$	$-\dfrac{3\pi}{4}$	$-\dfrac{5\pi}{6}$	$-\pi$
$\tan x$	$-\dfrac{1}{\sqrt{3}}$	-1	$-\sqrt{3}$	undefined	$\sqrt{3}$	1	$\dfrac{1}{\sqrt{3}}$	0

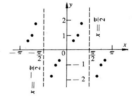

Figure 1.33

If x is just a little bit smaller than $\pi/2$, $\sin x$ is very close to 1 and $\cos x$ is positive and very close to 0. In this situation, $\sin x/\cos x$ gets very large. Using this idea and a similar analysis when x is just a little bit larger than $\pi/2$ or very close to $-\pi/2$, we can connect the points with smooth curves to get the colored portion of the graph in Figure 1.34. The periodicity of the tangent function is used to extend the graph beyond the interval $[-\pi, \pi]$.

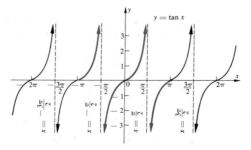

Figure 1.34

It appears that the tangent function has π as its fundamental period, and this is the case. Observe that

$$\tan (x + \pi) = \frac{\sin (x + \pi)}{\cos (x + \pi)}$$

$$= \frac{-\sin x}{-\cos x}$$

$$= \tan x.$$

The range of the tangent function is the entire set of real numbers.

The development of the graphs of the cosecant function and the cotangent function, shown in Figures 1.35 and 1.36, respectively, is left for the student in the exercises.

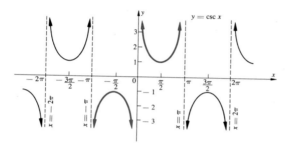

Figure 1.35

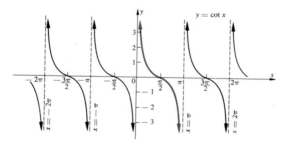

Figure 1.36

Exercises 1.7

1.   a.   Prove that if $x \neq n\pi$, where $n \in J$, $\cot (x + 2\pi) = \cot x$.
      b.   What are the numbers in the interval $[-\pi, \pi]$ for which $\cot x$ is undefined?
      c.   Construct a table of function values for the other numbers in the interval $[-\pi, \pi]$ for which you know the function values.

   d.   Put dotted vertical lines at appropriate places on the graph. Then plot the function values from part c.

   e.   Draw a smooth curve through these points, remembering not to intersect the dotted lines.

   f.   Extend the graph in both directions by using the periodicity of the cotangent function.

   g.   What is the fundamental period of the cotangent function?

2.   a.   Prove that if $x \neq n\pi$, where $n \in J$, $\csc(x + 2\pi) = \csc x$.

   b.   What are the numbers in the interval $[-\pi, \pi]$ for which $\csc x$ is undefined?

   c.   Construct a table of function values for the other numbers in the interval $[-\pi, \pi]$ for which you know the function values.

   d.   Put dotted vertical lines at appropriate places on the graph; then plot the function values from part c.

   e.   Draw a smooth curve through these points, remembering not to intersect the vertical lines.

   f.   Extend the graph in both directions by using the periodicity of the cosecant function.

   g.   What is the fundamental period of the cosecant function?

Make a sketch of the graphs of the functions in Problems 3–12.

Example

$y = \tan 2x.$

Solution

Since the fundamental period of the tangent function is π, we may start by letting $2x$ vary from $-\pi/2$ to $\pi/2$. Fill in the second row of the table with special numbers for which we know the function values, and then fill in the other rows appropriately.

x	$-\dfrac{\pi}{4}$	$-\dfrac{\pi}{6}$	$-\dfrac{\pi}{8}$	$-\dfrac{\pi}{12}$	0	$\dfrac{\pi}{12}$	$\dfrac{\pi}{8}$	$\dfrac{\pi}{6}$	$\dfrac{\pi}{4}$
$2x$	$-\dfrac{\pi}{2}$	$-\dfrac{\pi}{3}$	$-\dfrac{\pi}{4}$	$-\dfrac{\pi}{6}$	0	$\dfrac{\pi}{6}$	$\dfrac{\pi}{4}$	$\dfrac{\pi}{3}$	$\dfrac{\pi}{2}$
$\tan 2x$	undefined	$-\sqrt{3}$	-1	$-\dfrac{1}{\sqrt{3}}$	0	$\dfrac{1}{\sqrt{3}}$	1	$\sqrt{3}$	undefined

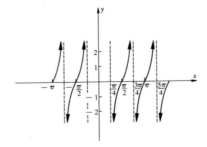

3. $y = \tan \dfrac{x}{2}$.

4. $y = 2 + \cot x$.

5. $y = 2 \sec x$.

6. $y = \dfrac{1}{3} \tan x$.

7. $y = \csc 2x$.

8. $y = \cot 4x$.

9. $y = \sec x - 1$.

10. $y = -\dfrac{1}{2} \csc x$.

11. $y = 2 \tan 2x$.

12. $y = \tan \left(x + \dfrac{\pi}{2} \right)$.

Review Exercises

1. Evaluate the following expressions.

a. $\cos \dfrac{\pi}{4}$

b. $\sin \dfrac{\pi}{3}$

c. $\tan \dfrac{\pi}{6}$

d. $\cot \dfrac{\pi}{2}$

e. $\sec 0$

f. $\csc \dfrac{\pi}{4}$

g. $\sin \dfrac{5\pi}{6}$

h. $\cos \dfrac{2\pi}{3}$

i. $\cot \dfrac{4\pi}{3}$

j. $\tan \left(-\dfrac{3\pi}{4} \right)$

k. $\csc \left(-\dfrac{\pi}{3} \right)$

l. $\sec \left(-\dfrac{5\pi}{6} \right)$

Make a rough sketch of the graph of each of the following functions. Determine the fundamental period and phase shift in each problem.

2. $y = \sin 2x$.

3. $y = \cos (-3x)$.

4. $y = 2 \cos (2x + \pi)$.

5. $y = 3 \sin \left(-2x + \dfrac{\pi}{2} \right)$.

6. $y = -2 \tan x$.

7. $y = \sec \left(2x - \dfrac{\pi}{2} \right)$.

8. $y = \cot \left(x + \dfrac{\pi}{4} \right)$.

9. $y = 3 \csc \left(x - \dfrac{\pi}{2} \right)$.

10. $y = 3 \sec \dfrac{x}{2}$.

11. $y = \tan \left(\dfrac{x}{2} + \dfrac{\pi}{4} \right)$.

12. Evaluate each of the following expressions.

a. $\sin \dfrac{23\pi}{4}$

b. $\cos \left(-\dfrac{11\pi}{3} \right)$

c. $\tan \dfrac{21\pi}{4}$

d. $\cot \dfrac{13\pi}{6}$

e. $\csc \dfrac{13\pi}{2}$

f. $\sec (-7\pi)$

g. $\cos \dfrac{125\pi}{6}$

h. $\sin \left(-\dfrac{74\pi}{3} \right)$

i. $\sec \dfrac{17\pi}{3}$

j. $\tan -\dfrac{49\pi}{6}$

2

Trigonometric identities

2.1 Identities and equations

You should recall from your study of algebra that mathematical expressions that involve an equals sign are called equations. An equation, actually a statement that two expressions are equal, is sometimes called a statement of equality. A statement of equality may be either true or false. Some examples of equations appear below.

$$(x - 1)(x + 1) = x^2 - 1. \qquad 3x - 4 = 5.$$

We are actually considering two types of algebraic equations here. The first equation is intended to indicate that if x represents any number for which $(x - 1)(x + 1)$ and $x^2 - 1$ are both meaningful expressions, then $(x - 1)(x + 1)$ and $x^2 - 1$ are different names for the same number. An equation of this type is called an **identity**.

The second equation expresses a different idea. The two expressions, $3x - 4$ and 5, may or may not be different names for the same number. Clearly, if $x = 3$, we have a true statement of equality and if $x \neq 3$, we have a false statement of equality. Equations of this type are called **conditional equations.**

The *replacement set* for an equation in one variable is a set of numbers any one of which may be used to replace the variable. Sometimes we agree beforehand what set of numbers this will be. It may be the set of natural numbers, the set of integers, the set of complex numbers, or any other set of numbers. Often we assume that the replacement set for an equation is the set of all real numbers for which each expression in the equation is a meaningful expression.

A conditional equation may be defined more accurately as *an equation for which at least one element in the replacement set results in a false statement of equality*. The equation $3x - 4 = 5$ is a conditional equation, since 2 is in the replacement set for $3x - 4 = 5$, and $3 \cdot 2 - 4 = 5$ is a *false* statement of equality.

An identity may be defined as *an equation for which each element in the replacement set results in a true statement of equality*.

From these two definitions, you can see that every equation is either a conditional equation or an identity.

One should keep in mind that in algebra different replacement sets are used for the variables on different occasions. For example, if the replacement set for the equation $x^2 + 1 = 0$ were the set of real numbers, there would be no elements in the replacement set that result in a true statement of equality. If the replacement set for the equation $x^2 + 1 = 0$ is the set of complex numbers, both i and $-i$ result in true statements of equality. In each of these cases, the equation $x^2 + 1 = 0$ is a conditional equation, since, in each case, 2 is in the replacement set and 2 results in a false statement of equality.

In this section we shall extend the ideas of identities and conditional equations to trigonometric equations. This chapter deals with techniques for verifying that some trigonometric equations are identities, and Chapter 3 explores methods of solving conditional trigonometric equations.

In dealing with trigonometric expressions, we consider the replacement set to be *all real numbers for which the expression is meaningful*. The replacement set of a trigonometric equation is *the set of all real numbers for which each member of the equation is a real number*, whether or not the resulting statement of equality is true.

There are three ways in which substituting a particular real number for the variable might fail to result in a meaningful expression:

1. It might leave a trigonometric function undefined.
2. It might create a situation which calls for dividing by 0.
3. It might create a situation which calls for taking an even root of a negative number.

The first of these three difficulties is illustrated in the equation $\sec x \sin x = \tan x$. You will remember that if x is a real number of the form $\pi/2 + n\pi$, where $n \in J$, both $\sec x$ and $\tan x$ are undefined. Thus, the replacement set for $\sec x \sin x = \tan x$ is

$$R - \left\{ x \mid x = \frac{\pi}{2} + n\pi, n \in J \right\}.$$

The second difficulty is illustrated in the equation

$$\sin x = \frac{1}{1 - \cos x}.$$

The right-hand member of the equation will not be defined if $\cos x = 1$, since this would involve division by 0. Since $\cos x = 1$ if $x = 2n\pi$, where $n \in J$, the replacement set for $\sin x = 1/(1 - \cos x)$ is the set

$$R - \{x \,|\, x = 2n\pi, n \in J\}.$$

We will use the symbol $\mathscr{D}$ to represent the replacement set for the expression or equation under consideration in any problem. Thus, in this last example we could have written

$$\mathscr{D} = R - \{x \,|\, x = 2n\pi, n \in J\}.$$

The discussion here has been basically algebraic in nature, and the student should recognize that the last two of the three difficulties listed can also occur in algebra. In practice, we must be alert to avoid the first two difficulties. The third will occur relatively infrequently in this book.

As indicated earlier, a conditional equation is an equation for which at least one number in the replacement set results in a false statement of equality. One way of proving that an equation is conditional is to demonstrate that such a number is in the replacement set. Take, for example, the equation $\sin x = 1/(1 - \cos x)$ for which the replacement set is $\mathscr{D} = R - \{x \,|\, x = 2n\pi, n \in J\}$. We note that

$$\pi \in \mathscr{D}, \quad \sin \pi = 0, \quad \frac{1}{1 - \cos \pi} = \frac{1}{1 - (-1)} = \frac{1}{2}, \quad \text{and} \quad 0 \neq \frac{1}{2}.$$

Thus, $\sin \pi \neq 1/(1 - \cos \pi)$, and $\sin x = 1/(1 - \cos x)$ is a conditional equation.

There are times when it is quite helpful to know whether a given trigonometric equation is an identity or a conditional equation. We have just demonstrated the basic method of proving that a trigonometric equation is a conditional equation—by showing that the use of a particular number in the replacement set results in a false statement of equality.

If we cannot find a number which proves that a trigonometric equation is a conditional equation, this does not necessarily mean that the equation in question is an identity. It may mean that we have not tried an appropriate number. If we suspect that a trigonometric equation is an identity, we can attempt to justify our suspicions by using techniques which are discussed throughout the remainder of this chapter. The equation $\sec x \sin x = \tan x$ is an identity, as you will be asked to verify in Exercises 2.2.

So far we have used only symbols with which the student is familiar to represent variables. In trigonometry it is common to use lowercase Greek letters to represent variables. We will use θ, ϕ, α, β, and γ as variables frequently. Their names are *theta, phi, alpha, beta,* and *gamma,* respectively.

Exercises 2.1

Prove that the equations are conditional equations. State the replacement set for each equation.

Example

$\sin x + \cos x = 1.$

Solution

$\mathcal{D} = R.$

$\frac{\pi}{4} \in \mathcal{D}, \sin \frac{\pi}{4} + \cos \frac{\pi}{4} = \frac{\sqrt{2}}{2} + \frac{\sqrt{2}}{2} = \sqrt{2} \neq 1.$

1. $\cos x - \sin x = 1.$
2. $\sec x - \tan x = 1.$
3. $\cos x = \frac{1}{\sin x}.$
4. $\sin 2x = 2 \sin x.$
5. $\cos 2x = 2 \cos x.$
6. $\sin x - \cos x = \cos x - \sin x.$
7. $\sec x - \csc x = \tan x - \cot x.$
8. $\cos \frac{x}{2} = \frac{1}{2} \cos x.$
9. $\sin \frac{x}{2} = \frac{1}{2} \sin x.$
10. $\tan \frac{x}{2} = \frac{1}{2} \tan x.$
11. $\tan 2x = 2 \tan x.$
12. $\frac{\tan x + 1}{\sin x} = \sec x.$
13. $2 \sin x - \cos x + 1 = 0.$
14. $\cos x - 2 \tan x + \sec x = 0.$
15. $\csc x - \sec x = \sin x - \cos x.$

2.2   The fundamental identities

In Chapter 1 we defined the sine function and the cosine function. Then the other trigonometric functions were defined in terms of the sine and cosine functions. These four definitions give us four of the basic trigonometric identities.

1. $\tan \theta = \dfrac{\sin \theta}{\cos \theta},$ $\mathcal{D} = R - \left\{ \theta \mid \theta = \dfrac{\pi}{2} + n\pi, n \in J \right\}.$

2. $\cot \theta = \dfrac{\cos \theta}{\sin \theta},$ $\mathcal{D} = R - \{ \theta \mid \theta = n\pi, n \in J \}.$

3. $\sec \theta = \dfrac{1}{\cos \theta},$ $\mathcal{D} = R - \left\{ \theta \mid \theta = \dfrac{\pi}{2} + n\pi, n \in J \right\}.$

4. $\csc \theta = \dfrac{1}{\sin \theta},$ $\mathcal{D} = R - \{ \theta \mid \theta = n\pi, n \in J \}.$

There is nothing in the equation $\tan \theta = \sin \theta / \cos \theta$ to tell us that this is an identity rather than a conditional equation. We shall use the symbol $\equiv$ to represent the idea that one member of an equation is equal to the other member of the equation for each number in the replacement set for the equation. Thus, the four identities above could have been written

$$\text{1.} \quad \tan \theta \equiv \frac{\sin \theta}{\cos \theta}, \qquad \text{2.} \quad \cot \theta \equiv \frac{\cos \theta}{\sin \theta},$$

$$\text{3.} \quad \sec \theta \equiv \frac{1}{\cos \theta}, \qquad \text{4.} \quad \csc \theta \equiv \frac{1}{\sin \theta},$$

with the replacement set for each equation.

As indicated earlier, the replacement set for an equation is the set of all real numbers for which each member of the equation is a real number. If there is a single real number for which the two members of the equation are both real numbers, but not equal, then that equation is not an identity.

We shall use $\equiv$ in only two cases—when we have proved that an equation is an identity and when we state a problem in which you are to prove that the given equation is an identity.

Three very important identities that were developed in Chapter 1 appear below.

$\text{5.} \quad \sin^2 \theta + \cos^2 \theta \equiv 1, \qquad \mathscr{D} = R.$

$\text{6.} \quad \tan^2 \theta + 1 \equiv \sec^2 \theta, \qquad \mathscr{D} = R - \left\{ \theta \,\middle|\, \theta = \frac{\pi}{2} + n\pi, n \in J \right\}.$

$\text{7.} \quad \cot^2 \theta + 1 \equiv \csc^2 \theta, \qquad \mathscr{D} = R - \{ \theta \,|\, \theta = n\pi, n \in J \}.$

Several other identities were developed in the exercises. These are usually called reduction formulas, since, when we are trying to evaluate a trigonometric expression, we can use them to reduce the problem to the evaluation of a trigonometric expression where the variable represents a number between 0 and $\pi/2$. These reduction formulas appear below.

$\text{8.} \quad \sin(-\theta) \equiv -\sin \theta, \qquad \mathscr{D} = R.$

$\text{9.} \quad \cos(-\theta) \equiv \cos \theta, \qquad \mathscr{D} = R.$

$\text{10.} \quad \tan(-\theta) \equiv -\tan \theta, \qquad \mathscr{D} = R - \left\{ \theta \,\middle|\, \theta = \frac{\pi}{2} + n\pi, n \in J \right\}.$

$\text{11.} \quad \cot(-\theta) \equiv -\cot \theta, \qquad \mathscr{D} = R - \{ \theta \,|\, \theta = n\pi, n \in J \}.$

$\text{12.} \quad \sec(-\theta) \equiv \sec \theta, \qquad \mathscr{D} = R - \left\{ \theta \,\middle|\, \theta = \frac{\pi}{2} + n\pi, n \in J \right\}.$

$\text{13.} \quad \csc(-\theta) \equiv -\csc \theta, \qquad \mathscr{D} = R - \{ \theta \,|\, \theta = n\pi, n \in J \}.$

$\text{14.} \quad \sin(\theta + \pi) \equiv -\sin \theta, \qquad \mathscr{D} = R.$

$\text{15.} \quad \cos(\theta + \pi) \equiv -\cos \theta, \qquad \mathscr{D} = R.$

$\text{16.} \quad \tan(\theta + \pi) \equiv \tan \theta, \qquad \mathscr{D} = R - \left\{ \theta \,\middle|\, \theta = \frac{\pi}{2} + n\pi, n \in J \right\}.$

17. $\cot(\theta + \pi) \equiv \cot\theta,$ $\mathscr{D} = R - \{\theta \,|\, \theta = n\pi, n \in J\}.$

18. $\sec(\theta + \pi) \equiv -\sec\theta,$ $\mathscr{D} = R - \left\{\theta \,|\, \theta = \dfrac{\pi}{2} + n\pi, n \in J\right\}.$

19. $\csc(\theta + \pi) \equiv -\csc\theta,$ $\mathscr{D} = R - \{\theta \,|\, \theta = n\pi, n \in J\}.$
20. $\sin(\pi - \theta) \equiv \sin\theta,$ $\mathscr{D} = R.$
21. $\cos(\pi - \theta) \equiv -\cos\theta,$ $\mathscr{D} = R.$

22. $\tan(\pi - \theta) \equiv -\tan\theta,$ $\mathscr{D} = R - \left\{\theta \,|\, \theta = \dfrac{\pi}{2} + n\pi, n \in J\right\}.$

23. $\cot(\pi - \theta) \equiv -\cot\theta,$ $\mathscr{D} = R - \{\theta \,|\, \theta = n\pi, n \in J\}.$

24. $\sec(\pi - \theta) \equiv -\sec\theta,$ $\mathscr{D} = R - \left\{\theta \,|\, \theta = \dfrac{\pi}{2} + n\pi, n \in J\right\}.$

25. $\csc(\pi - \theta) \equiv \csc\theta,$ $\mathscr{D} = R - \{\theta \,|\, \theta = n\pi, n \in J\}.$
26. $\sin(\theta + 2n\pi) \equiv \sin\theta, n \in J,$ $\mathscr{D} = R.$
27. $\cos(\theta + 2n\pi) \equiv \cos\theta, n \in J,$ $\mathscr{D} = R.$

28. $\tan(\theta + n\pi) \equiv \tan\theta, n \in J,$ $\mathscr{D} = R - \left\{\theta \,|\, \theta = \dfrac{\pi}{2} + n\pi, n \in J\right\}.$

29. $\cot(\theta + n\pi) \equiv \cot\theta, n \in J,$ $\mathscr{D} = R - \{\theta \,|\, \theta = n\pi, n \in J\}.$

30. $\sec(\theta + 2n\pi) \equiv \sec\theta, n \in J,$ $\mathscr{D} = R - \left\{\theta \,|\, \theta = \dfrac{\pi}{2} + n\pi, n \in J\right\}.$

31. $\csc(\theta + 2n\pi) \equiv \csc\theta, n \in J,$ $\mathscr{D} = R - \{\theta \,|\, \theta = n\pi, n \in J\}.$

The student should learn all these identities. They seem like a lot to remember all at once, but in practice many of them can be remembered in other ways. The last six identities refer to the periodicity of the trigonometric functions. One way of remembering the others is to remember which functions are positive and which are negative in each quadrant.

2.3   Verifying trigonometric identities

The 31 basic identities considered in the last section were originally developed in several fashions. We proved the identity $\sin^2\theta + \cos^2\theta \equiv 1$ by using the fact that we were considering a point on the unit circle. The first four identities were simply definitions. The last 24 in the list were developed primarily in the homework problems, through the consideration of the relative positions of different points on the unit circle.

These techniques which we have used so far are helpful, but they will be of relatively little help in the development of further identities. As an aid to developing techniques of proving identities, let us consider two different ways of proving the identity

$$\tan^2\theta + 1 \equiv \sec^2\theta.$$

We will consider the development given in the preceding chapter first.

(1) $\sin^2 \theta + \cos^2 \equiv 1$

(2) $\dfrac{\sin^2 \theta}{\cos^2 \theta} + \dfrac{\cos^2 \theta}{\cos^2 \theta} = \dfrac{1}{\cos^2 \theta} \qquad \theta \neq \dfrac{\pi}{2} + n\pi, \ n \in J$

(3) $\left(\dfrac{\sin \theta}{\cos \theta}\right)^2 + 1 = \left(\dfrac{1}{\cos \theta}\right)^2$

(4) $\tan^2 \theta + 1 = \sec^2 \theta$

$\therefore$ **$\tan^2 \theta + 1 \equiv \sec^2 \theta, \quad \mathscr{D} = R - \left\{\theta \,|\, \theta = \dfrac{\pi}{2} + n\pi, \, n \in J\right\}.$**

In this proof we started with a known identity. Then we divided both sides by the same quantity ($\cos^2 \theta$) and indicated that those numbers which would cause division by 0 were not in the replacement set for the equation. The third step was simply an algebraic manipulation, so that we could apply the definitions of $\tan \theta$ and $\sec \theta$ in the fourth step. It is important to note here that we started with a known identity, not what we wanted to prove. One difficulty with this particular technique is that most students lack sufficient insight to see which known identity, if any, could be used to start proving that a given equation is an identity.

A second technique that can be used to verify identities consists of the following steps:

1. *State the desired identity,*
2. *Indicate the appropriate replacement set,*
3. *Start with one of the two sides of the equation,* and
4. *Attempt to transform that expression into the other side of the equation through a series of steps involving*
   a. *Algebraic manipulations* and
   b. *The use of previously proven identities.*

This technique is demonstrated below.

To prove: $\tan^2 \theta + 1 \equiv \sec^2 \theta, \quad \mathscr{D} = R - \left\{\theta \,|\, \theta = \dfrac{\pi}{2} + n\pi, \, n \in J\right\}.$

(1) $\tan^2 \theta + 1 = \left(\dfrac{\sin \theta}{\cos \theta}\right)^2 + 1$

(2) $\qquad\qquad = \dfrac{\sin^2 \theta}{\cos^2 \theta} + 1$

(3) $\qquad\qquad = \dfrac{\sin^2 \theta}{\cos^2 \theta} + \dfrac{\cos^2 \theta}{\cos^2 \theta}$

(4) $\qquad\qquad = \dfrac{\sin^2 \theta + \cos^2 \theta}{\cos^2 \theta}$

(5) $\qquad\qquad = \dfrac{1}{\cos^2 \theta}$

(6) $$= \left(\frac{1}{\cos \theta}\right)^2$$

(7) $$= \sec^2 \theta$$

$$\therefore \ \tan^2 \theta + 1 \equiv \sec^2 \theta, \quad \mathcal{D} = R - \left\{\theta \,\middle|\, \theta = \frac{\pi}{2} + n\pi, \ n \in J\right\}.$$

This proof has not combined any two steps into a single step. The first step applies the definition of the tangent function. The second, fourth, and sixth steps apply rules of algebra. The third step expresses 1 as $\cos^2 \theta/\cos^2 \theta$ so that we will have a common denominator for the addition of fractions. The fifth step applies a previously proven identity. The seventh step used the definition of $\sec \theta$.

This proof could be abbreviated quite satisfactorily as follows:

To prove: $\tan^2 \theta + 1 \equiv \sec^2 \theta, \quad \mathcal{D} = R - \left\{\theta \,\middle|\, \theta = \frac{\pi}{2} + n\pi, \ n \in J\right\}.$

(1) $\tan^2 \theta + 1 = \dfrac{\sin^2 \theta}{\cos^2 \theta} + \dfrac{\cos^2 \theta}{\cos^2 \theta}$

(2) $= \dfrac{\sin^2 \theta + \cos^2 \theta}{\cos^2 \theta}$

(3) $= \dfrac{1}{\cos^2 \theta}$

(4) $= \sec^2 \theta$

$$\therefore \ \tan^2 \theta + 1 \equiv \sec^2 \theta, \quad \mathcal{D} = R - \left\{\theta \,\middle|\, \theta = \frac{\pi}{2} + n\pi, \ n \in J\right\}.$$

In practice, most students will prefer to combine steps as was done in this last proof rather than giving each step separately, as was done in the first proof. It should be noted that in using this technique we started with the more complicated side of the equation and worked to obtain the less complicated side.

Let us consider another example.

To prove: $\dfrac{1 - \sin x}{\cos x} \equiv \dfrac{\cos x}{1 + \sin x}.$ What is $\mathcal{D}$?

The two sides of the equation are of about the same complexity. One might start by noting that the given equation will be an identity if and only if

$$(1 - \sin x)(1 + \sin x) = (\cos x)(\cos x).$$

Noticing that $(1 - \sin x)(1 + \sin x) = 1 - \sin^2 x$, by a rule of algebra, and that $1 - \sin^2 x = \cos^2 x$, we now have enough clues to start the following proof.

(1) $1 = \sin^2 x + \cos^2 x$

(2) $1 - \sin^2 x = \cos^2 x$

(3) $(1 - \sin x)(1 + \sin x) = (\cos x)(\cos x)$

(4) $\dfrac{1 - \sin x}{\cos x} = \dfrac{\cos x}{1 + \sin x}$ (what restrictions here?)

$$\therefore \dfrac{1 - \sin x}{\cos x} \equiv \dfrac{\cos x}{1 + \sin x}, \quad \mathscr{D} = R - \left\{x \mid x = \dfrac{\pi}{2} + n\pi, n \in J\right\}.$$

The student should be able to provide justification for each step in the proof. In this particular proof, the analysis we made before starting helped us see where we might start. There are several other ways that this identity could be proved. One of them appears below.

We observe that the right side of the equation is $\cos x/(1 + \sin x)$. We might multiply the left side of the equation by 1, expressed in the form $(1 + \sin x)/(1 + \sin x)$, in order to get the expression $1 + \sin x$ in the denominator. If we are fortunate, we will see where to go from there.

(1) $\dfrac{1 - \sin x}{\cos x} = \left(\dfrac{1 - \sin x}{\cos x}\right)\left(\dfrac{1 + \sin x}{1 + \sin x}\right)$ (restrictions?)

(2) $\qquad\qquad = \dfrac{1 - \sin^2 x}{\cos x\,(1 + \sin x)}$

(3) $\qquad\qquad = \dfrac{\cos^2 x}{\cos x\,(1 + \sin x)}$

(4) $\qquad\qquad = \dfrac{\cos x}{1 + \sin x}$

$$\therefore \dfrac{1 - \sin x}{\cos x} \equiv \dfrac{\cos x}{1 + \sin x}, \quad \mathscr{D} = R - \left\{x \mid x = \dfrac{\pi}{2} + n\pi, n \in J\right\}.$$

As was suggested, we multiplied the left side of the equation by 1, expressed in an appropriate form. Once we had done this, the following steps were largely a matter of observation.

It should be noted that in proving trigonometric identities the most important tool is the power of observation. One needs to observe what he has and what he wants to get. Then he needs to select appropriate identities which have been proved for making the desired manipulations. There is no series of steps which will aıways work. The best way to develop the necessary power of observation is to practice. This practice can be obtained in only one way, through attempting to prove identities.

Another example appears below.

To prove: $\cos^6 \phi + \sin^6 \phi \equiv \cos^4 \phi - \cos^2 \phi \sin^2 \phi + \sin^4 \phi, \quad \mathscr{D} = R.$

In order to prove the identity above, it helps if we notice that $\cos^6 \phi + \sin^6 \phi$ is in the form $x^6 + y^6$, which can be factored as the sum of two cubes,

$$x^6 + y^6 = (x^2 + y^2)(x^4 - x^2 y^2 + y^4).$$

Thus,

$$\cos^6 \phi + \sin^6 \phi = (\cos^2 \phi + \sin^2 \phi)(\cos^4 \phi - \cos^2 \phi \sin^2 \phi + \sin^4 \phi)$$

$$= 1 \cdot (\cos^4 \phi - \cos^2 \phi \sin^2 \phi + \sin^4 \phi)$$
$$= \cos^4 \phi - \cos^2 \phi \sin^2 \phi + \sin^4 \phi.$$
$$\therefore \cos^6 \phi + \sin^6 \phi \equiv \cos^4 \phi - \cos^2 \phi \sin^2 \phi + \sin^4 \phi, \quad \mathscr{D} = R.$$

Exercises 2.2

Most of the following equations are identities. Some may be conditional equations. Determine in which category each belongs and prove your conclusion. Give the replacement set for each equation.

1. $\sec x \sin x \equiv \tan x.$
2. $\sec \phi \cot \phi \equiv \csc \phi.$
3. $\tan y \csc y \equiv \sec y.$
4. $\csc \theta \cos \theta \equiv \cot \theta.$
5. $\sin \alpha \cot \alpha \equiv \cos \alpha.$
6. $\cos \beta \tan \beta \equiv \sin \beta.$
7. $\sec^2 x - \tan^2 x \equiv 1.$
8. $\csc^2 \beta - \cot^2 \beta \equiv 1.$
9. $\csc^2 y - \sec^2 y \equiv \sin^2 y.$
10. $\cos(-\theta)\cos\theta - \sin\theta\sin(-\theta) \equiv 1.$
11. $\tan^2 \theta \csc^2 \theta - \sec^2 \theta \sin^2 \theta \equiv 1.$
12. $\cos^2 y \tan^2 y + \sin^2 y \cot^2 y \equiv 1.$
13. $\sec^2 \phi \cot^2 \phi - \csc^2 \phi \cos^2 \phi \equiv 1.$
14. $\cos^4 \alpha - \sin^4 \alpha \equiv \cos^2 \alpha - \sin^2 \alpha.$
15. $\sec^4 x - \tan^4 x \equiv \sec^2 x + \tan^2 x.$
16. $\sec^4 \phi - 1 \equiv \tan^2 \phi (\sec^2 \phi + 1).$
17. $\csc^4 z - \cot^4 z \equiv \csc^2 z + \cot^2 z.$
18. $\tan^3 \alpha + 1 \equiv (\tan \alpha + 1)(\sec^2 \alpha - \tan \alpha).$
19. $\tan^3 \alpha - 1 \equiv (\tan \alpha - 1)(\tan \alpha + \sec^2 \alpha).$
20. $\cot^3 \beta + 1 \equiv (\cot \beta + 1)(\csc^2 \beta - \cot \beta).$
21. $\cot^3 \beta - 1 \equiv (\cot \beta - 1)(\cot \beta + \csc^2 \beta).$
22. $\cos^6 \gamma - \sin^6 \gamma \equiv \cos^2 \gamma + \cos^4 \gamma.$
23. $\cos^6 \phi - \sin^6 \phi \equiv \cos^4 \phi + \sin^2 \phi.$
24. $\cos^3 x + \sin^3 x \equiv \cos x(1 - \cos x \sin x) + \sin x(1 - \cos x \sin x).$
25. $\cos^3 y + \sin^3 y \equiv \cos y(1 - \cos y \sin y) - \sin y(\cos y \sin y - 1).$
26. $\cos^3 \alpha - \sin^3 \alpha \equiv \cos \alpha(1 + \sin \alpha \cos \alpha) - \sin \alpha(1 + \sin \alpha \cos \alpha).$
27. $(\tan^2 \gamma + 1)^2 \equiv (-\sec \gamma)^4.$
28. $(\cos x - \sin x)^2 \equiv 1 - 2 \sin x \cos x.$
29. $(\tan \alpha - 1)^2 \equiv \sec^2 \alpha - 2 \tan \alpha.$
30. $(1 + \cot z)^2 \equiv 2 \cot z + \csc^2 z.$
31. $(\cos \beta + \sin \beta)^4 \equiv \cos^2 \beta + \sin^2 \beta + 4 \cos^2 \beta \sin^2 \beta + 4 \cos \beta \sin \beta.$

32. $(\cos \alpha - \sin \alpha)^4 \equiv \cos^2 \alpha + \sin^2 \alpha + 4 \cos^2 \alpha \sin^2 \alpha - 4 \cos \alpha \sin \alpha.$

33. $(\sin \theta + \cos \theta)^3 \equiv \sin \theta + 2 \sin \theta \cos \theta (\sin \theta + \cos \theta) + \cos \theta.$

34. $\cos^2 x - \sin^2 x \equiv 1 - 2 \sin^2 x.$

35. $\cos^2 \alpha - \sin^2 \alpha \equiv 2 \cos^2 \alpha - 1.$

36. $\cos^4 \theta \equiv 1 - 2 \sin^2 \theta + \sin^4 \theta.$

37. $\sec^2 \phi + \csc^2 \phi \equiv \sec^2 \phi \csc^2 \phi.$

38. $\sec^4 x - \tan^4 x \equiv \dfrac{\sin^2 x + 1}{\cos^2 x}.$

39. $\csc^4 \beta - \cot^4 \beta \equiv \dfrac{\cos^2 \beta + 1}{\sin^2 \beta}.$

40. $\csc^4 \alpha - 1 \equiv \cot^2 \alpha (\csc^2 \alpha + 1).$

41. $\tan^2 \gamma - \cot^2 \gamma \equiv \dfrac{\sin^2 \gamma - \cos^2 \gamma}{\cos^2 \gamma \sin^2 \gamma}.$

42. $\tan^2 z + \cot^2 z \equiv \dfrac{2 \sin^4 z - 2 \sin^2 z + 1}{\sin^2 z \cos^2 z}.$

43. $\tan^2 \phi + \cot^2 \phi \equiv 2 \tan^2 \phi - 2 \sec^2 \phi + \sec^2 \phi \csc^2 \phi.$

44. $\dfrac{\tan y + \cot y}{\sec y \csc y} \equiv 1.$

45. $\dfrac{\sin \phi + \cos^2 \phi \csc \phi}{\csc \phi} \equiv 1.$

2.4   Sum and difference identities

Some of the many identities useful in trigonometry deal with expressions such as $\cos (\alpha \pm \beta)$ and $\sin (\alpha \pm \beta)$. Identities involving these expressions will be developed in this section.

First we shall develop the identity

$$\cos (\alpha + \beta) \equiv \cos \alpha \cos \beta - \sin \alpha \sin \beta$$

if $\alpha, \beta \in R$. To do this we use the unit circle and the distance formula. Consider Figure 2.1, where the arcs $\overset{\frown}{PQ}$ and $\overset{\frown}{PR}$ are assumed to have lengths α and β, respectively. This means that the points Q and R must have the coordinates indicated. The points S and T depend upon the points P and Q. S is the point

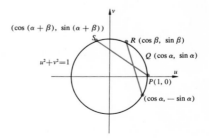

Figure 2.1

corresponding to $\alpha + \beta$, and T is the point corresponding to $-\alpha$. This determines the coordinates for the points S and T. Note that identities for $\cos(-\alpha)$ and $\sin(-\alpha)$ have been used in giving the coordinates of T.

Because of the way in which the points S and T were selected, the arcs $\overset{\frown}{PS}$ and $\overset{\frown}{TR}$ have the same length, $\alpha + \beta$. Since, within the same circle, equal arcs subtend equal chords, the lengths of the segments $\overline{PS}$ and $\overline{TR}$ are equal. This leads us to the following development.

$$d(PS) = \sqrt{[\cos(\alpha + \beta) - 1]^2 + [\sin(\alpha + \beta) - 0]^2}$$
$$= \sqrt{\cos^2(\alpha + \beta) - 2\cos(\alpha + \beta) + 1 + \sin^2(\alpha + \beta)}$$
$$= \sqrt{2 - 2\cos(\alpha + \beta)}.$$
$$d(TR) = \sqrt{(\cos\beta - \cos\alpha)^2 + [\sin\beta - (-\sin\alpha)]^2}$$
$$= \sqrt{(\cos\beta - \cos\alpha)^2 + (\sin\beta + \sin\alpha)^2}$$
$$= \sqrt{\cos^2\beta - 2\cos\beta\cos\alpha + \cos^2\alpha + \sin^2\beta + 2\sin\beta\sin\alpha + \sin^2\alpha}$$
$$= \sqrt{2 - 2\cos\beta\cos\alpha + 2\sin\beta\sin\alpha}.$$

Since $d(PS) = d(TR)$, we have

$$\sqrt{2 - 2\cos(\alpha + \beta)} = \sqrt{2 - 2\cos\beta\cos\alpha + 2\sin\beta\sin\alpha},$$
$$2 - 2\cos(\alpha + \beta) = 2 - 2\cos\beta\cos\alpha + 2\sin\beta\sin\alpha,$$
$$-2\cos(\alpha + \beta) = -2\cos\beta\cos\alpha + 2\sin\beta\sin\alpha,$$
$$\cos(\alpha + \beta) = \cos\beta\cos\alpha - \sin\beta\sin\alpha,$$
$$\cos(\alpha + \beta) = \cos\alpha\cos\beta - \sin\alpha\sin\beta.$$
$$\therefore \cos(\alpha + \beta) \equiv \cos\alpha\cos\beta - \sin\alpha\sin\beta, \quad \alpha \in R, \beta \in R.$$

Any real numbers α and β could have been selected. α and β were chosen to be positive with a sum less than π for the convenience of the illustration. You may wish to experiment with other real numbers to demonstrate the generality of the identity for yourself.

If we wish to use an expression for $\cos(\alpha - \beta)$, we note that $\alpha - \beta = \alpha + (-\beta)$. This enables us to develop

$$\cos(\alpha - \beta) \equiv \cos\alpha\cos\beta + \sin\alpha\sin\beta$$

as follows:

$$\cos(\alpha - \beta) = \cos[\alpha + (-\beta)]$$
$$= \cos\alpha\cos(-\beta) - \sin\alpha\sin(-\beta)$$
$$= \cos\alpha\cos\beta - \sin\alpha(-\sin\beta)$$
$$= \cos\alpha\cos\beta + \sin\alpha\sin\beta.$$
$$\therefore \cos(\alpha - \beta) \equiv \cos\alpha\cos\beta + \sin\alpha\sin\beta, \quad \alpha \in R, \beta \in R.$$

From the identity $\cos(\alpha - \beta) \equiv \cos\alpha\cos\beta + \sin\alpha\sin\beta$ we can develop the identity

$$\cos\left(\frac{\pi}{2} - \theta\right) \equiv \sin\theta.$$

This identity will be most helpful in developing expressions for $\sin(\alpha + \beta)$ and $\sin(\alpha - \beta)$. We note that

$$\cos\left(\frac{\pi}{2} - \theta\right) = \cos\frac{\pi}{2}\cos\theta + \sin\frac{\pi}{2}\sin\theta$$

$$= (0)\cos\theta + (1)\sin\theta$$

$$= \sin\theta.$$

$$\therefore \cos\left(\frac{\pi}{2} - \theta\right) \equiv \sin\theta, \quad \mathcal{D} = R.$$

It is also true that $\sin(\pi/2 - \theta) \equiv \cos\theta$ for any real number θ. We note that

$$\cos\left[\frac{\pi}{2} - \left(\frac{\pi}{2} - \theta\right)\right] = \sin\left(\frac{\pi}{2} - \theta\right).$$

But since

$$\frac{\pi}{2} - \left(\frac{\pi}{2} - \theta\right) = \frac{\pi}{2} - \frac{\pi}{2} + \theta = \theta,$$

we have

$$\cos\theta = \cos\left[\frac{\pi}{2} - \left(\frac{\pi}{2} - \theta\right)\right]$$

$$= \sin\left(\frac{\pi}{2} - \theta\right).$$

$$\therefore \sin\left(\frac{\pi}{2} - \theta\right) \equiv \cos\theta, \quad \mathcal{D} = R.$$

We now note that $\cos[\pi/2 - (\alpha + \beta)] = \sin(\alpha + \beta)$. But since

$$\frac{\pi}{2} - (\alpha + \beta) = \left(\frac{\pi}{2} - \alpha\right) - \beta,$$

we have

$$\sin(\alpha + \beta) = \cos\left[\frac{\pi}{2} - (\alpha + \beta)\right]$$

$$= \cos\left[\left(\frac{\pi}{2} - \alpha\right) - \beta\right]$$

$$= \cos\left(\frac{\pi}{2} - \alpha\right)\cos\beta + \sin\left(\frac{\pi}{2} - \alpha\right)\sin\beta$$

$$= \sin\alpha\cos\beta + \cos\alpha\sin\beta.$$

$$\therefore \sin(\alpha + \beta) \equiv \sin\alpha\cos\beta + \cos\alpha\sin\beta, \quad \alpha \in R, \beta \in R.$$

To develop an expression for $\sin(\alpha - \beta)$, we note that $\alpha - \beta = \alpha + (-\beta)$ and use identities involving $\sin(-\beta)$ and $\cos(-\beta)$. The development of

$$\sin(\alpha - \beta) \equiv \sin\alpha\cos\beta - \cos\alpha\sin\beta$$

appears below.

$$\sin (\alpha - \beta) = \sin [\alpha + (-\beta)]$$
$$= \sin \alpha \cos (-\beta) + \cos \alpha \sin (-\beta)$$
$$= \sin \alpha \cos \beta + \cos \alpha (-\sin \beta)$$
$$= \sin \alpha \cos \beta - \cos \alpha \sin \beta.$$
$$\therefore \sin (\alpha - \beta) \equiv \sin \alpha \cos \beta - \cos \alpha \sin \beta, \quad \alpha \in R, \beta \in R.$$

In this section we have derived the six identities which appear below. In each of them, α and β may be any real numbers.

1. $\cos (\alpha + \beta) \equiv \cos \alpha \cos \beta - \sin \alpha \sin \beta.$
2. $\cos (\alpha - \beta) \equiv \cos \alpha \cos \beta + \sin \alpha \sin \beta.$
3. $\cos \left(\dfrac{\pi}{2} - \alpha \right) \equiv \sin \alpha.$
4. $\sin \left(\dfrac{\pi}{2} - \alpha \right) \equiv \cos \alpha.$
5. $\sin (\alpha + \beta) \equiv \sin \alpha \cos \beta + \cos \alpha \sin \beta.$
6. $\sin (\alpha - \beta) \equiv \sin \alpha \cos \beta - \cos \alpha \sin \beta.$

These six identities are all important in trigonometry, and they are used frequently. The student should learn them. Some applications of these identities are included in the exercises.

Exercises 2.3

Use the identities of this section to evaluate the following.

Example

$\cos \dfrac{\pi}{12}$

Solution

$\dfrac{\pi}{12} = \dfrac{\pi}{4} - \dfrac{\pi}{6}$, so

$$\cos \frac{\pi}{12} = \cos \left(\frac{\pi}{4} - \frac{\pi}{6} \right)$$
$$= \cos \frac{\pi}{4} \cos \frac{\pi}{6} + \sin \frac{\pi}{4} \sin \frac{\pi}{6}$$
$$= \left(\frac{\sqrt{2}}{2} \right) \left(\frac{\sqrt{3}}{2} \right) + \left(\frac{\sqrt{2}}{2} \right) \left(\frac{1}{2} \right)$$
$$= \frac{\sqrt{6} + \sqrt{2}}{4}.$$

Trigonometric identities

$$\frac{\pi}{4} + \frac{\pi}{6}$$

$$= \frac{\pi}{2} + \frac{5\pi}{12}$$

2.4

1. $\sin \frac{\pi}{12}$ 2. $\sin \frac{5\pi}{12}$ 3. $\cos \frac{5\pi}{12}$ 4. $\sin \frac{11\pi}{12}$

5. $\cos \frac{11\pi}{12}$ 6. $\cos \frac{7\pi}{12}$ 7. $\sin \frac{7\pi}{12} = \pi - \frac{5\pi}{12}$

Verify that each of the following equations is an identity.

8. $\cos \left(\frac{\pi}{6} + x \right) \equiv \frac{\sqrt{3}}{2} \cos x - \frac{1}{2} \sin x.$

9. $\sin \left(x + \frac{\pi}{4} \right) \equiv \frac{\sqrt{2}}{2} (\sin x + \cos x).$

10. $\sin \left(\theta + \frac{\pi}{2} \right) \equiv \cos \theta.$

11. $\cos \left(\theta + \frac{\pi}{2} \right) \equiv -\sin \theta.$

12. $\sin (\theta + \pi) \equiv -\sin \theta.$

13. $\cos (\theta + \pi) \equiv -\cos \theta.$

14. $\cos 4\theta \equiv \cos 3\theta \cos \theta - \sin 3\theta \sin \theta.$

15. $\sin 7x \equiv \sin 4x \cos 3x + \cos 4x \sin 3x.$

16. $\sin 3\phi \equiv \sin 5\phi \cos 2\phi - \cos 5\phi \sin 2\phi.$

17. $\cos 5y \equiv \cos 9y \cos 4y + \sin 9y \sin 4y.$

18. $\sin (x + \pi) - \sin (x - \pi) \equiv 0.$

19. $(\sin x + \cos \beta)^2 + (\cos x + \sin \beta)^2 \equiv 2[\sin (x + \beta) + 1].$

20. $1 - \tan \theta \tan \phi \equiv \dfrac{\cos (\theta + \phi)}{\cos \theta \cos \phi}.$

21. $\cos (\alpha + \beta) \cos (\alpha - \beta) \equiv (\cos \alpha \cos \beta)^2 - (\sin \alpha \sin \beta)^2.$

22. $(\cos \alpha \cos \beta)^2 - (\sin \alpha \sin \beta)^2 \equiv \cos^2 \alpha - \sin^2 \beta.$

23. $\tan (\alpha + \beta) \equiv \dfrac{\tan \alpha + \tan \beta}{1 - \tan \alpha \tan \beta}$ [Use $\sin (\alpha + \beta)$ and $\cos (\alpha + \beta)$.]

24. $\cot (\theta + \phi) \equiv \dfrac{\cot \theta \cot \phi - 1}{\cot \phi + \cot \theta}.$

25. $\sec (x + y) \equiv \dfrac{\sec x \sec y}{1 - \tan x \tan y}.$

26. $\csc (\alpha + \beta) \equiv \dfrac{\csc \alpha \csc \beta}{\cot \beta + \cot \alpha}.$

27. $\tan (\theta - \phi) \equiv \dfrac{\tan \theta - \tan \phi}{1 + \tan \theta \tan \phi}.$

28. $\cot (x - y) \equiv \dfrac{\cot x \cot y + 1}{\cot y - \cot x}.$

29. $\sec (\alpha - \beta) \equiv \dfrac{\sec \alpha \sec \beta}{1 + \tan \alpha \tan \beta}.$

30. $\csc (\theta - \phi) \equiv \dfrac{\csc \theta \csc \phi}{\cot \phi - \cot \theta}.$

31. $\tan \left(\theta + \frac{\pi}{2} \right) \equiv -\cot \theta.$

32. $\cot \left(\alpha + \frac{\pi}{2} \right) \equiv -\tan \alpha.$

- 33. $\sin 2\phi \equiv 2 \sin \phi \cos \phi.$
  34. $\cos 2x \equiv \cos^2 x - \sin^2 x.$
- 35. $\cos 2y \equiv 2 \cos^2 y - 1.$
  36. $\cos 2z \equiv 1 - 2 \sin^2 z.$
  37. $\tan 2\alpha \equiv \dfrac{2 \tan \alpha}{1 - \tan^2 \alpha}.$
- 38. $\tan (\alpha + \beta) \equiv \dfrac{\cot \beta + \cot \alpha}{\cot \alpha \cot \beta - 1}.$
  39. $(\sin x \cos y)^2 - (\cos x \sin y)^2 \equiv \sin^2 x - \sin^2 y.$
  40. $\sin (x + y) \sin (x - y) \equiv \sin^2 x - \sin^2 y.$

2.5   The "double-angle" identities

In Section 2.4 we developed the identities

$$\cos (\alpha + \beta) \equiv \cos \alpha \cos \beta - \sin \alpha \sin \beta$$

and

$$\sin (\alpha + \beta) \equiv \sin \alpha \cos \beta + \cos \alpha \sin \beta.$$

These identities are the basis for the development of the so-called **double-angle** formulas, which give expressions equal to $\cos 2\theta$ and $\sin 2\theta$. You may have derived these identities from the previous exercises.

First we shall derive the identity

$$\sin 2\theta \equiv 2 \sin \theta \cos \theta, \quad \mathscr{D} = R.$$

If, in the identity $\sin (\alpha + \beta) \equiv \sin \alpha \cos \beta + \cos \alpha \sin \beta$, we let $\alpha = \theta$ and $\beta = \theta$, we have

$$\sin (\theta + \theta) = \sin \theta \cos \theta + \cos \theta \sin \theta,$$
$$\sin 2\theta = 2 \sin \theta \cos \theta,$$
$$\therefore \ \sin 2\theta \equiv 2 \sin \theta \cos \theta, \quad \mathscr{D} = R.$$

In a similar fashion we can develop the identity

$$\cos 2\theta \equiv \cos^2 \theta - \sin^2 \theta, \quad \mathscr{D} = R.$$

The derivation appears below.

$$\cos (\theta + \theta) = \cos \theta \cos \theta - \sin \theta \sin \theta,$$
$$\cos 2\theta = \cos^2 \theta - \sin^2 \theta,$$
$$\therefore \ \cos 2\theta \equiv \cos^2 \theta - \sin^2 \theta, \quad \mathscr{D} = R.$$

There are two other commonly used identities involving $\cos 2\theta$, which we can derive easily from the identity $\cos 2\theta \equiv \cos^2 \theta - \sin^2 \theta$. First,

$$\cos 2\theta = \cos^2 \theta - \sin^2 \theta$$
$$= \cos^2 \theta + \cos^2 \theta - \sin^2 \theta - \cos^2 \theta$$

$$= 2 \cos^2 \theta - (\sin^2 \theta + \cos^2 \theta)$$
$$= 2 \cos^2 \theta - 1.$$
$$\therefore \textbf{cos } 2\boldsymbol{\theta} \equiv 2 \textbf{ cos}^2 \boldsymbol{\theta} - \textbf{1}, \quad \mathscr{D} = \textbf{R}.$$

Second,

$$\cos 2\theta = \cos^2 \theta - \sin^2 \theta$$
$$= \cos^2 \theta + \sin^2 \theta - \sin^2 \theta - \sin^2 \theta$$
$$= 1 - 2 \sin^2 \theta.$$
$$\therefore \textbf{cos } 2\boldsymbol{\theta} \equiv \textbf{1} - \textbf{2 sin}^2 \boldsymbol{\theta}, \quad \mathscr{D} = \textbf{R}.$$

These last two identities involving cos 2θ are quite useful in developing the so-called "half-angle" formulas, that is identities involving $\sin \theta/2$ and $\cos \theta/2$, which will be developed in the next section.

The identities developed in these two sections are also most helpful in deriving identities involving larger multiples of the variable. We would like to derive an identity expressing $\sin 3\theta$ in terms of $\sin \theta$.

$$\sin 3\theta = \sin (2\theta + \theta)$$
$$= \sin 2\theta \cos \theta + \cos 2\theta \sin \theta$$
$$= (2 \sin \theta \cos \theta) \cos \theta + (1 - 2 \sin^2 \theta) \sin \theta$$
$$= 2 \sin \theta \cos^2 \theta + \sin \theta - 2 \sin^3 \theta$$
$$= 2 \sin \theta (1 - \sin^2 \theta) + \sin \theta - 2 \sin^3 \theta$$
$$= 2 \sin \theta - 2 \sin^3 \theta + \sin \theta - 2 \sin^3 \theta$$
$$= 3 \sin \theta - 4 \sin^3 \theta.$$
$$\therefore \textbf{sin } 3\boldsymbol{\theta} \equiv \textbf{3 sin } \boldsymbol{\theta} - \textbf{4 sin}^3 \boldsymbol{\theta}, \quad \mathscr{D} = \textbf{R}.$$

The tangent of the sum of two numbers can be expressed, since we have developed identities for $\sin (\alpha + \beta)$ and $\cos (\alpha + \beta)$. You may already have derived this identity from the exercises.

$$\tan (\alpha + \beta) = \frac{\sin (\alpha + \beta)}{\cos (\alpha + \beta)}, \quad \alpha + \beta \neq \frac{\pi}{2} + n\pi, n \in J,$$
$$= \frac{\sin \alpha \cos \beta + \cos \alpha \sin \beta}{\cos \alpha \cos \beta - \sin \alpha \sin \beta}$$
$$= \frac{\dfrac{\sin \alpha \cos \beta}{\cos \alpha \cos \beta} + \dfrac{\cos \alpha \sin \beta}{\cos \alpha \cos \beta}}{\dfrac{\cos \alpha \cos \beta}{\cos \alpha \cos \beta} - \dfrac{\sin \alpha \sin \beta}{\cos \alpha \cos \beta}}, \quad \begin{array}{l} \alpha \neq \dfrac{\pi}{2} + n\pi, n \in J, \\[2mm] \beta \neq \dfrac{\pi}{2} + n\pi, n \in J, \end{array}$$
$$= \frac{\tan \alpha + \tan \beta}{1 - \tan \alpha \tan \beta}.$$
$$\therefore \textbf{tan } (\boldsymbol{\alpha} + \boldsymbol{\beta}) \equiv \frac{\textbf{tan } \boldsymbol{\alpha} + \textbf{tan } \boldsymbol{\beta}}{\textbf{1} - \textbf{tan } \boldsymbol{\alpha} \textbf{ tan } \boldsymbol{\beta}}, \quad \alpha, \beta, \alpha + \beta \neq \frac{\pi}{2} + n\pi, n \in J.$$

We should also note that if $\alpha = \beta = \theta$, we have

$$\textbf{tan } 2\boldsymbol{\theta} \equiv \frac{\textbf{2 tan } \boldsymbol{\theta}}{\textbf{1} - \textbf{tan}^2 \boldsymbol{\theta}}, \quad \theta, 2\theta \neq \frac{\pi}{2} + n\pi, n \in J.$$

Exercises 2.4

Using $\cos \pi/6 = \sqrt{3}/2$, $\sin \pi/6 = 1/2$, and $\tan \pi/6 = 1/\sqrt{3}$ and the double-angle formulas, evaluate the following.

1. $\sin \dfrac{\pi}{3}$

2. $\cos \dfrac{\pi}{3}$

3. $\tan \dfrac{\pi}{3}$

Using $\cos \pi/4 = \sqrt{2}/2 = \sin \pi/4$ and the double-angle formulas, evaluate the following.

4. $\sin \dfrac{\pi}{2}$

5. $\cos \dfrac{\pi}{2}$

Using $\sin \pi/2 = 1$ and $\cos \pi/2 = 0$, evaluate the following.

6. $\sin \pi$

7. $\cos \pi$

Verify that each of the following equations is an identity.

8. $\cos 3\theta \equiv 4 \cos^3 \theta - 3 \cos \theta.$

9. $\sin 4\phi \equiv 4 \cos \phi (\sin \phi - 2 \sin^3 \phi).$

10. $\cos 4\alpha \equiv 8 \cos^4 \alpha - 8 \cos^2 \alpha + 1.$

11. $\sin 5x \equiv 16 \sin^5 x - 20 \sin^3 x + 5 \sin x.$

12. $\cos 5y \equiv 16 \cos^5 y - 20 \cos^3 y + 5 \cos y.$

13. $\sin \dfrac{x}{2} \cos \dfrac{x}{2} \equiv \dfrac{1}{2} \sin x.$ $\left[Hint: \quad x = 2\left(\dfrac{x}{2}\right) \right]$

14. $\cos^2 \dfrac{z}{2} - \sin^2 \dfrac{z}{2} \equiv \cos z.$

15. $\left(\cos \dfrac{\beta}{2} - \sin \dfrac{\beta}{2}\right)^2 \equiv 1 - \sin \beta.$

16. $\sin 2\alpha \equiv \dfrac{2 \tan \alpha}{1 + \tan^2 \alpha}$

17. $\tan 3\phi \equiv \dfrac{3 \tan \phi - \tan^3 \phi}{1 - 3 \tan^2 \phi}.$

18. $\tan 2y \equiv \dfrac{2}{\cot y - \tan y}.$

19. $\cos 2x \equiv \cos^4 x - \sin^4 x.$

20. $1 - 2 \sin^2 \left(\dfrac{\pi}{4} - \theta\right) \equiv \sin 2\theta.$

21. $\cos 2z + 2 \sin^2 z \equiv 1.$

22. $\sin^2 \dfrac{\beta}{2} \equiv \dfrac{1 - \cos \beta}{2}.$

23. $\cos 2\gamma - 2 \cos^2 \gamma \equiv -1.$

24. $\sec 2\phi \equiv \dfrac{\sec^2 \phi}{1 - \tan^2 \phi}.$

25. $\sin \theta \sin 3\theta \equiv \sin^2 2\theta - \sin^2 \theta.$

26. $\cot 2y \equiv \dfrac{\cot^2 y - 1}{2 \cot y}.$

27. $\sec y \csc y \equiv 2 \csc 2y.$

28. $\cos 4\alpha \equiv 1 - 8 \sin^2 \alpha \cos^2 \alpha.$

29. $\cos 4z \equiv 8 \sin^4 z - 8 \sin^2 z + 1.$

30. $(\cos y - \sin y)^2 \equiv 1 - \sin 2y.$

31. $2 \sin (\alpha + \beta) \cdot \cos (\alpha - \beta) \equiv \sin 2\alpha + \sin 2\beta.$

32. $\dfrac{\sin 3\phi}{\sin \phi} - \dfrac{\cos 3\phi}{\cos \phi} \equiv 2.$

33. $2 \csc 2x \equiv \cot x + \tan x.$

34. $\cot \alpha - \cot 2\alpha \equiv \csc 2\alpha.$

35. $\csc^2 2y - \sec^2 2y \equiv 4 \cot 4y \csc 4y.$

36. $\cos \theta \cos 3\theta \equiv \cos^2 \theta - \sin^2 2\theta.$

37. $\tan \beta \equiv \dfrac{\sin 2\beta}{1 + \cos 2\beta}.$

38. $\cot^2 \phi - \tan^2 \phi \equiv \dfrac{4 \cos 2\phi}{\sin^2 2\phi}.$

39. $8 \sin^4 \gamma \equiv 3 - 4 \cos 2\gamma + \cos 4\gamma.$

40. $\dfrac{1 + \sin 2x + \cos 2x}{1 + \sin 2x - \cos 2x} \equiv \cot x.$

2.6   The "half-angle" identities

In Section 2.5 we developed the double-angle identities or formulas. These identities will be used in this section to develop **the half-angle** identities, involving $\sin \theta/2$, $\cos \theta/2$, and $\tan \theta/2$.

We derived three different expressions for $\cos 2\alpha$. One of these was

$$\cos 2\alpha \equiv 1 - 2 \sin^2 \alpha.$$

If we substitute $\theta/2$ for α, we have the following derivation.

$$\cos 2\alpha = 1 - 2 \sin^2 \alpha,$$

$$\cos 2\left(\frac{\theta}{2}\right) = 1 - 2 \sin^2 \frac{\theta}{2},$$

$$\cos \theta = 1 - 2 \sin^2 \frac{\theta}{2},$$

$$2 \sin^2 \frac{\theta}{2} = 1 - \cos \theta,$$

$$\sin^2 \frac{\theta}{2} = \frac{1 - \cos \theta}{2}.$$

$$\therefore \sin^2 \frac{\theta}{2} \equiv \frac{1 - \cos \theta}{2}, \quad \mathscr{D} = R.$$

Using this identity we can find the value of $\sin^2 \theta/2$ if we know $\cos \theta$. In order to evaluate $\sin \theta/2$, we need to know whether $\sin \theta/2$ is positive or negative. If $\theta/2$ is in the first or the second quadrant, $\sin \theta/2 > 0$, and we take the positive square root of $\sin^2 \theta/2$. If $\theta/2$ is in the third or the fourth quadrant, $\sin \theta/2 < 0$, and we take the negative square root of $\sin^2 \theta/2$. Thus, we cannot say in general which square root is appropriate. It is for this reason that we did not solve explicitly for $\sin \theta/2$.

In a similar fashion, we use the identity

$$\cos 2\alpha \equiv 2 \cos^2 \alpha - 1$$

to develop the identity

$$\cos^2 \frac{\theta}{2} \equiv \frac{1 + \cos \theta}{2}, \quad \mathscr{D} = R.$$

Thus,

$$\cos 2\alpha = 2 \cos^2 \alpha - 1,$$
$$\cos \theta = 2 \cos^2 \frac{\theta}{2} - 1,$$
$$1 + \cos \theta = 2 \cos^2 \frac{\theta}{2},$$
$$\frac{1 + \cos \theta}{2} = \cos^2 \frac{\theta}{2}.$$
$$\therefore \cos^2 \frac{\theta}{2} \equiv \frac{1 + \cos \theta}{2}, \quad \mathscr{D} = R.$$

Here we determine whether $\cos \theta/2$ is positive or negative by determining the quadrant in which $\cos \theta/2$ is located. If $\theta/2$ is in the first or the fourth quadrant, $\cos \theta/2 > 0$. If $\theta/2$ is in the second quadrant or the third quadrant, $\cos \theta/2 < 0$.

These two identities can be used to derive an identity for $\tan^2 \theta/2$. We have the following derivation.

$$\tan^2 \frac{\theta}{2} = \frac{\sin^2 \frac{\theta}{2}}{\cos^2 \frac{\theta}{2}}$$
$$= \frac{\left(\frac{1 - \cos \theta}{2}\right)}{\left(\frac{1 + \cos \theta}{2}\right)}$$
$$= \frac{1 - \cos \theta}{1 + \cos \theta}.$$
$$\therefore \tan^2 \frac{\theta}{2} \equiv \frac{1 - \cos \theta}{1 + \cos \theta}, \quad \mathscr{D} = R - \{\theta \,|\, \theta = \pi + 2n\pi, n \in J\}.$$

We see that if $\theta/2$ is in the first or the third quadrant, $\tan \theta/2$ is positive. If $\theta/2$ is in the second or the fourth quadrant, $\tan \theta/2$ is negative.

These identities can be used to evaluate some trigonometric expressions which we would not be able to evaluate otherwise. In some cases when we use these formulas, the results look different from the results obtained by other means. For example,

$$
\begin{aligned}
\cos^2 \frac{\pi}{12} &= \frac{1 + \cos \frac{\pi}{6}}{2} \\
&= \frac{1 + \frac{\sqrt{3}}{2}}{2} \\
&= \frac{2 + \sqrt{3}}{4}.
\end{aligned}
$$

$\cos \pi/12 = (\sqrt{2 + \sqrt{3}})/2$, since $\pi/12$ is in the first quadrant. But from the example in Exercises 3.3 we found that $\cos \pi/12 = (\sqrt{6} + \sqrt{2})/4$. Is $(\sqrt{6} + \sqrt{2})/4 = (\sqrt{2 + \sqrt{3}})/2$? We now show that it is.

$$
\begin{aligned}
\frac{\sqrt{6} + \sqrt{2}}{4} &= \sqrt{\left(\frac{\sqrt{6} + \sqrt{2}}{4}\right)^2} \\
&= \sqrt{\frac{6 + 2\sqrt{12} + 2}{16}} \\
&= \sqrt{\frac{8 + 2\sqrt{12}}{16}} \\
&= \sqrt{\frac{8 + 2(2\sqrt{3})}{16}} \\
&= \sqrt{\frac{2 + \sqrt{3}}{4}} \\
&= \frac{\sqrt{2 + \sqrt{3}}}{2}.
\end{aligned}
$$

$$\therefore \frac{\sqrt{6} + \sqrt{2}}{4} = \frac{\sqrt{\sqrt{2} + \sqrt{3}}}{2}.$$

This illustrates that sometimes expressions which look very different are actually equal and that either may be the solution to a given problem.

Exercises 2.5

Use the identities developed in this section to evaluate the following expressions.

1. $\sin \frac{\pi}{12}$ 2. $\sin \frac{\pi}{8}$ 3. $\cos \frac{\pi}{8}$ 4. $\sin \frac{\pi}{24}$

5. $\cos \dfrac{\pi}{24}$ 6. $\cos \dfrac{\pi}{16}$ 7. $\sin \dfrac{\pi}{16}$ 8. $\tan \dfrac{\pi}{8}$

9. $\tan \dfrac{\pi}{12}$ 10. $\tan \dfrac{\pi}{16}$ 11. $\tan \dfrac{5\pi}{12}$ 12. $\sin \dfrac{3\pi}{8}$

13. $\cos \dfrac{3\pi}{8}$ 14. $\cos \dfrac{7\pi}{8}$ 15. $\sin \dfrac{7\pi}{8}$ 16. $\sin \dfrac{11\pi}{12}$

17. $\cos \dfrac{11\pi}{12}$ 18. $\tan \dfrac{3\pi}{8}$ 19. $\tan \dfrac{7\pi}{8}$ 20. $\tan \dfrac{11\pi}{12}$

Verify that each of the following equations is an identity.

[handwritten: $\sin 2\alpha = 2 \sin \alpha \cos \alpha$]

21. $\sin \dfrac{\alpha}{2} \cos \dfrac{\alpha}{2} \equiv \dfrac{1}{2} \sin \alpha.$ 22. $\cos^2 \dfrac{\theta}{4} - \cos \dfrac{\theta}{2} \equiv \sin^2 \dfrac{\theta}{4}.$

23. $\tan \dfrac{\beta}{2} \equiv \dfrac{1 - \cos \beta}{\sin \beta}.$ 24. $\tan \dfrac{\gamma}{2} \equiv \dfrac{\sin \gamma}{1 + \cos \gamma}.$

25. $\cot \dfrac{x}{2} \equiv \dfrac{1 + \cos x}{\sin x}.$ 26. $\cot \dfrac{z}{2} \equiv \dfrac{\sin z}{1 - \cos z}.$

27. $\tan \dfrac{y}{2} \equiv \csc y - \cot y.$ 28. $\sec^2 \dfrac{\phi}{2} \equiv \dfrac{2}{1 + \cos \phi}.$

29. $\sin \alpha \cot \dfrac{\alpha}{2} \equiv 2 \cos^2 \dfrac{\alpha}{2}.$ 30. $\left(\sin \dfrac{y}{2} + \cos \dfrac{y}{2}\right)^2 \equiv 1 + \sin y.$

31. $\tan^2 \dfrac{\beta}{2} + 1 \equiv 2 \csc \beta \tan \dfrac{\beta}{2}.$ 32. $\csc^2 \dfrac{x}{2} \equiv \dfrac{2}{1 - \cos x}.$

[handwritten: ex 25. $1 + \cos + \sin$]

33. $\tan \dfrac{\phi}{2} \sin \phi \equiv 2 \sin^2 \dfrac{\phi}{2}.$ 34. $\dfrac{1 + \tan \dfrac{z}{2}}{1 - \tan \dfrac{z}{2}} \equiv \sec z + \tan z.$

[handwritten near 34: $\to \dfrac{\sin x}{1 + \cos x}$]

35. $2 \tan \dfrac{\alpha}{2} \csc \alpha \equiv \sec^2 \dfrac{\alpha}{2}.$ 36. $\cot y + \csc y \equiv \cot \dfrac{y}{2}.$

37. $\csc (\alpha + \beta) - \cot (\alpha + \beta) \equiv$ $\tan \left(\dfrac{\alpha + \beta}{2}\right).$ *[handwritten: ex 25]*   38. $2 \sin^2 \dfrac{y}{6} - \sin^2 \dfrac{y}{7} \equiv \cos^2 \dfrac{y}{7} - \cos \dfrac{y}{3}.$

[handwritten near 36: $1 - \cos^2$]

39. $\cos^2 \dfrac{x}{18} \equiv \sin^2 \dfrac{x}{18} + \cos \dfrac{x}{9}.$ 40. $\dfrac{1 - \tan \dfrac{\alpha}{2}}{1 + \tan \dfrac{\alpha}{2}} \equiv \dfrac{\cos \alpha}{1 + \sin \alpha}.$

[handwritten near 40: $\dfrac{1}{\cos}$ ... K 34]

2.7   Other important identities

There are occasions when we would like to work with expressions like $\sin \theta \cos \phi$, $\sin \theta \sin \phi$, and $\cos \theta \cos \phi$. There are identities involving each of these expressions, but they are involved and probably difficult to remember. The basic knowledge that the student should gain from this section is how to develop the necessary identities if he needs them.

We remember that for any θ and ϕ which belong to R, $\sin (\theta + \phi) \equiv$ $\sin \theta \cos \phi + \cos \phi \sin \theta$ and $\cos (\theta + \phi) \equiv \cos \theta \cos \phi - \sin \theta \sin \phi$. We can develop the desired expressions by manipulating these identities.

First we will develop the identity of the form $\sin \theta \cos \phi \equiv$ _____ for $\theta, \phi \in R$. We observe that the identity

$$\sin (\theta + \phi) \equiv \sin \theta \cos \phi + \cos \theta \sin \phi$$

contains the desired expression, but it also contains the expression $\cos \theta \sin \phi$. However, the identity

$$\sin (\theta - \phi) \equiv \sin \theta \cos \phi - \cos \theta \sin \phi$$

contains the same two expressions with a difference in sign that is just what we need. The formal development appears below.

$$\sin (\theta + \phi) \equiv \sin \theta \cos \phi + \cos \theta \sin \phi$$
$$\underline{(+) \sin (\theta - \phi) \equiv \sin \theta \cos \phi - \cos \theta \sin \phi}$$
$$\sin (\theta + \phi) + \sin (\theta - \phi) = 2 \sin \theta \cos \phi,$$

$$\sin \theta \cos \phi = \frac{1}{2}[\sin (\theta + \phi) + \sin (\theta - \phi)].$$

$$\therefore \ \mathbf{\sin \theta \cos \phi} \equiv \frac{1}{2}[\sin (\theta + \phi) + \sin (\theta - \phi)], \quad \boldsymbol{\theta, \phi \in R.}$$

The development of the identity for $\cos \theta \cos \phi$ is quite similar. We observe that the identity

$$\cos (\theta + \phi) \equiv \cos \theta \cos \phi - \sin \theta \sin \phi$$

contains the desired expression and one other. This is also true of the identity

$$\cos (\theta - \phi) \equiv \cos \theta \cos \phi + \sin \theta \sin \phi.$$

Adding these two identities gives us the following derivation.

$$\cos (\theta + \phi) \equiv \cos \theta \cos \phi - \sin \theta \sin \phi$$
$$\underline{(+) \cos (\theta - \phi) \equiv \cos \theta \cos \phi + \sin \theta \sin \phi}$$
$$\cos (\theta + \phi) + \cos (\theta - \phi) = 2 \cos \theta \cos \phi,$$

$$\cos \theta \cos \phi = \frac{1}{2}[\cos (\theta + \phi) + \cos (\theta - \phi)].$$

$$\therefore \ \mathbf{\cos \theta \cos \phi} \equiv \frac{1}{2}[\cos (\theta + \phi) + \cos (\theta - \phi)], \quad \boldsymbol{\theta, \phi \in R.}$$

We can see that the identities

$$\cos (\theta + \phi) \equiv \cos \theta \cos \phi - \sin \theta \sin \phi$$

and

$$\cos (\theta - \phi) \equiv \cos \theta \cos \phi + \sin \theta \sin \phi$$

both contain the expression $\sin \theta \sin \phi$ as well as the expression $\cos \theta \cos \phi$. Adding these two identities gave us an expression equivalent to $\cos \theta \cos \phi$. If we subtract the first of these two identities from the second, we can derive an identity for $\sin \theta \sin \phi$.

$$\cos(\theta - \phi) \equiv \cos\theta\cos\phi + \sin\theta\sin\phi$$
$$-\cos(\theta + \phi) \equiv -\cos\theta\cos\phi + \sin\theta\sin\phi$$
$$\overline{\cos(\theta - \phi) - \cos(\theta + \phi) = 2\sin\theta\sin\phi,}$$
$$\sin\theta\sin\phi = \frac{1}{2}[\cos(\theta - \phi) - \cos(\theta + \phi)].$$
$$\therefore\ \sin\theta\sin\phi \equiv \frac{1}{2}[\cos(\theta - \phi) - \cos(\theta + \phi)], \quad \theta, \phi \in R.$$

Exercises 2.6

Use the identities developed in this section to evaluate the following expressions.

1. $\sin\dfrac{5\pi}{12}\sin\dfrac{\pi}{12}$ 2. $\sin\dfrac{\pi}{4}\cos\dfrac{\pi}{12}$ 3. $\cos\dfrac{\pi}{8}\cos\dfrac{3\pi}{8}$

4. $\cos\dfrac{7\pi}{12}\cos\dfrac{\pi}{12}$ 5. $\cos\dfrac{11\pi}{8}\sin\dfrac{3\pi}{8}$ 6. $\sin\dfrac{\pi}{24}\sin\dfrac{5\pi}{24}$

Verify that each of the following equations is an identity.

7. $\cos x + \cos y \equiv 2\cos\left(\dfrac{x+y}{2}\right)\cos\left(\dfrac{x-y}{2}\right).$

8. $\cos x - \cos y \equiv -2\sin\left(\dfrac{x+y}{2}\right)\sin\left(\dfrac{x-y}{2}\right).$

9. $\sin x + \sin y \equiv 2\sin\left(\dfrac{x+y}{2}\right)\cos\left(\dfrac{x-y}{2}\right).$

10. $\sin x - \sin y \equiv 2\cos\left(\dfrac{x+y}{2}\right)\sin\left(\dfrac{x-y}{2}\right).$

11. $\sin 3x \sin 7x \equiv \dfrac{1}{2}[\cos 4x - \cos 10x].$

12. $2\cos 2\alpha \sin 4\alpha \equiv \sin 6\alpha + \sin 2\alpha.$

13. $\cos 4x \cos 2x \equiv \dfrac{1}{2}[\cos 6x + \cos 2x].$

14. $\sin 5x \sin(-x) \equiv \dfrac{1}{2}[\cos 6x - \cos 4x].$

15. $\sin 3\phi \cos 7\phi \equiv \dfrac{1}{2}[\sin 10\phi - \sin 4\phi].$

16. $\cos 3x \cos(-3x) \equiv \dfrac{1}{2}[1 + \cos 6x].$

17. $\cos 2\theta\,[2\cos 4\theta - 1] \equiv \cos 6\theta.$

18. $\sin 2\beta\,[1 + 2\cos 4\beta] \equiv \sin 6\beta.$

19. $2\sin 2x \cos 2x \equiv 4\cos x\,(\sin x - 2\sin^3 x).$

20. $\sin\dfrac{\phi}{4}\cos\dfrac{\phi}{4} \equiv \dfrac{1}{2}\sin\dfrac{\phi}{2}.$

21.　$\cos 3x \cos \left(\dfrac{\pi}{2} - 3x\right) \sec \left(6x - \dfrac{\pi}{2}\right) \equiv \dfrac{1}{2}.$

22.　$2 \cos 2\theta \equiv \dfrac{\sin 4\theta}{\sin 2\theta}.$

23.　$\sin (u + h) - \sin u \equiv 2 \cos \left(u + \dfrac{h}{2}\right) \sin \dfrac{h}{2}.$

×　24.　$4 \sin x \sin 2x \sin 3x \equiv \sin 4x + \sin 2x - \sin 6x.$

25.　$\sin 5\phi \cos 5\phi \csc 10\phi \equiv \dfrac{1}{2}.$

26.　$4 \cos x \cos 2x \cos 3x \equiv 1 + \cos 2x + \cos 4x + \cos 6x.$

27.　$2 \cos 2\alpha \cos 2\alpha \equiv 2 + 8 \cos^4 \alpha - 8 \cos^2 \alpha.$

28.　$\sin 5x \cos x \equiv \sin 3x \cos 3x + \sin 2x \cos 2x.$

29.　$2 \cos 6\theta \cos 2\theta \equiv (2 \cos 4\theta - 1)(\cos 4\theta + 1).$

Review Exercises

Verify the following identities.

1.　$\sec^2 x \, (1 - \sin^2 x) \equiv 1.$

2.　$\left(\sin \dfrac{\phi}{2} - \cos \dfrac{\phi}{2}\right)^2 \equiv 1 - \sin \phi.$

3.　$\sin 5y \equiv \sin 7y \cos 2y - \cos 7y \sin 2y.$

4.　$\cos 2\beta \equiv \cos^4 \beta - \sin^4 \beta.$

5.　$\sin \alpha + \cos \alpha \cot \alpha \equiv \csc \alpha.$

6.　$\sin 2z \equiv \dfrac{2 \tan z}{\sec^2 z}.$

7.　$\dfrac{1 - \cos 2\theta}{\sin 2\theta} \equiv \tan \theta.$

8.　$\sec^2 \dfrac{y}{2} \equiv 2 \csc y \tan \dfrac{y}{2}.$

9.　$\tan \beta \, (\sin \beta + \cot \beta \cos \beta) \equiv \sec \beta.$

10.　$\sin 3\phi \sin \phi \equiv \sin^2 2\phi - \sin^2 \phi.$

11.　$\cos (x + \pi) - \cos (x - \pi) \equiv 0.$

12.　$2 \csc 2\gamma \equiv \cot \gamma + \tan \gamma.$

13.　$\tan^2 \phi + \cot^2 \phi \equiv \dfrac{1 - 2 \sin^2 \phi + 2 \sin^4 \phi}{\sin^2 \phi - \sin^4 \phi}.$

14.　$\csc^2 \dfrac{\beta}{2} \equiv \dfrac{2}{1 - \cos \beta}.$

15.　$(\cos x \cos z)^2 - (\sin x \sin z)^2 \equiv \cos^2 z - \sin^2 x.$

16.　$\cos 2\gamma - 2 \cos^2 \gamma \equiv -1.$

17.　$\dfrac{\cos y + \sin^2 y \sec y}{\sec y} \equiv 1.$

18.　$\tan \dfrac{\alpha}{2} \equiv \csc \alpha - \cot \alpha.$

19. $\cot(\theta + \phi) \equiv \dfrac{\cot \theta \cot \phi - 1}{\cot \theta + \cot \phi}$.

20. $\tan 3z \equiv \dfrac{3 \tan z - \tan^3 z}{1 - 3 \tan^2 z}$.

21. $(\cos \alpha + \sin \alpha)^4 \equiv 1 + 4 \cos^2 \alpha \sin^2 \alpha + 4 \cos \alpha \sin \alpha$.

22. $\cos 4\alpha \equiv 1 - 8 \sin^2 \alpha \cos^2 \alpha$.

23. $(\sin \alpha \cos \theta)^2 - (\cos \alpha \sin \theta)^2 \equiv \sin^2 \alpha - \sin^2 \theta$.

24. $\dfrac{1 + \sin 2x + \cos 2x}{1 - \cos 2x + \sin 2x} \equiv \cot x$.

25. $\dfrac{1 - \tan \dfrac{\alpha}{2}}{1 + \tan \dfrac{\alpha}{2}} \equiv \sec \alpha - \tan \alpha$.

Evaluate the following expressions.

26. $\sin \dfrac{\pi}{12}$

27. $\tan \dfrac{\pi}{8}$

28. $\cos\left(-\dfrac{\pi}{8}\right)$

29. $\sin \dfrac{3\pi}{8}$

30. $\tan \dfrac{\pi}{12}$

31. $\cos\left(-\dfrac{5\pi}{12}\right)$

32. $\sin\left(-\dfrac{\pi}{16}\right)$

33. $\tan \dfrac{\pi}{16}$

Trigonometric equations

3.1 Introduction

In Chapter 2 we defined two kinds of equations, identities and conditional equations. Also, trigonometric identities were discussed in detail. A conditional equation was defined to be an equation for which there is at least one number in the replacement set for the equation which results in a false statement of equality. For example, $\cos x = \sin x$ is a conditional equation. We note that the replacement set for $\cos x = \sin x$ is $\mathscr{D} = R$, that $0 \in R$, and that $\cos 0 = 1 \neq 0 = \sin 0$.

The problem confronting us in this chapter is not proving that a particular equation is a conditional equation. Rather, we shall assume that we are starting with a conditional equation and we shall seek the solution set of the equation —that is, the set of all the numbers in the replacement set which result in a true statement of equality. S will to represent the solution set. We use the uppercase letter for the solution set, since we are representing a set.

If we should discover that the solution set S is equal to the replacement set $\mathscr{D}$, the equation with which we started is an identity, and there should be other means at our disposal to prove that the equation is an identity.

In the example above we showed that $\cos x = \sin x$ is a conditional equation with replacement set $\mathscr{D} = R$. To solve this equation we might do the following:

$$\cos x = \sin x,$$

$$1 = \frac{\sin x}{\cos x} = \tan x, \qquad x \neq \frac{\pi}{2} + n\pi, n \in J.$$

We remember that $\tan \pi/4 = 1$. This means that $\pi/4 \in S$, but it does not necessarily mean that $\{\pi/4\} = S$. The student should remember that

$$\tan(\theta + n\pi) \equiv \tan \theta$$

for $n \in J$. This tells us that if $\theta = \pi/4 + n\pi$, where $n \in J$, then $\tan \theta = 1$.

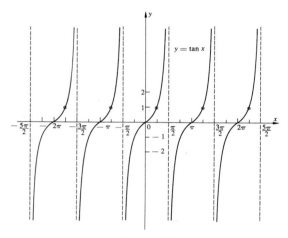

Figure 3.1

If we study Figure 3.1, we see that $\pi/4$ is the only number θ in the interval $[-\pi/2, \pi/2]$ for which $\tan \theta = 1$. In fact, we can conclude from Figure 3.1 that if $\tan \theta = 1$, then

$$\theta \in \left\{ x \,\middle|\, x = \frac{\pi}{4} + n\pi, n \in J \right\}.$$

These two paragraphs tell us that the solution set for the equation $\cos x = \sin x$, is

$$S = \left\{ x \,\middle|\, x = \frac{\pi}{4} + n\pi, n \in J \right\}.$$

The solution set which we have found is the **general solution** to the given equation. Sometimes it is only necessary to find solutions in one fundamental period of the functions which occur in the equation. The solutions which lie in this fundamental period are often called the **principal solutions** to the equation. The principal solution to the equation $\cos x = \sin x$ is $\pi/4$, since this is the only solution to the equation in the fundamental period $[-\pi/2, \pi/2]$.

Many trigonometric equations cannot be solved out of the knowledge we have developed so far. Over the years tables of values of the trigonometric functions have been developed that enable us to solve many trigonometric equations which we could not hope to solve otherwise.

Table I in the Appendix, page 178, is such a table. Note that the real numbers in the left-hand column are given to the nearest hundredth. We can read from the table that

sin .23 = .2280   or   csc .47 = 2.208.

These function values are not exact. The statement that sin .23 = .2280, means that, if we round off the value of sin .23 to the nearest ten-thousandth, sin .23 = .2280.

Although the left-hand column only gives real numbers to the nearest hundredth, we can find the function value of a real number x, if x is given to the nearest thousandth, by using straight-line interpolation.

For example, find cos .324. We note that

cos .32 = .9492   and   cos .33 = .9460.

In this case, we have a difference of .0032, and we note that the cosine function is a decreasing function in this interval. We find four-tenths of the difference in function values, since .324 is four-tenths of the way from .32 to .33:

$$(.4)(.0032) = .00128.$$

Since function values are given to the nearest ten-thousandth, we use .0013 as an approximation of (.4)(.0032). The number .0013 is *subtracted* from .9492, since the cosine function is a *decreasing* function in this interval. Thus,

cos .324 = .9492 − .0013 = .9479.

This is just an approximation of the value of cos .324, but it is a very close approximation, based upon the assumption that the graph of $y = \cos x$ is a straight line between $x = .32$ and $x = .33$. Actually, this segment of the graph is not a straight line, but it is very close to being one.

Table I can be used to solve some trigonometric equations in the fashion illustrated in the following examples.

Example

Solve $2 \sin x - 3 = 6 \sin x - 2$.

Solution

$$-3 + 2 = 6 \sin x - 2 \sin x$$
$$-1 = 4 \sin x$$
$$\sin x = -\frac{1}{4} = -.2500$$

To solve this equation from this point, we find a solution for sin x = .2500 and then use the identity

$$\sin (-x) \equiv -\sin x$$

to find a solution for sin $x = -.2500$. We observe that

$$\sin .25 = .2474$$

and

$$\sin .26 = .2571.$$

We use straight-line interpolation to find a value of x to the nearest thousandth.

$$.2571 - .2474 = .0097 \quad \text{and} \quad .2500 - .2474 = .0026,$$

$$\frac{.0026}{.0097} = .3 \quad \text{(when rounded to the nearest tenth).}$$

The approximate solution to sin $x = .2500$ is $x = .253$, since .253 is three-tenths of the way from .25 to .26. Thus, an approximate solution to sin $x = -2500$ is $x = -.253$.

Since $\sin (\pi + x) = -\sin x$,

$$\sin (\pi + .253) = -.2500 \quad \text{and} \quad x = \pi + .253$$

is also a solution to sin $x = -.2500$. We use the periodicity of the sine function to obtain the complete solution set for the equation $2 \sin x - 3 = 6 \sin x - 2$. The complete solution set is

$$S = \{x \mid x = -.253 + 2n\pi, n \in J\} \cup \{x \mid x = \pi + .253 + 2n\pi, n \in J\}.$$

Example

Solve cot $x = 3$.

Solution

We observe that cot $.32 = 3.018$ and cot $.33 = 2.920$. The cotangent function is *decreasing* here.

$$3.018 - 3 = .018, \quad 3.018 - 2.920 = .098, \quad \text{and} \quad \frac{.018}{.098} = .2$$

to the nearest tenth. Thus, the solution is approximately two-tenths of the way from .32 to .33, or $x = .322$ is an approximate solution of cot $x = 3$. Since the cotangent function has fundamental period π, the complete solution is given by

$$S = \{x \mid x = .322 + n\pi, n \in J\}.$$

Exercises 3.1

Find the solution sets for the following equations.

1. $3 \sin x + 2 = 0$.
2. $4 \cos y - 3 = 0$.
3. $2 + \tan z = 0$.
4. $4 \sin \theta - 1 = 0$.
5. $5 \cos \alpha + 1 = 0$.
6. $3 \tan x - 2 = 0$.
7. $2 \sin y - 5 = 0$.
8. $3 \cos z - 1 = 0$.

9. $3 \tan \theta - 7 = 0$.

10. $2 \sec \alpha - 3 = 0$.

11. $3 \csc x - 1 = 0$.

12. $2 \cot y + 5 = 0$.

13. $3 - \sin z = -2 + 5 \sin z$.

14. $2 + \cos \theta = 1 + 3 \cos \theta$.

15. $\tan \alpha + 2 = 3 - \tan \alpha$.

16. $\sin x - 3 = 3 \sin x - 2$.

17. $\cos y - 2 = 4 \cos y + 3$.

18. $2 + 3 \tan z = 4 - 2 \tan z$.

19. $\sec \theta + 2 = 2 \sec \theta + 1$.

20. $\csc \alpha - 3 = 4 + 2 \csc \alpha$.

21. $2 + 3 \cot \beta = 6 - 2 \cot \beta$.

Example

$\sin^2 x + 7 \sin x + 6 = 0$.

Solution

$$(\sin x + 1)(\sin x + 6) = 0,$$
$$\sin x = -1 \quad \text{or} \quad \sin x = -6.$$

The solution set for $\sin x = -1$ is

$$S = \left\{ x \mid x = \frac{3\pi}{2} + 2n\pi, n \in J \right\}.$$

$\sin x = -6$ has no solution, since -6 is not in the range of the sine function. Thus, the solution set for $\sin^2 x + 7 \sin x + 6 = 0$ is

$$S = \left\{ x \mid x = \frac{3\pi}{2} + 2n\pi, n \in J \right\}.$$

22. $\sin^2 x - \sin x - 2 = 0$.

23. $3 \cos^2 y - 4 \cos y + 1 = 0$.

24. $2 \tan^2 z - 5 \tan z + 3 = 0$.

25. $6 \sin^2 \alpha + 5 \sin \alpha - 1 = 0$.

26. $12 \cos^2 \theta - 7 \cos \theta + 1 = 0$.

27. $\tan^2 \beta - 9 = 0$.

28. $\sec^2 \gamma + 4 \sec \gamma + 4 = 0$.

29. $2 \csc^2 t - 3 = 0$.

30. $\cot^2 w - 4 \cot w + 3 = 0$.

3.2 More conditional equations

In the preceding section we considered two variations of the same type of trigonometric equation—that is, each equation involved a single trigonometric function of one variable. In some equations, the highest degree of the function was the first degree, as in $3 \sin x + 2 = 0$. In other equations, the highest degree of the function was the second degree, as in $3 \cos^2 y - 4 \cos y + 1 = 0$. In problems of this latter type, the factoring should have been relatively easy for you, and, once the equation was factored, the work was quite similar to that required to solve the earlier problems.

The types of problems explored in this section will be slightly more involved than those in Section 3.1. For one thing, they may involve expressions such as $\sin 3x$ and $\sin x/2$, rather than simply $\sin x$. Also, some equations will require use of some of the basic identities. Examples of these various types of problems follow.

Example 1

Solve $2 \sin 4x = 1$.

Solution

This may be solved by temporarily letting $4x = \theta$.
Then

$$2 \sin \theta = 1,$$
$$\sin \theta = \frac{1}{2},$$
$$\theta = \frac{\pi}{6} + 2n\pi, \quad n \in J \quad \text{or} \quad \theta = \frac{5\pi}{6} + 2n\pi, \quad n \in J.$$

Since $\theta = 4x$, we have

$$4x = \frac{\pi}{6} + 2n\pi, \quad n \in J \quad \text{or} \quad 4x = \frac{5\pi}{6} + 2n\pi, \quad n \in J.$$

Thus,

$$x = \frac{\pi}{24} + \frac{n\pi}{2}, \quad n \in J \quad \text{or} \quad x = \frac{5\pi}{24} + \frac{n\pi}{2}, \quad n \in J.$$

Thus,

$$S = \left\{ x \mid x = \frac{\pi}{24} + \frac{n\pi}{2}, \quad n \in J \right\} \cup \left\{ x \mid x = \frac{5\pi}{24} + \frac{n\pi}{2}, \quad n \in J \right\}.$$

Example 2

Solve $3 \cos \frac{y}{3} + 2 = 0$.

Solution

Let $\frac{y}{3} = \theta$. Then

$$3 \cos \theta + 2 = 0,$$
$$3 \cos \theta = -2,$$
$$\cos \theta = -\frac{2}{3}.$$
$$\theta = \pi - .841 + 2n\pi, \, n \in J$$

or

$$\theta = \pi + .841 + 2n\pi, \, n \in J \text{ (by methods of Sec. 3.1).}$$

Since $\theta = \frac{y}{3}$,

$$\frac{y}{3} = \pi - .841 + 2n\pi, \quad n \in J \quad \text{or} \quad \frac{y}{3} = \pi + .841 + 2n\pi, \quad n \in J.$$
$$y = 3\pi - 2.523 + 6n\pi, \quad n \in J \quad \text{or} \quad y = 3\pi + 2.523 + 6n\pi, \quad n \in J.$$

Thus,

$$S = \{ y \mid y = 3\pi - 2.523 + 6n\pi, n \in J \} \cup \{ y \mid y = 3\pi + 2.523 + 6n\pi, n \in J \}.$$

Example 3

Solve $\sec^2 \alpha + \tan^2 \alpha = 3$.

Solution

Since $\sec^2 \alpha - 1 \equiv \tan^2 \alpha$, we have

$$\sec^2 \alpha + (\sec^2 \alpha - 1) = 3,$$
$$2 \sec^2 \alpha - 1 = 3,$$
$$\sec^2 \alpha = 2.$$
$$\sec \alpha = \sqrt{2} \quad \text{or} \quad \sec \alpha = -\sqrt{2}.$$
$$\alpha = \frac{\pi}{4} + 2n\pi, \, n \in J \quad \text{or} \quad \alpha = -\frac{\pi}{4} + 2n\pi, \, n \in J$$

or

$$\alpha = \frac{3\pi}{4} + 2n\pi, \, n \in J \quad \text{or} \quad \alpha = \frac{5\pi}{4} + 2n\pi, \, n \in J.$$

Thus,

$$S = \left\{ \alpha \,\middle|\, \alpha = \frac{\pi}{4} + \frac{n\pi}{2}, \, n \in J \right\}.$$

Example 4

Solve $\sin x - \cos x = 1$.

Solution

$$\sin x = 1 + \cos x.$$

We observe that $1 - \cos^2 x = \sin^2 x$ and that $\sin^2 x$ can be obtained by squaring both sides of the equation.

$$\sin^2 x = 1 + 2 \cos x + \cos^2 x,$$
$$1 - \cos^2 x = 1 + 2 \cos x + \cos^2 x,$$
$$-\cos^2 x = 2 \cos x + \cos^2 x,$$
$$2 \cos x + 2 \cos^2 x = 0,$$
$$2 \cos x \,(1 + \cos x) = 0,$$
$$\cos x = 0 \quad \text{or} \quad \cos x = -1.$$
$$x = \frac{\pi}{2} + 2n\pi, \, n \in J \quad \text{or} \quad x = \frac{3\pi}{2} + 2n\pi, \, n \in J \quad \text{or} \quad x = \pi + 2n\pi, \, n \in J.$$

Since we squared each side of the equation, we may have obtained some extraneous roots. To guard against this possibility, we check each of the above.

If $x = \frac{\pi}{2} + 2n\pi$, $\sin x = 1$, $\cos x = 0$, $\sin x - \cos x = 1$. (OK)

If $x = \frac{3\pi}{2} + 2n\pi$, $\sin x = -1$, $\cos x = 0$, $\sin x - \cos x = -1$. (No)

If $x = \pi + 2n\pi$, $\sin x = 0$, $\cos x = -1$, $\sin x - \cos x = 1$. (OK)

$$S = \left\{ x \,\middle|\, x = \frac{\pi}{2} + 2n\pi, \, n \in J \right\} \cup \{ x \,|\, x = \pi + 2n\pi, \, n \in J \}.$$

Exercises 3.2

Find the solution sets for the following equations.

1. $2 \sin 3x - 1 = \sin 3x - 2.$

2. $2 \cos \frac{\alpha}{2} + 1 = 4 \cos \frac{\alpha}{2} + 2.$

3. $3 \tan 2\beta - 1 = 4 \tan 2\beta - 2.$

4. $4 \sin \frac{y}{3} + 2 = 2 - \sin \frac{y}{3}.$

5. $3 \cos 3z - 1 = 2 \cos 3z + 3.$

6. $6 \tan \frac{x}{5} - 1 = \tan \frac{x}{5} - 3.$

7. $2 \sec 4y + 3 = \sec 4y + 5.$

8. $3 \csc \frac{\alpha}{2} + 1 = 1 - 4 \csc \frac{\alpha}{2}.$

9. $5 \cot 5\beta - 1 = 3 + \cot 5\beta.$

10. $4 \sin 2z - 1 = \sin 2z + 3.$

11. $\cos 2x - 1 = 3 \cos 2x - 1.$

12. $3 \tan \frac{\beta}{3} = \sqrt{3}.$

13. $2 \csc 2\alpha - 1 = 3 \csc 2\alpha + 4.$

14. $3 \csc \frac{y}{3} - 3 = 3 - \csc \frac{y}{3}.$

15. $\cot \frac{z}{4} - 4 = 4 \cot \frac{z}{4} - 1.$

16. $\cos x - \sin x = 1.$

17. $\tan y - \sec y = 1.$

18. $\csc \alpha - \cot \alpha = 1.$

19. $\sin^2 \beta - \cos \beta + 1 = 0.$

20. $\tan^2 z + \sec z - 3 = 0.$

21. $\cot^2 x + 4 = 2 \csc^2 x.$

22. $\sin y - 3 \cos y = 0.$

23. $\sec \alpha - \tan \alpha = 0.$

24. $\csc \beta - 2 \cot \beta = 0.$

25. $\sin z + 2 \cos z = 2.$

26. $\sec x - 3 \tan x = -1.$

27. $2 \csc y - 2 \cot y = 3.$

28. $\cos^2 \alpha + \sin \alpha = -1.$

29. $\sec^2 \beta - \tan \beta = 3.$

30. $\csc^2 z + \cot z = 3.$

31. $\sin \frac{\alpha}{2} - \csc \frac{\alpha}{2} = 0.$

32. $\cos 2\beta + \sec 2\beta = -2.$

33. $\tan 3x + 2 \cot 3x = 3.$

3.3 Some involved trigonometric equations

Among the several types of conditional trigonometric equations which we have not considered yet, some are quite difficult to solve. Equations involving both a variable and trigonometric equations of that variable, such as

$$x \sin x - 1 = 0$$

or

$$x^2 + 2 \tan x - \sec x = 10$$

are beyond the scope of this book. Another type involves two functions with different fundamental periods. In order to solve these, we must resort to the reduction formulas summarized on pages 74 and 75.

Before we look at examples of this type we must determine whether or not the equation **sin** x = **sin** z tells us that for some integer n, $z = x + 2n\pi$. The answer to this question is no. For example,

$$\sin \frac{\pi}{4} = \frac{\sqrt{2}}{2} = \sin \frac{3\pi}{4}$$

even though we cannot express $3\pi/4$ in the form $\pi/4 + 2n\pi$ for any $n \in J$. The reason for this can be seen in the graph of the sine function, shown in Figure 3.2. If y is some number between -1 and 1, we can see that there are two values of x in the interval $[0, 2\pi]$ for which $\sin x = y$. The same is true for any other interval of length 2π. This should not be surprising, since we remember that **sin** $(\pi - x)$ = **sin** x. Although we shall not formally do so here, it can be shown that $\sin x = \sin z$ if and only if (i) for some integer n, $z = x + 2n\pi$ or (ii) for some integer n, $z = (\pi - x) + 2n\pi$.

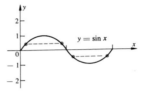

Figure 3.2

Example 1

Solve $\sin 3x = \sin 7x$.

Solution

From the reduction formulas and consideration of the periodicity of the trigonometric functions, we see that $\sin 3x = \sin 7x$ if

$$7x = 3x + 2n\pi, \quad n \in J \quad \text{or} \quad 7x = (\pi - 3x) + 2n\pi, \quad n \in J,$$
$$4x = 2n\pi, \quad n \in J \quad \text{or} \quad 10x = \pi + 2n\pi, \quad n \in J,$$
$$x = \frac{n\pi}{2}, \quad n \in J \quad \text{or} \quad x = \frac{\pi}{10} + \frac{n\pi}{5}, \quad n \in J.$$

$$S = \left\{ x \mid x = \frac{n\pi}{2}, n \in J \right\} \cup \left\{ x \mid x = \frac{\pi}{10} + \frac{n\pi}{5}, n \in J \right\}.$$

Example 2

Solve $\cos 5x = -\cos 2x$.

Solution

The two reduction formulas which are appropriate here are

$$\cos (\pi - \theta) = -\cos \theta \quad \text{and} \quad \cos (\pi + \theta) = -\cos \theta.$$

If we combine these reduction formulas with the periodicity of the cosine function, we see that $\cos 5x = -\cos 2x$ if

$$2x = (\pi - 5x) + 2n\pi, \quad n \in J \quad \text{or} \quad 2x = (\pi + 5x) + 2n\pi, \quad n \in J,$$

$$7x = \pi + 2n\pi, \quad n \in J \quad \text{or} \quad -3x = \pi + 2n\pi, \quad n \in J,$$

$$x = \frac{\pi}{7} + \frac{2n\pi}{7}, \quad n \in J \quad \text{or} \quad x = -\frac{\pi}{3} + -\frac{2n\pi}{3}, \quad n \in J.$$

Since $\cos(-x) = \cos x$, we could write

$$x = \frac{\pi}{7} + \frac{2n\pi}{7}, \quad n \in J \quad \text{or} \quad x = \frac{\pi}{3} + \frac{2n\pi}{3}, \quad n \in J.$$

$$S = \left\{ x \mid x = \frac{\pi}{7} + \frac{2n\pi}{7}, \quad n \in J \right\} \cup \left\{ x \mid x = \frac{\pi}{3} + \frac{2n\pi}{3}, \quad n \in J \right\}.$$

Sometimes the identities $\sin(\pi/2 - x) = \cos x$ and $\cos(\pi/2 - x) = \sin x$ are quite helpful. This is illustrated in Example 3.

Example 3

Solve $\sin 2\theta = \cos 3\theta$.

Solution

We observe that $\cos 3\theta$ can be expressed in another form by using one of the identities above,

$$\cos 3\theta = \sin\left(\frac{\pi}{2} - 3\theta\right).$$

We now have the following solution.

$$\sin 2\theta = \sin\left(\frac{\pi}{2} - 3\theta\right)$$

$$\frac{\pi}{2} - 3\theta = 2\theta + 2n\pi, \quad n \in J \quad \text{or} \quad \frac{\pi}{2} - 3\theta = \pi - 2\theta + 2n\pi, \quad n \in J.$$

$$-5\theta = -\frac{\pi}{2} + 2n\pi, \quad n \in J \quad \text{or} \quad -\theta = \frac{\pi}{2} + 2n\pi, \quad n \in J.$$

$$\theta = \frac{\pi}{10} - \frac{2n\pi}{5}, \quad n \in J \quad \text{or} \quad \theta = -\frac{\pi}{2} - 2n\pi, \quad n \in J.$$

Since n can be either a positive or a negative integer, we can rewrite the above in the following form.

$$\theta = \frac{\pi}{10} + \frac{2n\pi}{5}, \quad n \in J \quad \text{or} \quad \theta = -\frac{\pi}{2} + 2n\pi, \quad n \in J.$$

$$S = \left\{ \theta \mid \theta = \frac{\pi}{10} + \frac{2n\pi}{5}, \quad n \in J \right\} \cup \left\{ \theta \mid \theta = -\frac{\pi}{2} + 2n\pi, \quad n \in J \right\}.$$

Exercises 3.3

Find the solution sets for the following equations.

1. $\sin 4\theta = -\sin 3\theta$.
2. $\cos 3y = \cos 6y$.
3. $\tan 3x = -\tan x$.
4. $\sin 5\alpha = \sin \alpha$.
5. $\cos 4\beta = -\cos 3\beta$.
6. $\tan 2z = \tan 5z$.

7. $\sec 2y = \sec y.$ 8. $\csc 3\theta = -\csc 2\theta.$ 9. $\cot 5\alpha = \cot 2\alpha.$

10. $\cos 2x = \sin 5x.$ 11. $\sin 4z = -\cos 3z.$ 12. $\cos 6\beta = \sin 3\beta.$

13. $\tan 2x = \cot 3x.$ 14. $\sec 5\alpha = \csc 3\alpha.$ 15. $\csc 2\theta = -\sec 4\theta.$

Review Exercises

Find the solution set for each of the following equations.

1. $5 \sin x + 2 = 0.$
2. $4 \sin 3\beta = 2.$
3. $3 \sin^2 \alpha - 5 \sin \alpha + 2 = 0.$
4. $6 \cos z + 1 = 0.$
5. $\sin 2x - \sin 3x = 0.$
6. $\sin x + \cos x = 1.$
7. $3 \cos 2\beta + 1 = 0.$
8. $4 \cos^2 x - 1 = 0.$
9. $3 - 2 \tan \alpha = -1.$
10. $\cos 4\theta + \cos 5\theta = 0.$

11. $\cot y - \csc y = 1.$
12. $4 \sin \left(\alpha + \frac{\pi}{4} \right) = -2.$

13. $3 \tan 3\gamma - \sqrt{3} = 0.$
14. $3 + 5 \cot z = 2 \cot z - 5.$
15. $\tan^2 x - 7 \tan x + 12 = 0.$
16. $\sin 4\theta + \sin \theta = 0.$

17. $\sin 6\theta - 4 = 2 \sin 6\theta - 3.$
18. $\cos \left(\gamma - \frac{\pi}{2} \right) = 1.$

19. $4 \sec z - 2 = 5 \sec z.$
20. $2 \sin^2 \alpha - 3 \sin \alpha + 1 = 0.$
21. $\sec x + \tan x = 1.$
22. $3 - 2 \csc x = 6 - \csc x.$
23. $\cos 2\theta - \cos 7\theta = 0.$
24. $4 \cos 2\beta - 1 = \cos 2\beta + 2.$

25. $5 \sin \left(2x + \frac{2\pi}{3} \right) - 4 = 0.$

3.1   8,10

32   5 25

33   1 2,3
)
          1

Inverse trigonometric functions

4.1   Inverse functions

In Section 0.7, where the terms relation and function were defined, we said that a relation in A is *any subset of $A \times A$* and that a function is *a relation in which each element in the domain occurs in only one ordered pair in the relation.* For example, consider the following sets of ordered pairs, each of which is a subset of $R \times R$.

$$A = \left\{ (1, 4), (2, 6), (-1, 0), \left(\frac{1}{2}, 3\right), (-2, 2), \left(-\frac{3}{2}, 1\right) \right\}.$$

$$B = \left\{ (0, 0), (1, 1), (-1, 1), (2, 4), (-2, 4), \left(\frac{1}{2}, \frac{1}{4}\right), \left(-\frac{3}{2}, \frac{9}{4}\right) \right\}.$$

$$C = \{ (0, 0), (1, 3), (4, 5), (2, -1), (-1, 5), (1, -2), (2, 2) \}.$$

The sets A, B, and C are shown graphically in Figures 4.1, 4.2, and 4.3, respectively. We see that A, B, and C are all relations in R, since each is a subset of $R \times R$. C is not a function, since $(1, 3)$ and $(1, -2)$ are distinct ordered pairs in C with the same first element and different second elements. A and B are both functions. However, there is one basic difference that can be observed between them. Each ordered pair in A has a *different* second element, while in B the ordered pairs $(1, 1)$ and $(-1, 1)$ have the same second element. $(2, 4)$ and

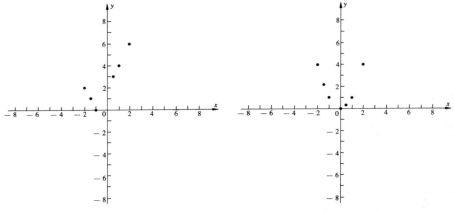

Figure 4.1   Figure 4.2

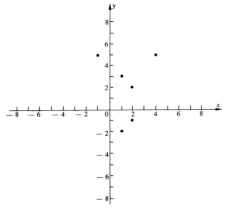

Figure 4.3

$(-2, 4)$ also have the same second element. This difference illustrates the desirability of a definition for what we call a **one-to-one function.**

*Let f be a function. f is a **one-to-one function** if and only if for any pairs (x_1, y_1) and (x_2, y_2) which belong to f, if $x_1 \neq x_2$, then $y_1 \neq y_2$.*

In the function given by B we could let the pairs $(1, 1)$ and $(-1, 1)$ be (x_1, y_1) and (x_2, y_2), respectively. Since $1 \neq -1$, we have $x_1 \neq x_2$, but $y_1 = y_2$, since $1 = 1$. This tells us that B is *not* a one-to-one function, but A is a one-to-one function. The last of this definition is often expressed in either of two ways using functional notation. Instead of saying if $x_1 \neq x_2$, then $y_1 \neq y_2$, we might say that if $x_1 \neq x_2$, then $f(x_1) \neq f(x_2)$ or that if $f(x_1) = f(x_2)$, then $x_1 = x_2$.

While these three phrases all say the same thing, the last one is the easiest to use. When checking a given function by listing a set of ordered pairs to determine whether it is a one-to-one function, all we need to do is to check the second components of the ordered pairs to see if some element occurs twice as a second component. If not, the function is one-to-one. If we do find some element occurring twice as a second component, then we check the first components to determine whether or not they are the same element.

This is illustrated in the functions given above by A and B. Since no element occurs twice as a second component in A, A is a one-to-one function. In B we can see that 1 is the second component in both the second and third ordered pairs listed, and the first elements of these pairs are different, since 1 $\neq -1$, and we conclude that B is not a one-to-one function.

It is also easy to check the graphical representation of a function to determine whether the function is one-to-one. If some horizontal line intersects the graph of the function at more than one point, the function is *not* one-to-one. If *no* horizontal line intersects the graph at more than one point, the function is one-to-one. This is illustrated in Figures 4.4, 4.5, and 4.6. The function graphed in Figure 4.5 is one-to-one, while the other two graphs do not represent one-to-one functions.

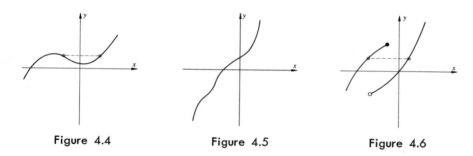

Figure 4.4   Figure 4.5   Figure 4.6

Every one-to-one function has associated with it a special function called its **inverse function.**

Let f be a one-to-one function. Then the set $\{(y, x) \mid (x, y) \in f\}$ *is the **inverse function** of f. This is usually denoted by* f^{-1}.

For example, the set $A = \{(1, 4), (2, 6), (-1, 0), (1/2, 3), (-2, 2), (-3/2, 1)\}$ has been identified as a one-to-one function. The set which we might represent by $A^{-1} = \{(4, 1), (6, 2), (0, -1), (3, 1/2), (2, -2), (1, -3/2)\}$ is the inverse function of A. We note that A^{-1} is a function and that it is one-to-one. In fact, *the inverse function of each one-to-one function is both a function and one-to-one.*

In most cases when we are concerned with inverse functions, we are dealing with infinite sets of ordered pairs. In these cases we cannot define the inverse function by simply listing the appropriate ordered pairs. We must use other techniques.

Consider the function $f = \{(x, y) \mid y = 2x + 3\}$. We observe that for any real number x there is exactly one real number y which can be paired with x as a second component. Let us assume that (x_1, y_1) and (x_2, y_2) are both in f and that $y_1 = y_2$. We might also represent this situation by saying that $f(x_1) = f(x_2)$. We have the following:

$$f(x_1) = f(x_2),$$
$$2x_1 + 3 = 2x_2 + 3,$$
$$2x_1 = 2x_2,$$
$$x_1 = x_2.$$

Thus, if $f(x_1) = f(x_2)$, then $x_1 = x_2$, and we know that f is a one-to-one function.

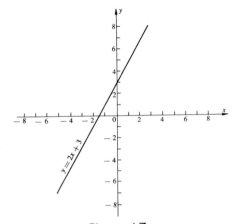

Figure 4.7

We could also determine this by checking the graph of f in Figure 4.7, which tells us that f has an inverse function. We could say

$$f^{-1} = \{(y, x) \mid y = 2x + 3\},$$

but it is more customary to express the second component in terms of the first component. In addition, we would like to express f^{-1} as a set of ordered pairs (x, y). The reason for this is involved with the graphing of f^{-1}. Since the horizontal axis is usually designated as the x-axis and the vertical axis as the y-axis, it is more meaningful to let x be the first component of the ordered pair and y be the second component of the ordered pair.

If (x, y) is in f^{-1}, we know that (y, x) is in f. Thus, $y = f^{-1}(x)$ if and only if $f(y) = x$. We let $x = f(y)$ and then solve for y to find what $f^{-1}(x)$ looks like.

$$x = f(y) = 2y + 3,$$
$$x - 3 = 2y,$$

$$\frac{x-3}{2} = y,$$

$$f^{-1} = \left\{(x, y) \mid y = \frac{x-3}{2}\right\}.$$

You should be able to demonstrate in a similar fashion that if $g = \{(w, z) \mid z = w - 5\}$, then

(1) g is a one-to-one function, and

(2) $g^{-1} = \{(w, z) \mid z = w + 5\}$.

Let f be any one-to-one function and f^{-1} be the inverse function of f. These two functions are related in a special way. Let us consider any pair $(y, x) \in f$. This means that $(x, y) \in f^{-1}$. If we use functional notation, $f(y) = x$ and $f^{-1}(x) = y$. If we look at the composite function $f^{-1}(f(y))$, we have

$$f^{-1}(f(y)) = f^{-1}(x) = y.$$

In similar fashion,

$$f(f^{-1}(x)) = f(y) = x.$$

Thus, we see that either of the composite functions formed by combining f and f^{-1} is actually the identity function, composed of the ordered pairs of the form (x, x).

For example, let us use the function

$$f = \{(x, y) \mid y = 2x + 3\}$$

and the inverse f^{-1} of f. It was shown above that $f^{-1} = \{(x, y) \mid y = (x - 3)/2\}$. We see that $(2, 7) \in f$ and $(7, 2) \in f^{-1}$.

$$f^{-1}(f(2)) = f^{-1}(7) = 2 \quad \text{and} \quad f(f^{-1}(7)) = f(2) = 7.$$

Thus $f(2) = 7$ and $f^{-1}(7) = 2$.

If we wish to be more general, $f(x) = 2x + 3$ and $f^{-1}(x) = (x - 3)/2$.

$$f^{-1}(f(x)) = \frac{f(x) - 3}{2}$$

$$= \frac{(2x + 3) - 3}{2}$$

$$= \frac{2x}{2}$$

$$= x.$$

We see that $f^{-1}(f(x)) = x$. In addition,

$$f(f^{-1}(x)) = 2(f^{-1}(x)) + 3$$

$$= 2\left(\frac{x-3}{2}\right) + 3$$

$$= (x - 3) + 3$$

$$= x.$$

This shows us that $f(f^{-1}(x)) = x.$

There are some cases where we would like to develop an inverse function for a function that is not one-to-one. What we do in a case of this type is to *restrict the domain* of the original function until we get a function that is one-to-one. For example, let

$$h = \{(x, y) \mid y = x^2\}.$$

Ordinarily, the domain of h is the entire set of real numbers. Unfortunately, while h is a function, it is not a one-to-one function, since

$$h(-1) = (-1)^2 = 1 = 1^2 = h(1).$$

We can, however, consider a subset of h which is a one-to-one function. Let

$$h_1 = \{(x, y) \mid x \geq 0 \text{ and } y = x^2\}.$$

h_1 is a one-to-one function, and we can find an inverse function for h_1. h_1^{-1} may be given by

$$h_1^{-1} = \{(x, y) \mid y = \sqrt{x}\}.$$

We also note that the inverse function of h_1^{-1} is simply h_1.

Exercises 4.1

Determine whether each of the following functions is one-to-one. If it is, give an inverse function.

1. $f = \{(1, 17), (2, 1), (3, 5), (4, -2), (5, 1), (6, 3), (7, 9)\}$.
2. $g = \{(6, -1), (-6, 1), (5, 13), (-5, -13), (4, 19), (0, 1024)\}$.
3. $h = \{(1, 5), (-1, 3), (3, 9), (-3, 1), (5, 13), (-5, -1)\}$.
4. $f = \{(1, 1), (2, 1), (3, 1), (4, 1), (5, 1), (6, 1)\}$.
5. $g = \{(x, y) \mid y = 4x - 13\}$.
6. $h = \left\{(x, y) \mid y = \dfrac{x}{2} + 5\right\}$.
7. $f = \{(w, z) \mid z = w^2 - 4\}$.
8. $g = \{(w, z) \mid z = w^3 - 8\}$.
9. $h = \{(x, y) \mid y = 1 - 3x\}$.
10. $f = \{(x, y) \mid y = |x|\}$.
11. $g = \{(w, z) \mid z = 3w + 2\}$.
12. $h = \{(w, z) \mid z = w^2 + 5w + 6\}$.

For each of the following functions, give an inverse function. If it is necessary to restrict the domain of the function first, do so.

13. $f = \{(x, y) \mid y = x^2 - 1\}$.
14. $g = \{(x, y) \mid y = x^3 - 1\}$.

15. $h = \{(w, z)\,|\,z = w^2 + 6w + 9\}$.

16. $j = \{(w, z)\,|\,z = \sqrt[3]{w}\}$.

17. $j = \{(u, v)\,|\,v = u^2 + 4u + 1\}$.

18. $h = \left\{(u, v)\,\middle|\,v = \dfrac{1}{u + 3}\right\}$.

19. $g = \left\{(x, z)\,\middle|\,z = \dfrac{1}{x^2 - 2x + 2}\right\}$.

20. $f = \{(x, z)\,|\,z = |x|\}$.

4.2 The inverse trigonometric functions

The trigonometric functions, like all periodic functions, are not one-to-one functions. Recall from Section 4.1 that although the function $\{(x, y)\,|\,y = x^2\}$ is not one-to-one, if we restrict the domain of this function appropriately, we create a new function which is one-to-one. We shall also restrict the domains of the trigonometric functions in order to get one-to-one functions.

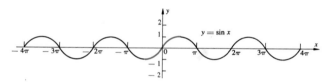

Figure 4.8

Let us consider the graph of the sine function in Figure 4.8. We observe that each function value (or y-value) occurs many times. We might also observe that if we restrict our attention to an appropriate interval, we can get a function that is one-to-one. The interval $[-\pi/2, \pi/2]$ is one in which the sine function is one-to-one, as we can see from the green portion of the graph. We shall define the **Sine function** as follows.

Sine function $= \{(x, y)\,|\,-\pi/2 \leq x \leq \pi/2 \text{ and } y = \sin x\}$. *This is often denoted by* $y = \text{Sin } x$.

The Sine function is a subset of the sine function, but the two functions are not the same. The **domain** of the Sine function is the interval $[-\pi/2, \pi/2]$ while the domain of the sine function is the entire set of real numbers. In the interval $[-\pi/2, \pi/2]$,

$$\text{Sin } x = \sin x.$$

Outside that interval, $\sin x$ is defined while $\text{Sin } x$ is not defined. The colored portion of Figure 4.8 is the graph of the Sine function.

We should also notice that the Sine function is a one-to-one function. Although the Sine function does not have the same domain as the sine function, they both have the same **range**—the interval $[-1, 1]$.

Since the Sine function is a one-to-one function, it has an inverse, called the **inverse Sine function,** which we define formally as follows:

inverse Sine function $= \{(x, y) \mid (y, x) \in$ Sine *function*$\}$. *This is often denoted by* $y = \text{Sin}^{-1} x$ *or* $y = \text{Arcsin } x$.

We could define this function by saying that (x, y) belongs to the inverse Sine function if and only if $x = \text{Sin } y$, a definition that would be equivalent to the one above. The **domain** of the inverse Sine function is the interval $[-1, 1]$, and its **range** is the interval $[-\pi/2, \pi/2]$. Its graph is given in Figure 4.9. We will notice, for example, that

$$\text{Sin}^{-1} 0 = 0, \quad \text{Sin}^{-1} 1 = \frac{\pi}{2}, \quad \text{and} \quad \text{Sin}^{-1}\left(-\frac{1}{2}\right) = -\frac{\pi}{6}.$$

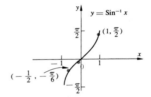

Figure 4.9

These three points are shown in Figure 4.9. If you learned the trigonometric function values of the basic numbers, as they are given in the tables on page 46, you should have relatively little difficulty giving the values of the inverse Sines of such numbers as $0, \pm 1/2, \pm\sqrt{2}/2, \pm\sqrt{3}/2$, and ± 1.

The graph of the cosine function is shown in Figure 4.10, where you can easily see that the cosine function is not one-to-one. If we wish to restrict the domain of the cosine function as we restricted the domain of the sine function, the interval $[-\pi/2, \pi/2]$ is not appropriate, since $\pi/4$ and $-\pi/4$ are both in the interval $[-\pi/2, \pi/2]$, and

$$\cos \frac{\pi}{4} = \frac{\sqrt{2}}{2} = \cos\left(-\frac{\pi}{4}\right),$$

as shown in Figure 4.10. We can see from Figure 4.10 that in the interval $[0, \pi]$ the cosine function is a one-to-one function. We define the **Cosine function** over the interval $[0, \pi]$.

Cosine function $= \{(x, y) \mid 0 \leq x \leq \pi \text{ and } y = \cos x\}$. *This is denoted by* $y = \text{Cos } x$.

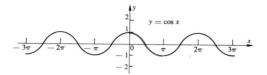

Figure 4.10

The colored portion of Figure 4.10 is the graph of the Cosine function. We can see that the Cosine function is a subset of the cosine function and that the Cosine function is a one-to-one function. The **domain** of the Cosine function is the interval $[0, \pi]$, and the **range** of the Cosine function is the interval $[-1, 1]$. The Cosine function has an inverse function, which is defined below.

> *inverse Cosine function* $= \{(x, y)\,|\,(y, x) \in \text{Cosine function}\}$. *This is denoted by* $y = \text{Cos}^{-1} x$ *or* $y = \text{Arccos } x$.

The *domain* of the inverse Cosine function is the interval $[-1, 1]$, and its range is the interval $[0, \pi]$. The graph of the inverse Cosine function is shown in Figure 4.11. Once again, if you are familiar with the basic function values given

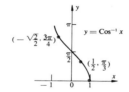

Figure 4.11

in the tables on pages 47 and 48, you should have relatively little difficulty determining the values of the inverse Cosines of numbers like 0, $\pm 1/2$, $\pm\sqrt{2}/2$, $\pm\sqrt{3}/2$, and ± 1. For example

$$\text{Cos}^{-1} 1 = 0, \quad \text{Arccos}\left(-\frac{\sqrt{2}}{2}\right) = \frac{3\pi}{4}, \quad \text{and} \quad \text{Cos}^{-1}\frac{1}{2} = \frac{\pi}{3}.$$

These three function values are shown in Figure 4.11.

We now define the **Tangent function.**

> *Tangent function* $= \{(x, y)\,|\,-\pi/2 < x < \pi/2 \text{ and } y = \tan x\}$. *This is denoted by* $y = \text{Tan } x$.

The Tangent function, a subset of the tangent function, is a one-to-one function. Its **domain** is the interval $(-\pi/2, \pi/2)$ and its range is the entire set of real numbers. Its graph is given in Figure 4.12.

Since the Tangent function is one-to-one, it has an inverse, the **inverse Tangent function,** defined below.

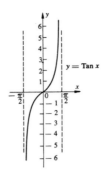

Figure 4.12

inverse Tangent function $= \{(x, y) \mid (y, x) \in \text{Tangent function}\}$.
This is denoted by $y = \text{Tan}^{-1} x$ *or* $y = \text{Arctan } x$.

The graph of the inverse Tangent function appears in Figure 4.13. Notice that its domain is the entire set of real numbers and its range is the interval $(-\pi/2, \pi/2)$. You should be able to observe, for example that

$$\text{Tan}^{-1}(-1) = -\frac{\pi}{4} \quad \text{and} \quad \text{Tan}^{-1}\sqrt{3} = \frac{\pi}{3}.$$

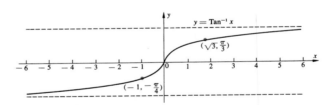

Figure 4.13

There are three other inverse trigonometric functions. They are the **inverse Cotangent function, the inverse Secant function,** and **the inverse Cosecant function.** These functions are frequently omitted when the inverse trigonometric functions are studied. However, we shall consider the inverse Secant function, because of the applications it has in the calculus. First, we define the Secant function.

Secant function $= \{(x, y) \mid 0 \leq x < \pi/2 \text{ or } \pi \leq x < 3\pi/2 \text{ and } y = \sec x\}$.
This is denoted by $y = \text{Sec } x$.

We have restricted the domain of the secant function in what probably seems to be an unusual fashion. If we examine the graph of the secant function

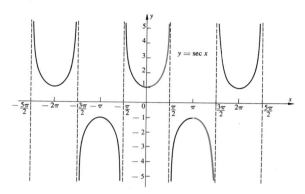

Figure 4.14

(Figure 4.14), we can see why the domain of the Secant function could not be a single interval. One reason for selecting the intervals we did is that the tangent function is non-negative in the domain of the Secant function. This is important in the applications you will have in the calculus. The graph of the Secant function is shown in color in Figure 4.14.

We now define the inverse Secant function.

inverse Secant function = {$(x, y) | (y, x) \in$ Secant function}.
This is denoted by $y = \text{Sec}^{-1} x$ *or* $y = \text{Arcsec } x$.

The *domain* of the inverse Secant function is $(-\infty, -1] \cup [1, \infty)$, and the range is $[0, \pi/2) \cup [\pi, 3\pi/2)$. The graph of the inverse Secant function appears in Figure 4.15.

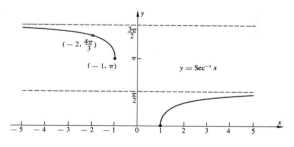

Figure 4.15

To evaluate an expression like $\text{Sec}^{-1}(-2)$, we might proceed in the following manner. We know that the secant function is negative in the second and third quadrants. When we consider the range of the inverse Secant function, we know that we want to find a number y such that $\pi \le y < 3\pi/2$ and Sec $y = \sec y = -2$. The appropriate value of y is $4\pi/3$, so

$$\text{Sec}^{-1}(-2) = \frac{4\pi}{3}.$$

Exercises 4.2

1. a. $\text{Sin}^{-1}(-1)$

    b. $\text{Sin}^{-1}\frac{\sqrt{3}}{2}$

    c. $\text{Sin}^{-1}\left(-\frac{\sqrt{2}}{2}\right)$

    d. $\text{Arcsin}\frac{\sqrt{2}}{2}$

    e. $\text{Arcsin}\left(-\frac{\sqrt{3}}{2}\right)$

    f. $\text{Arcsin}\frac{1}{2}$

2. a. $\text{Cos}^{-1}(-1)$

    b. $\text{Cos}^{-1}\left(-\frac{\sqrt{3}}{2}\right)$

    c. $\text{Cos}^{-1}\left(-\frac{1}{2}\right)$

    d. $\text{Arccos}\frac{\sqrt{2}}{2}$

    e. $\text{Arccos } 0$

    f. $\text{Arccos}\frac{\sqrt{3}}{2}$

3. a. $\text{Tan}^{-1}\frac{1}{\sqrt{3}}$

    b. $\text{Tan}^{-1} 1$

    c. $\text{Tan}^{-1}(-\sqrt{3})$

    d. $\text{Arctan } 0$

    e. $\text{Arctan}(-1)$

    f. $\text{Arctan}\left(-\frac{1}{\sqrt{3}}\right)$

4. a. $\text{Sec}^{-1} 1$

    b. $\text{Sec}^{-1}(-2)$

    c. $\text{Sec}^{-1}\left(-\frac{2\sqrt{3}}{3}\right)$

    d. $\text{Arcsec}\frac{2\sqrt{3}}{3}$

    e. $\text{Arcsec } 2$

    f. $\text{Arcsec}(-1)$

5. $\text{Sin}^{-1}\left[\cos\left(-\frac{\pi}{3}\right)\right]$

6. $\dfrac{\text{Sin}^{-1} 1}{\text{Cos}^{-1} 1}$

7. $\sin\left[\text{Sin}^{-1}\left(-\frac{1}{2}\right)\right]$

8. $\tan\left[\text{Cos}^{-1}\frac{\sqrt{3}}{2}\right]$

9. $\text{Cos}^{-1}\left[\sin\left(-\frac{\pi}{3}\right)\right]$

10. $\tan[\text{Arctan}\sqrt{3}]$

11. $\cos[\text{Sec}^{-1}(-\sqrt{2})]$

12. $\text{Sin}^{-1}\frac{1}{2} + \text{Cos}^{-1}\frac{1}{2}$

13. $\text{Cos}^{-1}\left(-\frac{\sqrt{2}}{2}\right) + \text{Sin}^{-1}\left(-\frac{\sqrt{2}}{2}\right)$

14. $\text{Sin}^{-1}(-1) + \text{Cos}^{-1}(-1)$

15. $\text{Sin}^{-1}\left[\cos\left(-\frac{\pi}{4}\right)\right]$

16. $\text{Cos}^{-1}\left[\sin\left(-\frac{\pi}{4}\right)\right]$

17. $\sin\left[\text{Cos}^{-1}\frac{\sqrt{2}}{2}\right]$

18. $\sin\left[\text{Cos}^{-1}\frac{1}{2}\right]$

19. $\cos\left[\text{Sin}^{-1}\frac{\sqrt{3}}{2}\right]$

20. $\cos[\text{Sin}^{-1} 1]$

4.3 Identities involving the inverse trigonometric functions

In Section 4.2 we defined four of the inverse trigonometric functions, each in such a way that it was the inverse function to a previously defined function. Taking this into account, you should readily recognize each of the following to be an identity.

1. $\text{Sin}^{-1}(\text{Sin } x) \equiv x$ $\quad \mathscr{D} = \left\{ x \,\middle|\, -\dfrac{\pi}{2} \le x \le \dfrac{\pi}{2} \right\}.$

2. $\text{Sin }(\text{Sin}^{-1} x) \equiv x$ $\quad \mathscr{D} = \{ x \,|\, -1 \le x \le 1 \}.$

3. $\text{Cos}^{-1}(\text{Cos } x) \equiv x$ $\quad \mathscr{D} = \{ x \,|\, 0 \le x \le \pi \}.$

4. $\text{Cos }(\text{Cos}^{-1} x) \equiv x$ $\quad \mathscr{D} = \{ x \,|\, -1 \le x \le 1 \}.$

5. $\text{Tan}^{-1}(\text{Tan } x) \equiv x$ $\quad \mathscr{D} = \left\{ x \,\middle|\, -\dfrac{\pi}{2} < x < \dfrac{\pi}{2} \right\}.$

6. $\text{Tan }(\text{Tan}^{-1} x) \equiv x$ $\quad \mathscr{D} = R.$

7. $\text{Sec}^{-1}(\text{Sec } x) \equiv x$ $\quad \mathscr{D} = \left\{ x \,\middle|\, 0 \le x < \dfrac{\pi}{2} \text{ or } \pi \le x < \dfrac{3\pi}{2} \right\}.$

8. $\text{Sec }(\text{Sec}^{-1} x) \equiv x$ $\quad \mathscr{D} = \{ x \,|\, x \le -1 \text{ or } x \ge 1 \}.$

Examples of two of these identities were included in the exercises at the end of the previous section, where you should have concluded that

$$\sin \left[\text{Sin}^{-1} \left(-\frac{1}{2} \right) \right] = -\frac{1}{2} \quad \text{and} \quad \tan (\text{Arctan } \sqrt{3}) = \sqrt{3}.$$

When we consider the way in which we restricted the domains of the regular trigonometric functions to define the Sine function, the Cosine function, the Tangent function, and the Secant function, we realize that the identities written above can be rewritten as shown below. For example, we know that if θ is in the domain of $\text{Sin } \theta$, then $\sin \theta = \text{Sin } \theta$. Thus,

$$\sin (\text{Sin}^{-1} x) = \text{Sin }(\text{Sin}^{-1} x),$$

so we know that $\sin (\text{Sin}^{-1} x) = x$. Identities 4′, 6′, and 8′ can be developed in a similar fashion.

4′. $\cos (\text{Cos}^{-1} x) \equiv x$ $\quad \mathscr{D} = \{ x \,|\, -1 \le x \le 1 \}.$

6′. $\tan (\text{Tan}^{-1} x) \equiv x$ $\quad \mathscr{D} = R.$

8′. $\sec (\text{Sec}^{-1} x) \equiv x$ $\quad \mathscr{D} = \{ x \,|\, x \le -1 \text{ or } x \ge 1 \}.$

Five other identities involving the inverse trigonometric functions which are not so obvious are given next. Four of these identities are developed in this section and the remaining identity is included in the exercises.

9. $\text{Cos}^{-1} (\text{Sin } x) \equiv \frac{\pi}{2} - x \qquad \mathscr{D} = \left\{ x \middle| -\frac{\pi}{2} \le x \le \frac{\pi}{2} \right\}.$

10. $\text{Sin}^{-1} (\text{Cos } x) \equiv \frac{\pi}{2} - x \qquad \mathscr{D} = \{ x \mid 0 \le x \le \pi).$

11. $\text{Sin}^{-1} x + \text{Cos}^{-1} x \equiv \frac{\pi}{2} \qquad \mathscr{D} = \{ x \mid -1 \le x \le 1 \}.$

12. $\sin (\text{Cos}^{-1} x) \equiv \sqrt{1 - x^2} \qquad \mathscr{D} = \{ x \mid -1 \le x \le 1 \}.$

13. $\cos (\text{Sin}^{-1} x) \equiv \sqrt{1 - x^2} \qquad \mathscr{D} = \{ x \mid -1 \le x \le 1 \}.$

The first two identities in the list can be proved quite easily. To prove that

$$\text{Cos}^{-1} (\text{Sin } x) \equiv \frac{\pi}{2} - x,$$

we use the identity

$$\text{Cos} \left(\frac{\pi}{2} - x \right) \equiv \text{Sin } x.$$

If $-\pi/2 \le x \le \pi/2$, then

$$-\frac{\pi}{2} - \frac{\pi}{2} \le x - \frac{\pi}{2} \le \frac{\pi}{2} - \frac{\pi}{2},$$

$$-\pi \le x - \frac{\pi}{2} \le 0,$$

$$0 \le -\left(x - \frac{\pi}{2} \right) \le -(-\pi),$$

$$0 \le \frac{\pi}{2} - x \le \pi.$$

Thus, if $-\pi/2 \le x \le \pi/2$, then $0 \le \pi/2 - x \le \pi$. This tells us that if $-\pi/2 \le x \le \pi/2$, then $\pi/2 - x$ is in the domain of the Cosine function, and we have the following derivation.

$$\text{Cos}^{-1} (\text{Sin } x) = \text{Cos}^{-1} \left[\text{Cos} \left(\frac{\pi}{2} - x \right) \right]$$

$$= \frac{\pi}{2} - x.$$

$\therefore$ $\text{Cos}^{-1} (\text{Sin } x) \equiv \frac{\pi}{2} - x, \qquad \mathscr{D} = \left\{ x \middle| -\frac{\pi}{2} \le x \le \frac{\pi}{2} \right\}.$

In a similar fashion, we can use the identity

$$\text{Sin} \left(\frac{\pi}{2} - x \right) \equiv \text{Cos } x$$

to develop the identity

$$\text{Sin}^{-1} (\text{Cos } x) \equiv \frac{\pi}{2} - x.$$

If $0 \le x \le \pi$, you should be able to show that $-\pi/2 \le \pi/2 - x \le \pi/2$.

Thus, if $0 \leq x \leq \pi$, then $\pi/2 - x$ is in the domain of the Sine function. The derivation of the identity $\text{Sin}^{-1} (\text{Cos } x) \equiv \pi/2 - x$ follows.

$$\text{Sin}^{-1} (\text{Cos } x) = \text{Sin}^{-1} [\text{Sin } (\frac{\pi}{2} - x)]$$

$$= \frac{\pi}{2} - x.$$

$$\therefore \quad \text{Sin}^{-1} (\text{Cos } x) \equiv \frac{\pi}{2} - x, \qquad \mathcal{D} = \{x \,|\, 0 \leq x \leq \pi\}.$$

Let us now consider a development of the identity

$$\text{Sin}^{-1} x + \text{Cos}^{-1} x \equiv \frac{\pi}{2}.$$

We know that $y = \text{Sin}^{-1} x$ if and only if $x = \text{Sin } y$. Thus, by letting $x = \text{Sin } y$, we have the following steps.

$$\text{Sin}^{-1} x + \text{Cos}^{-1} x = \text{Sin}^{-1} (\text{Sin } y) + \text{Cos}^{-1} (\text{Sin } y)$$

$$= y + \text{Cos}^{-1} (\text{Sin } y)$$

$$= y + \left(\frac{\pi}{2} - y\right) \quad \text{(from an identity just proved)}$$

$$= \frac{\pi}{2}.$$

$$\therefore \quad \text{Sin}^{-1} x + \text{Cos}^{-1} x \equiv \frac{\pi}{2}, \qquad \mathcal{D} = \{x \,|\, -1 \leq x \leq 1\}.$$

Note that if $y = \text{Cos}^{-1} x$, then $x = \text{Cos } y = \cos y$ and $0 \leq y \leq \pi$. Since $0 \leq y \leq \pi$, $\sin y \geq 0$, and we have the following derivation.

$$\sin^2 y + \cos^2 y = 1,$$

$$\sin^2 y = 1 - \cos^2 y,$$

$$\sin y = \sqrt{1 - \cos^2 y} \quad \text{(since } \sin y \geq 0\text{)},$$

$$\sin y = \sqrt{1 - x^2} \quad \text{(since } x = \cos y\text{)}.$$

But since $y = \text{Cos}^{-1} x$,

$$\sin y = \sin (\text{Cos}^{-1} x),$$

$$\sin (\text{Cos}^{-1} x) = \sqrt{1 - x^2}.$$

$$\therefore \quad \sin (\text{Cos}^{-1} x) \equiv \sqrt{1 - x^2}. \qquad \mathcal{D} = \{x \,|\, -1 \leq x \leq 1\}.$$

Some of the identities we have developed here are useful in solving equations. For example, let us solve the equation

$$\text{Sin}^{-1} x - \text{Cos}^{-1} x = \frac{\pi}{6}.$$

Since we know that $\text{Sin}^{-1} x + \text{Cos}^{-1} x = \pi/2$, we can write

$$\text{Cos}^{-1} x = \frac{\pi}{2} - \text{Sin}^{-1} x,$$

and we have the following solution.

$$\text{Sin}^{-1} x - \text{Cos}^{-1} x = \frac{\pi}{6},$$

$$\text{Sin}^{-1} x - \left(\frac{\pi}{2} - \text{Sin}^{-1} x \right) = \frac{\pi}{6},$$

$$2 \text{Sin}^{-1} x - \frac{\pi}{2} = \frac{\pi}{6},$$

$$2 \text{Sin}^{-1} x = \frac{2\pi}{3},$$

$$\text{Sin}^{-1} x = \frac{\pi}{3},$$

$$\text{Sin} \left(\text{Sin}^{-1} x \right) = \text{Sin} \frac{\pi}{3},$$

$$x = \text{Sin} \frac{\pi}{3} = \frac{\sqrt{3}}{2}.$$

$$\therefore \quad S = \left\{ \frac{\sqrt{3}}{2} \right\}.$$

As another example, let us solve the equation $4 \text{ Arccos } x + 2 \text{ Arcsin } x = 3\pi/2$.

$$4 \text{ Arccos } x + 2 \left(\frac{\pi}{2} - \text{Arccos } x \right) = \frac{3\pi}{2},$$

$$2 \text{ Arccos } x + \pi = \frac{3\pi}{2},$$

$$2 \text{ Arccos } x = \frac{\pi}{2},$$

$$\text{Arccos } x = \frac{\pi}{4},$$

$$\text{Cos } (\text{Arccos } x) = \text{Cos } \frac{\pi}{4},$$

$$x = \text{Cos } \frac{\pi}{4} = \frac{\sqrt{2}}{2}.$$

$$\therefore \quad S = \left\{ \frac{\sqrt{2}}{2} \right\}.$$

Exercises 4.3

✗ 1. Prove the identity $\cos (\text{Sin}^{-1} x) = \sqrt{1 - x^2}$, $\mathscr{D} = \{x \mid -1 \leq x \leq 1\}$. Find the solution sets for the following equations.

2. $\text{Cos}^{-1} x - \text{Sin}^{-1} x = \frac{\pi}{6}.$

3. $2 \cos^{-1} x + \sin^{-1} x = \pi.$

4. $2 \arcsin x + \arccos x = \dfrac{\pi}{6}.$

5. $3 \arcsin x - \arccos x = \dfrac{\pi}{2}.$

6. $\arccos x + \arcsin x = \dfrac{\pi}{4}.$

7. $2 \arccos x - \arcsin x = \dfrac{3}{2} - \dfrac{\pi}{2}.$

8. $3 \cos^{-1} y + \sin^{-1} y = \dfrac{\pi}{2} + \dfrac{3}{4}.$

9. $3 \sin^{-1} y - \cos^{-1} y = \dfrac{4}{3} - \dfrac{\pi}{2}.$

10. $2 \sin^{-1} y - \cos^{-1} y = \dfrac{3}{4} - \dfrac{\pi}{2}.$

11. $4 \sin^{-1} y + 3 \cos^{-1} y = \dfrac{3\pi}{2} + \dfrac{1}{5}.$

Review Exercises

Evaluate the following.

1. $\sec^{-1} 1$

2. $\sin^{-1} \left(\dfrac{-\sqrt{3}}{2} \right)$

3. $\tan \left(\sin^{-1} \dfrac{1}{2} \right)$

4. $\cos(\tan^{-1} (-\sqrt{3})]$

5. $\sec \left(\cos^{-1} \left(\dfrac{-\sqrt{2}}{2} \right) \right)$

6. $\sin^{-1} \dfrac{1}{2} + \sin^{-1} \dfrac{\sqrt{3}}{2}$

7. $\tan^{-1} (-\sqrt{3}) - \tan^{-1} \dfrac{1}{\sqrt{3}}$

8. $\cos^{-1} \left(-\dfrac{\sqrt{3}}{2} \right) + \cos^{-1} \dfrac{\sqrt{3}}{2}$

Solve the following equations.

9. $\cos^{-1} x - \sin^{-1} x = \dfrac{\pi}{2}.$

10. $3 \arcsin x - \arccos x = \dfrac{5\pi}{6}.$

11. $3 \arccos x + \arcsin x = 2\pi.$

12. $4 \arcsin x + \arccos x = \pi.$

Determine whether or not the following functions are one-to-one functions. If they are, find their inverse functions.

13. $f(x) = x^3 - 1.$

14. $f(x) = 3x - 5.$

15. $f(x) = 3x^2 - 6.$

16. $f(x) = 4 - x.$

Solutions of triangles

5.1 Angles and radians

In the first five chapters of this book we developed the trigonometric functions as functions of real numbers, and we have worked with them in this fashion. Historically, the trigonometric functions were defined in terms of triangles and angles.

In this section we shall develop the relationships between two types of angle measure—degree measure and radian measure. Section 5.2 will show how the trigonometric functions could be expressed in terms of angles, measured in degrees, and triangles. The next three sections will show how our knowledge of the trigonometric functions can be used to solve triangles. By *solving* triangles, we mean that if we know the lengths of some of the sides of a triangle, and if we know the measure, in degrees, of some of the angles, then we can determine the lengths of the remaining sides and the measures, in degrees, of the remaining angles.

A **ray** may be defined to be the set consisting of all the points of a line which are on the same side of a given point and the given point. The given point is called the **end point of the ray**. If A and B are points on a line, the ray $\overrightarrow{AB}$ consists of the point A, the point B, and all the points on the same side of A as B. A is the end point of $\overrightarrow{AB}$. The ray $\overrightarrow{AB}$ is shown in color in Figure 5.1.

Figure 5.1   Figure 5.2

An **angle** may be defined to be the union of two rays with a common end point. Thus, if $\overrightarrow{AB}$ is one ray and $\overrightarrow{AC}$ is another ray, then the union of these two rays is an angle. The common end point of the two rays is usually called the **vertex** of the angle. Thus, in Figure 5.2, the point A is the vertex of the angle formed by the union of the two rays. The two rays which form the angle are often called the **sides** of the angle. We shall represent an angle in either of two ways: by using the name of the vertex, such as using $\angle A$ to represent the angle in Figure 5.2; or by naming three points, where the first point is a point on one of the sides of the angle, the second is the vertex, and third is a point on the remaining side of the angle. In this manner, the angle in Figure 5.2 could be denoted by $\angle BAC$ or by $\angle CAB$.

There are two standard units of measure of an angle, **degree measure** and **radian measure**. When we use *degree* measure, we imagine that a circle is drawn with the vertex of an angle at the center of the circle and the circle is divided into 360 arcs of equal length.

One degree is defined to be the measure of the angle subtended by any one of these 360 congruent arcs. The measure of an angle, in degrees, is then determined by the ratio of the arc subtended by the desired angle to the arc subtended by an angle of one degree.

Instead of representing fractional parts of one degree by decimal fractions, we divide an angle of one degree into 60 congruent parts, called **minutes**. An angle of one minute is divided into 60 congruent parts, called **seconds**.

The measure of an angle in degrees is not dependent upon the radius of the circle around the vertex of the angle. However, the circumference of the circle and the lengths of the various arcs described above are all proportional to the radius of the circle chosen.

When using *radian* measure, we begin in the same fashion as when using degree measure, by imagining that we have a circle with the vertex of the angle at the center of the circle.

One radian is defined to be the measure of any angle subtended by an arc on the circle which has the same length as the radius of the circle. The measure of an angle in radians is then determined by the ratio of the arc subtended by the angle in question to the arc subtended by an angle of one radian.

Once again, the measure of an angle in radians is independent of the radius of the circle chosen.

Since two different measures are used for angles, it is helpful to designate clearly the type of angle measure being used. We will write $m°(\angle A)$ if we are indicating the measure of $\angle A$ in degrees and $m^R(\angle A)$ if we are indicating the measure of $\angle A$ in radians.

Figure 5.3

Figure 5.3 shows a straight angle, $\angle AOB$. The straight angle, $\angle AOB$, subtends a semicircle. Since the circumference of a circle is 2π times the radius, the length of the semicircle in Figure 5.3 is π times the radius. Since the length of an arc subtended by an angle with a measure of one radian is equal to the radius, the measure of $\angle AOB$, in radians, is

$$\frac{m^R(\angle AOB)}{1} = \frac{\pi r}{r} = \pi.$$

Thus, the measure, in radians, of a straight angle is π.

In a similar fashion, if the circle with center O and radius $\overline{OA}$ is divided into 360 congruent arcs, the semicircle subtending $\angle AOB$ should contain 180 of these congruent arcs. This tells us that

$$m°(\angle AOB) = 180°.$$

Thus, $180°$ corresponds to π radians. We indicate this by writing

$$180° \approx \pi \text{ radians.}$$

From this, we conclude that

$$1° \approx \frac{\pi}{180} \text{ radians.}$$

Since π is approximately 3.14159, performing the indicated division enables us to determine that $1°$ corresponds to approximately 0.1745 radians.

In a similar fashion, we have the following development. Since

$$180° \approx \pi \text{ radians,}$$

$$\left(\frac{180}{\pi}\right)° \approx 1 \text{ radian.}$$

Performing the indicated division and converting the quotient into degree measure enables us to determine that 1 radian corresponds to approximately $57°17'45''$ (read 57 degrees, 17 minutes, 45 seconds).

You will not have much need of the two correspondences developed above, because Table I in the Appendix enables one to determine the degree measure, to the nearest minute, of an angle measured to the nearest 1/100th radian. For example,

$$.34 \text{ radians} \approx 19°29' \quad \text{and} \quad 1.23 \text{ radians} \approx 70°28'.$$

Table II enables us to determine the radian measure, to the nearest 1/10,000th radian, of an angle measured to the nearest 10 minutes. For example,

$$13°50' \approx .2414 \text{ radians} \quad \text{and} \quad 73°40' \approx 1.2857 \text{ radians}.$$

Our discussion so far enables us to determine the measure of an angle with certain restrictions. We have no provision yet that enables us to consider an angle with a measure greater than that of a straight angle (180° or π radians) or an angle with negative measure. It is possible to consider an angle having negative measure or having measure greater than that of a straight angle.

Two angles are **congruent** if and only if they have the same measure. We assume that each angle is congruent to some angle which has its vertex at the origin and has one side lying on the positive x-axis. In Figure 5.4, $\angle ABC$ is congruent to $\angle EOD$. An angle like $\angle EOD$ is said to be in **standard position**. The side $\overrightarrow{OE}$ of $\angle EOD$ is called the **initial side**, since it lies on the positive x-axis, and side $\overrightarrow{OD}$ is the **terminal side** of $\angle EOD$. We might visualize $\angle EOD$ being formed by *rotating* the initial side ($\overrightarrow{OE}$) of $\angle EOD$ into the terminal side ($\overrightarrow{OD}$) of the angle.

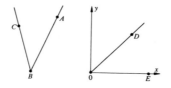

Figure 5.4

Rotation in a **counterclockwise** direction is said to be **positive**, while rotation in a **clockwise** direction is **negative**. In Figure 5.5 we see that $\angle EOD$ could be obtained by either of two different rotations. Observe that R_1 is a positive rotation, while R_2 is a negative rotation. Since we have demonstrated two different rotations which have the same terminal side, we see that $\angle EOD$ might be either of these two angles. The angle formed by rotation R_1 has *positive* measure, while the angle formed by rotation R_2 has *negative* measure. $\angle EOD$ might be any other angle in standard position which has the same terminal side as the two angles shown.

The example in the preceding paragraph involved **coterminal angles,** that is, angles which, when in standard position, have the same terminal side.

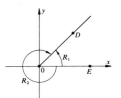

Figure 5.5

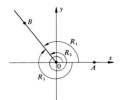

Figure 5.6

When we form an angle by rotating the initial side into the terminal side, it is possible to rotate the initial side through more than one complete rotation. This might be done in either the positive direction or the negative direction. Thus, we see that the $\angle AOB$ in Figure 5.6 could have been the angle formed by the positive rotation R_1 and have a measure less than 360° or 2π radians; the angle formed by the positive rotation R_2 and have a measure greater than 360° or 2π radians; or the angle formed by the negative rotation R_3 and have a measure between 0° and $-360°$ or between 0 radians and -2π radians. You can probably see that two angles which are coterminal have measures that differ by a multiple of 360° in degree measure or by a multiple of 2π radians in radian measure.

If the terminal side of an angle, when it is in standard position, lies in a quadrant, we often speak of the angle as being in that quadrant. For example, an angle of 120° lies in the second quadrant. If the terminal side of an angle lies on one of the coordinate axes, the angle is said to be a **quadrantal** angle. An angle of $-90°$ is a quadrantal angle.

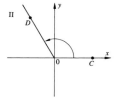

Figure 5.7

Figure 5.8

Exercises 5.1

Use Table I, if necessary, to convert the following radian measures to their equivalents in degree measure.

1. 1.32 radians   2. .35 radians   3. -1.09 radians
4. $-.73$ radians   5. 1.25 radians   6. -3.50 radians
7. $\dfrac{5\pi}{2}$ radians   8. -3π radians   9. $-\dfrac{9\pi}{2}$ radians
10. 13π radians

Use Table II, if necessary, to convert the following degree measures to their equivalents in radian measure.

11. $13°20'$ 12. $47°50'$ 13. $29°$ 14. $83°40'$
15. $-34°20'$ 16. $-59°30'$ 17. $-270°$ 18. $720°$
19. $390°$ 20. $-1830°$
21. Complete the following table.

degree measure	0°			60°	90°		360°
radian measure		$\dfrac{\pi}{6}$ rad	$\dfrac{\pi}{4}$ rad			π rad	$\dfrac{3\pi}{2}$ rad

Indicate the quadrant in which the angle with each of the following measures lies. If the angle is a quadrantal angle, so indicate.

22. $35°$ 23. $97°$ 24. $-48°$
25. $-347°$ 26. $450°$ 27. $\dfrac{3\pi}{4}$ radians
28. $-\dfrac{\pi}{3}$ radians 29. $-\dfrac{7\pi}{4}$ radians 30. $\dfrac{23\pi}{3}$ radians
31. $\dfrac{15\pi}{2}$ radians 32. $-1732°$ 33. $3201°$
34. $\dfrac{31\pi}{5}$ radians 35. $-\dfrac{95\pi}{7}$ radians 36. $\dfrac{21\pi}{4}$ radians.

In each of the following problems, give the measures of four other angles which would be coterminal with the angle having the given measure.

Example

$60°$

Solution

(i) $60° + 360° = 420°$
(ii) $60° - 360° = -300°$.

(iii) $60° + 2(360°) = 780°.$
(iv) $60° - 2(360°) = -660°.$

37. $21°$ 38. $-17°$ 39. $95°$

40. $392°$ 41. $-193°$ 42. $\dfrac{3\pi}{4}$ radians

43. $-\dfrac{\pi}{6}$ radians   44. $\dfrac{9\pi}{7}$ radians   45. $\dfrac{13\pi}{3}$ radians

46. $-\dfrac{5\pi}{2}$ radians

5.2 Solutions of right triangles

In order to discuss solutions of right triangles, we must first agree on the meanings of several terms. *If A, B, and C are 3 noncollinear points, the union of the three segments $\overline{AB}$, $\overline{BC}$, and $\overline{CA}$ is a **triangle**.* The end points of these three line segments are called the **vertices** of the triangle, and any one of them is a **vertex**. This triangle might be denoted by $\triangle ABC$ or, in a similar manner, with any other arrangement of the vertices. Note in Figure 5.9 that the union of the rays $\overrightarrow{AB}$ and $\overrightarrow{AC}$ forms an angle. We shall refer to this angle when we speak of $\angle BAC$ or $\angle A$ in $\triangle ABC$. In trigonometry we often "solve" a triangle denoted by $\triangle ABC$. During this operation, we shall use α, β, and γ to denote the measures in degrees of $\angle A$, $\angle B$, and $\angle C$, respectively.

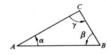

Figure 5.9

The segments $\overline{AB}$, $\overline{BC}$, and $\overline{AC}$ are called the **sides** of $\triangle ABC$. In $\triangle ABC$ we shall denote the measures of sides $\overline{AB}$, $\overline{BC}$, and $\overline{AC}$ by c, a, and b, respectively.

An angle which has measure 90° is called a **right** angle. If the measure of an angle is between 0° and 90°, the angle is an **acute** angle. If the measure of an angle is between 90° and 180°, the angle is called an **obtuse** angle. A **right triangle** is a one in which one of the angles is a right angle. The side opposite the right angle in a right triangle is called the **hypotenuse**.

If all three angles of a triangle are acute angles, the triangle is called an **acute triangle**. In an **obtuse triangle**, one of the angles is an obtuse angle. An acute triangle is shown in Figure 5.10, and an obtuse triangle in Figure 5.11.

We shall assume that the sum of the degree measures of the angles of a triangle is 180°. Thus, we can determine the measure of the third angle by finding the sum of the first two angle measures and subtracting that sum from 180°.

Figure 5.10

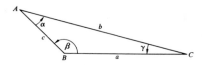

Figure 5.11

For example, if in $\triangle ABC$ $\alpha = 37°24'$ and $\gamma = 71°58'$, then

$$\alpha + \gamma = 109°22' \quad \text{and} \quad \beta = 180° - (\alpha + \gamma) = 70°38'.$$

The traditional way to define the six trigonometric functions of the measure of an acute angle of a right triangle was in terms of the ratios of the various sides of a right triangle. Let $\triangle ABC$ be a right triangle with the right angle at C. Then $0° < \alpha < 90°$, and $\angle A$ is an acute angle. The six trigonometric functions of α would be defined in the following way.

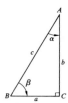

Figure 5.12

$$\sin \alpha = \frac{\text{side opposite } \angle A}{\text{hypotenuse}} = \frac{a}{c} \qquad \cot \alpha = \frac{\text{side adjacent } \angle A}{\text{side opposite } \angle A} = \frac{b}{a}$$

$$\cos \alpha = \frac{\text{side adjacent } \angle A}{\text{hypotenuse}} = \frac{b}{c} \qquad \sec \alpha = \frac{\text{hypotenuse}}{\text{side adjacent } \angle A} = \frac{c}{b}$$

$$\tan \alpha = \frac{\text{side opposite } \angle A}{\text{side adjacent } \angle A} = \frac{a}{b} \qquad \csc \alpha = \frac{\text{hypotenuse}}{\text{side opposite } \angle A} = \frac{c}{a}$$

These are not new definitions or redefinitions of the trigonometric functions. They are ways of expressing the trigonometric functions in terms of ratios of the various sides of a right triangle, and they are consistent with the definitions of the trigonometric functions, as the following development will show.

Consider the right triangle ABC in Figure 5.13. The circle with radius $\overline{AP}$ is the unit circle, with A as origin. Some real number x, between 0 and $\pi/2$, corresponds to the point P, which has coordinates (u, v). Observe that $\cos x = u$ and $\sin x = v$. $\triangle APQ$ and $\triangle ABC$ are similar right triangles, so

$$\frac{c}{m(\overline{AP})} = \frac{a}{m(\overline{PQ})} = \frac{b}{m(\overline{AQ})}.$$

But

$$m(\overline{AP}) = 1,$$

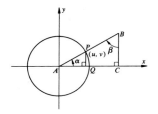

Figure 5.13

since $\overline{AP}$ is a radius of the unit circle, and

$$m(\overline{PQ}) = v = \sin x,$$

and

$$m(\overline{AQ}) = u = \cos x.$$

Thus, we have

$$\frac{c}{m(\overline{AP})} = \frac{b}{m(\overline{AQ})},$$

$$\frac{m(\overline{AQ})}{m(\overline{AP})} = \frac{b}{c},$$

$$\frac{\cos x}{1} = \frac{b}{c}.$$

$$\cos x = \frac{b}{c} = \cos \alpha.$$

Because of the way we defined the correspondence between the real numbers and the points on the unit circle in Chapter 1, the real number x which corresponds to the point P must be the measure of $\angle BAC$ in radians. In a similar fashion we can show that $\sin x = \sin \alpha$. You will be asked to show that the ways we have expressed the four remaining trigonometric functions in terms of ratios of the sides of a right triangle are consistent with the ways in which we defined these four functions in Chapter 1. It is important to note that the α in this development is the measure of $\angle A$ in degrees, since we use α, β, and γ to represent the degree measures of $\angle A$, $\angle B$, and $\angle C$ in $\triangle ABC$, respectively.

The identities which we developed in Chapters 1 and 2 still hold here, with certain changes. We must replace $\pi/2$ by $90°$, π by $180°$, and so forth. Through use of the reduction formulas, these ways of expressing the trigonometric functions of acute angles may be extended to angles of any size, provided that the measure of the angle corresponds to a number in the domain of the trigonometric function.

We can use Table II to find the trigonometric function values of angles measured in degrees and minutes. If the measure of the angle is between $0°$ and $45°$, we use the angle measures in the left-hand column and the column headings at the top of the column. If the measure of the angle is between $45°$ and $90°$, we use the angle measures in the right-hand column and the column headings at the bottom of the column. We will need to interpolate as we did before.

We shall now use the expressions for the trigonometric functions developed in this section to solve some triangles.

Example 1

If $\triangle ABC$ is a right triangle with $\angle C$ being the right angle, $c = 5$ inches, $b = 4$ inches, solve for the remaining parts of $\triangle ABC$. Assume that the given measurements are exact.

Solution

The given information is illustrated in Figure 5.14.
Since $\triangle ABC$ is a right triangle,

$$a = \sqrt{c^2 - b^2} = \sqrt{25 - 16} = \sqrt{9} = 3 \text{ inches.}$$

Figure 5.14

We have $\sin \beta = 4/5 = .8000$. By referring to Table II, we see that $\sin 53° = .7986$ and $\sin 53°10' = .8004$. By interpolation, we obtain $\beta = 53°8'$ to the nearest minute.

$$\alpha = 180° - (90° + 53°8') = 180° - 143°8' = 36°52'.$$

Thus, we have the following information:

Given	Found
$\gamma = 90°$	$a = 3''$
$c = 5''$	$\beta = 53°8'$
$b = 4''$	$\alpha = 36°52'$

We could also have found α by observing that $\sin \alpha = 3/5 = .6000$ or by observing that $\cos \alpha = 4/5 = .8000$.

Example 2

Solve $\triangle ABC$ if $\gamma = 90°$, $\alpha = 29°37'$, $b = 14$ feet. Assume that all these measurements are exact.

Solution

The given information is illustrated in Figure 5.15.

$$\beta = 180° - (\alpha + \gamma)$$
$$= 180° - (29°37' + 90°)$$
$$= 180° - 119°37'$$
$$= 60°23'.$$

Figure 5.15

Since $\cos 29°30' = .8704$ and $\cos 29°40' = .8689$, we have $\cos \alpha = .8694$ by interpolation. We also have $\cos \alpha = 14/c$, so

$$\frac{14}{c} = .8694, \qquad c = \frac{14}{.8694} = 16.10 \text{ feet.}$$

Since $\tan 29°30' = .5658$ and $\tan 29°40' = .5696$, we obtain $\tan \alpha = .5685$ by interpolation. We also know $\tan \alpha = a/14$, so

$$\frac{a}{14} = .5685, \qquad a = (14)(.5685) = 7.958 \text{ feet.}$$

Thus, we have the following information:

	Given	*Found*
	$\gamma = 90°$	$\beta = 60°23'$
	$\alpha = 29°37'$	$c = 16.10$ ft
	$b = 14$ ft	$a = 7.958$ ft

Once b and c are found, we could use the Pythagorean theorem to find a. However, the advantages to the method we used are that it is quicker and it forces one to use the relationships developed in this section.

Exercises 5.2

1. Show that the way of expressing $\tan \alpha$ in this section is consistent with the definition of the tangent function.
2. Show that the way of expressing $\sec \alpha$ in this section is consistent with the definition of the secant function.
3. Show that the way of expressing $\csc \alpha$ in this section is consistent with the definition of the cosecant function.
4. Show that the way of expressing $\cot \alpha$ in this section is consistent with the definition of the cotangent function.

In each of the problems 5–10 give the six trigonometric functions of α and β, first as fractions and then as decimals. Then use the given information to determine α and β to the nearest minute.

5.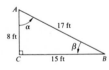

6.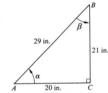

7.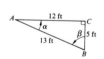

8.

9.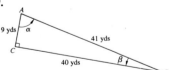

10.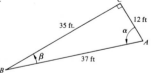

In each of the following problems use the given information to solve the triangle. Assume the given information is exact.

11. $\gamma = 90°$, $a = 3$ ft, $b = 3$ ft.

12. $\gamma = 90°$, $a = 8$ in. $b = 16$ in.

13. $\gamma = 90°$, $a = 3$ yds, $c = 6$ yds.

14. $\gamma = 90°$, $a = 4$ ft, $c = 7$ ft.

15. $\gamma = 90°$, $b = 7$ in., $c = 10$ in.

16. $\gamma = 90°$, $b = 13$ yds, $c = 20$ yds.

17. $\gamma = 90°$, $a = 5$ ft, $\alpha = 27°$.

18. $\gamma = 90°$, $a = 7$ in., $\alpha = 51°20'$.

19. $\gamma = 90°$, $b = 15$ yds, $\beta = 38°43'$.

20. $\gamma = 90°$, $b = 20$ ft, $\beta = 81°9'$

21. $\gamma = 90°$, $a = 5$ in., $\beta = 27°$.

22. $\gamma = 90°$, $a = 7$ yds, $\beta = 57°20'$.

23. $\gamma = 90°$, $b = 15$ ft, $\alpha = 62°27'$.

24. $\gamma = 90°$, $b = 20$ in., $\alpha = 19°14'$.

25. Find the height of a vertical tree that casts a shadow 85 feet long on level ground if the angle of elevation of the sun is 23°.

26. How long a shadow does a 6-foot-tall man cast on level ground if the angle of elevation of the sun is 40°?

27. A vacant rectangular lot is 80 feet long and 50 feet wide. A path has been trod which is a diagonal for the rectangular lot. Find the length of the path and the angle it makes with each of the adjacent sides of the lot.

28. Find the lengths of the congruent sides of an isosceles triangle if the length of the base is 12 inches and the measure of the angle opposite the base is 40°.

29. A 15-foot ladder is placed against the side of a building so that the top of the ladder is 13 feet above the ground. If the ground is level, how far is the base of the ladder from the building? What angle does the ladder make with the building?

30. A road is said to have a 5 per cent grade if the road rises 5 feet while moving forward 100 feet horizontally. How many feet does a 7 per cent road rise if the length of the road is 7 miles? (*Hint:* the road is the hypotenuse).

5 ft
100 ft
5% rise (right to left)

31. A boy is flying a kite. How much string must he have to get the kite 150 feet above the ground if the string makes an angle of 25° with the ground?

32. A 25-foot ladder is placed against a vertical wall so that the foot of the ladder is 6 feet from the wall on level ground. How high on the wall does the ladder reach? What angle does the ladder make with the wall?

5.3 Approximate measurement and significant digits

In Section 5.2 we solved certain types of triangles, but in one sense our solutions were not realistic, because we assumed that all measurements were exact. However, measurements on a physical triangle are only approximations, because our measuring instruments are not precise enough for exact measurement.

In the following sections we shall consider two kinds of triangles. In the problems at the start of the exercise sets, we shall assume that we are dealing with "mathematical" triangles. By this we mean that, theoretically, triangles exist which have the exact measurements given. In these problems we will want as many places in the answers as are available from the appropriate tables.

In the word problems, we shall assume that measurements have been taken of some parts of physical triangles. In these cases we shall use the following rules of thumb to determine the degree of accuracy to be included in the answers.

1. All the given figures are significant, including the zeros. (This differs from the general case, in which some zeros are not significant and in which there may be some question about the significance of other zeros.)

2. No part of the triangle that we "find" can include more significant figures than the least accurate given measurement.

3. a. Two significant figures in the measures of sides of a triangle correspond to angle measures to the nearest degree.

    b. Three significant figures in the measures of sides of a triangle correspond to angle measures to the nearest 10 minutes.

    c. Four significant figures in the measures of sides of a triangle correspond to angle measures to the nearest minute.

4. The usual rounding conventions will be used. Any remainder less than half of the last digit to be retained is dropped. Any remainder more than half of the last digit to be retained means that the preceding digit will be increased by one. A remainder of exactly one-half is rounded to the nearest even digit. For example, if only two significant figures are to be retained in the answer, a solution of 6.45 feet would be rounded to 6.4 feet. A solution of 6.55 feet would be rounded to 6.6 feet. A solution of 6.4532 feet would be rounded to 6.5 feet, since .0532 is more than half of 0.1.

5.4   The law of sines

In Section 5.2 we discussed the solving of right triangles. In each right triangle we knew that the measure of one of the angles was 90°. You may have observed that if we knew the measures of two additional parts (sides or angles) of the triangle, including at least one of the sides, we had enough information to solve the triangle.

However, we need additional techniques in order to solve other kinds of triangles. In this section we will develop and apply **the law of sines**, which enables one to solve any triangle in which the measures of two of the angles and one of the sides are known. It also enables us to work with cases in which we are given two of the sides and the angle opposite one of the given sides. This latter situation sometimes provides two possible solutions, and it sometimes offers no solution. We will consider this case further.

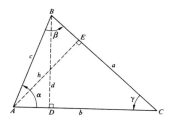

Figure 5.16

Consider the triangle in Figure 5.16. Note that the measure of $\overline{BD}$ is d and the measure of $\overline{AE}$ is h. $\triangle ABD$ is a right triangle, in which $\sin \alpha = d/c$. From this we get $d = c \sin \alpha$. In $\triangle BCD$, also a right triangle, we have $\sin \gamma = d/a$, so that $d = a \sin \gamma$. From these two facts we have

$$c \sin \alpha = a \sin \gamma,$$

$$\frac{\sin \alpha}{a} = \frac{\sin \gamma}{c}. \qquad (1)$$

In the right triangle ABE we have $\sin \beta = h/c$, so $h = c \sin \beta$. In the right triangle ACE we have $\sin \gamma = h/b$, so $h = b \sin \gamma$. From these we have

$$c \sin \beta = b \sin \gamma,$$

$$\frac{\sin \beta}{b} = \frac{\sin \gamma}{c}. \qquad (2)$$

From (1) and (2), we can say that

$$\frac{\sin \alpha}{a} = \frac{\sin \beta}{b} = \frac{\sin \gamma}{c}.$$

This is known as the law of sines. So far we have developed the law of sines for an acute triangle. You should have little difficulty verifying this in the case of a right triangle. You will have the opportunity to do so in the exercises at the end of the section.

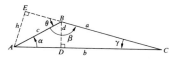

Figure 5.17

An obtuse triangle has one additional detail to be noted. In Figure 5.17 the acute angle at B in the right triangle ABE has measure θ, not measure β. We note that $\theta + \beta = 180°$, so that $\theta = 180° - \beta$. We have an identity that tells us that $\sin (180° - \beta) \equiv \sin \beta$, so $\sin \theta = \sin \beta$. Other than this, the development is much the same as the development of the law of sines for an acute triangle.

We now consider some applications involving the law of sines. All the given information will be considered to be exact.

Example 1

Solve $\triangle ABC$ if $\alpha = 37°23'$, $\beta = 75°29'$, $a = 3.25$ in.

Solution

The given information is pictured in Figure 5.18.

$$\gamma = 180° - (\alpha + \beta)$$
$$= 180° - (37°23' + 75°29')$$
$$= 180° - (112°52')$$
$$= 67°8'.$$

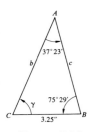

Figure 5.18

$$\frac{\sin \alpha}{a} = \frac{\sin \beta}{b}; \qquad b = \frac{a \sin \beta}{\sin \alpha} = \frac{(3.25)(.9680)}{.6072} = 5.182 \text{ in.}$$

$$\frac{\sin \alpha}{a} = \frac{\sin \gamma}{c}; \qquad c = \frac{a \sin \gamma}{\sin \alpha} = \frac{(3.25)(.9214)}{.6072} = 4.933 \text{ in.}$$

We now have the following information.

Given	*Found*
$\alpha = 37°23'$	$\gamma = 67°8'$
$\beta = 75°29'$	$b = 5.182$ in.
$a = 3.25$ in.	$c = 4.933$ in.

If we are given the measure of two sides of a triangle and the measure of the angle opposite one of the given sides, several possible situations might develop. Let us assume that we have been given a, b, and α. Then

$$\frac{\sin \beta}{b} = \frac{\sin \alpha}{a},$$

$$\sin \beta = \frac{b \sin \alpha}{a}.$$

Let us now consider the various possibilities for $\sin \beta$.

   (i)   **$\sin \beta > 1$.**   This is impossible, since the range of the sine function is the interval from -1 to 1. The triangle has no solution in this case.

  (ii) **$\sin \beta = 1$.**   In this case, $\beta = 90°$. If the given measure α is less than $90°$, the triangle has exactly one solution. If the given measure α is greater than or equal to $90°$, then $\alpha + \beta \geq 180°$, and the triangle has *no* solution.

 (iii) **$0 < \sin \beta < 1$.**   In this case, there are two possible solutions for β, β_1 and β_2, where $0 < \beta_1 < 90°$ and $90° < \beta_2 < 180°$, and $\beta_2 = 180° - \beta_1$. If $\alpha + \beta_2 < 180°$, the triangle has two solutions. If $\alpha + \beta_2 \geq 180°$, β_2 does not yield a solution. In this instance, there is one solution if $\alpha + \beta_1 < 180°$; there are no solutions if $\alpha + \beta_1 \geq 180°$.

Example 2

Solve $\triangle ABC$ if $\alpha = 47°$, $a = 25$ ft, and $b = 30$ ft.

Solution

The given information is shown in Figure 5.19.

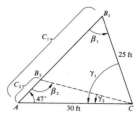

$$\frac{\sin \beta}{b} = \frac{\sin \alpha}{a}; \quad \sin \beta = \frac{b \sin \alpha}{a} = \frac{(30)(.7314)}{25} = .8776.$$

From Table II, we obtain $\beta_1 = 61°21'$. This means that

$$\beta_2 = 118°39'.$$

Since

Figure 5.19

$$47° + 118°39' = 165°39' < 180°,$$

there are two solutions. Completing the first solution, we have

$$\gamma_1 = 180° - (\alpha + \beta_1) = 180° - (47° + 61°21') = 180° - 108°21' = 71°39'.$$

$$\frac{\sin \alpha}{a} = \frac{\sin \gamma_1}{c_1}; \quad c_1 = \frac{a \sin \gamma_1}{\sin \alpha} = \frac{(25)(.9491)}{.7314} = 32.44 \text{ ft.}$$

Completing the second solution, we have

$$\gamma_2 = 180° - (\alpha + \beta_2) = 180° - 165°39' = 14°21'.$$

$$\frac{\sin \alpha}{a} = \frac{\sin \gamma_2}{c_2}; \quad c_2 = \frac{a \sin \gamma_2}{\sin \alpha} = \frac{(25)(.2479)}{.7314} = 8.474 \text{ ft.}$$

We now have the following information.

Given	1st Solution	2nd Solution
$\alpha = 47°$	$\beta_1 = 61°21'$	$\beta_2 = 118°39'$
$a = 25$ ft	$\gamma_1 = 71°39'$	$\gamma_2 = 14°21'$
$b = 30$ ft	$c_1 = 32.44$ ft	$c_2 = 8.474$ ft

Example 3

Solve $\triangle ABC$ if $\gamma = 85°$, $b = 52$ ft, $c = 31$ ft.

Solution

The given information is shown in Figure 5.20.

$$\frac{\sin \beta}{b} = \frac{\sin \gamma}{c};$$

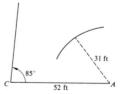

$$\sin \beta = \frac{b \sin \gamma}{c} = \frac{(52)(.9962)}{31} = 1.671.$$

Figure 5.20

Since **sin β = 1.671 > 1**, $\triangle ABC$ has *no* solution in this example.

You probably have observed from the illustrations accompanying these solutions that a careful sketch of the given information can be quite helpful in determining the number of solutions. There are some cases, though, when it is very difficult to make an accurate sketch of the given information.

Exercises 5.3

1. Prove the law of sines for $\triangle ABC$ if $\gamma = 90°$.
2. Finish the proof of the law of sines for an obtuse triangle. Figure 5.17 may be helpful.

Solve each of the following triangles, if possible. Consider all the given information to be exact.

3. $\alpha = 47°$, $\beta = 69°$, $b = 26$ ft.
4. $\alpha = 38°$, $\gamma = 75°$, $a = 40$ in.
5. $\beta = 21°49'$, $\gamma = 71°28'$, $c = 3.12$ ft.
6. $\alpha = 31°20'$, $\beta = 59°50'$, $a = 29$ yds.
7. $a = 35$ in., $b = 28$ in., $\alpha = 36°$.
8. $c = 17$ ft, $b = 28$ ft, $\gamma = 152°30'$.
9. $a = 23$ yds, $c = 18$ yds, $\gamma = 32°38'$.
10. $b = 15$ in., $c = 30$ in., $\beta = 30°$.
11. $a = 13$ ft, $b = 30$ ft, $\alpha = 74°10'$.
12. $a = 48$ yds, $c = 60$ yds, $\alpha = 63°13'$.
13. $b = 33$ in., $c = 11$ in., $\beta = 37°50'$.
14. $a = 24$ in., $c = 30$ in., $\alpha = 17°28'$.
15. Two men, 300 feet apart, observe an airplane that is in the same vertical plane as the two men. The angles of elevation of the plane from the two men are $47°10'$ and $63°28'$. If the men are standing on level ground, find the height of the plane above the ground if
    (a) the men are facing each other, and
    (b) the men are facing in the same direction.
16. Three towns are located in the plains. Town B is 35 miles due north of town A. Town C is 75 miles from town A and is $32°$ east of north from town B. How far is town C from town B? What direction is town C from town A?
17. A man is looking at a picture hanging on a wall. The picture is 6.0 feet high. The angle of elevation of the top of the picture from the man's line of sight is

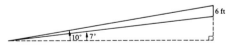

    $10°$ and the angle of elevation of the bottom of the picture is $7°$. How far is the man standing from the wall?
18. One diagonal of a parallelogram is 50 inches long. One end of the diagonal makes angles of $35°$ and $27°$ with the two sides. How long are the sides of the parallelogram?
19. Two men shoot at a deer, hitting it in exactly the same spot at the same time. There is an angle of $23°$ between the paths of the two bullets as they enter the deer. The first man is 150 feet from the deer and 75 feet from the second man. How far is the second man from the deer if he is *behind* the first man?

20. Two men in a building are looking at the top of a second building. The first man is 10 feet above the ground. The second man is 60 feet above the ground and directly above the first man. The angle of elevation of the top of the second building is 65° for the first man, 30° for the second man. How tall is the second building?

5.5   The law of cosines

It is also possible to solve a triangle if we know the measures of all three sides of the triangle or if we know the measures of two sides of the triangle and the measure of the angle included between the two sides. The **law of cosines**, which we will develop in this section, is the tool we need to solve these triangles.

Consider the triangle in Figure 5.21. We have located the vertex A at the origin and the vertex C on the positive half of the x-axis. The point C clearly has coordinates $(b, 0)$. In $\triangle ABD$, which has a right angle at D,

$$\frac{m(\overline{BD})}{c} = \sin \alpha \quad \text{and} \quad \frac{m(\overline{AD})}{c} = \cos \alpha,$$

so that the vertex B has coordinates $(c \cos \alpha, c \sin \alpha)$. The student is asked in the exercises to verify this if $\angle BAD$ is an obtuse angle.

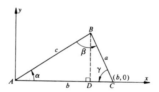

Figure 5.21

Recall that the distance formula states that the distance between two points (x_1, y_1) and (x_2, y_2) is $\sqrt{(x_2 - x_1)^2 + (y_2 - y_1)^2}$. Using this distance formula and the fact that a is equal to the distance between the vertices B and C, we have the following development.

$$a = \sqrt{(c \cos \alpha - b)^2 + (c \sin \alpha - 0)^2},$$
$$a^2 = (c \cos \alpha - b)^2 + (c \sin \alpha)^2,$$
$$a^2 = c^2 \cos^2 \alpha - 2bc \cos \alpha + b^2 + c^2 \sin^2 \alpha,$$
$$a^2 = b^2 + c^2(\cos^2 \alpha + \sin^2 \alpha) - 2 bc \cos \alpha,$$
$$a^2 = b^2 + c^2 - 2bc \cos \alpha.$$
$$\therefore \quad a^2 = b^2 + c^2 - 2bc \cos \alpha. \tag{1}$$

If we orient the triangle so that a different vertex is at the origin, we might obtain one of the following two equations.

$$b^2 = a^2 + c^2 - 2ac \cos \beta. \tag{2}$$

$$c^2 = a^2 + b^2 - 2ab \cos \gamma. \tag{3}$$

This particular form of the law of cosines is quite useful in solving a triangle in which we are given the measures of two of the sides of the triangle and the measure of the angle included by those two sides.

Example 1

Solve $\triangle ABC$ if $a = 23$ in., $c = 31$ in., and $\beta = 48°30'$.

Solution

The given information is shown in Figure 5.22.
$\cos \beta = .6626$. From (2) above, we have

$$b^2 = (23)^2 + (31)^2 - 2(23)(31)(.6626)$$
$$= 529 + 961 - 945$$
$$= 545$$
$$b = \sqrt{545} = 23.34 \text{ in.}$$

Now, using the law of sines,

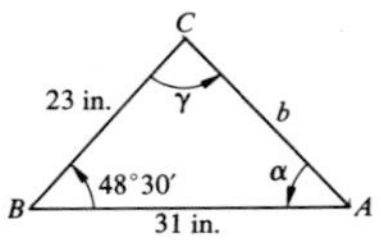

Figure 5.22

$$\frac{\sin \alpha}{a} = \frac{\sin \beta}{b};$$

$$\sin \alpha = \frac{a \sin \beta}{b} = \frac{(23)(.7490)}{23.34} = .7380,$$

$$\alpha_1 = 47°34' \quad \text{or} \quad \alpha_2 = 132°26'.$$

$\gamma = 180° - (\alpha_1 + \beta) = 180° - (48°30' + 47°34') = 180° - 96°4' = 83°56'.$

Since $\alpha_2 + \beta = 132°26' + 48°30' = 180°56'$, there is only one solution for the triangle.

We can obtain an alternate form for the law of cosines from (1) in the following manner.

$$a^2 = b^2 + c^2 - 2bc \cos \alpha,$$
$$2bc \cos \alpha = b^2 + c^2 - a^2,$$
$$\cos \alpha = \frac{b^2 + c^2 - a^2}{2bc}.$$

$$\therefore \quad \cos \alpha = \frac{b^2 + c^2 - a^2}{2bc}. \tag{4}$$

Note that if $\cos \alpha$ is negative, then $90° < \alpha < 180°$.

If we had begun with (2) or (3) and worked in a similar manner, we would have obtained

$$\cos \beta = \frac{a^2 + c^2 - b^2}{2ac} \tag{5}$$

or

$$\cos \gamma = \frac{a^2 + b^2 - c^2}{2ab}. \tag{6}$$

Any one of these three formulas may be used to solve a triangle in which we are given the measures of the three sides.

Example 2

Solve $\triangle ABC$ if $a = 47$ yds, $b = 39$ yds, $c = 62$ yds.

Solution

The given information is shown in Figure 5.23.
From (4),

$$\cos \alpha = \frac{b^2 + c^2 - a^2}{2bc} = \frac{(39)^2 + (62)^2 - (47)^2}{2(39)(62)}$$

$$= \frac{1521 + 3844 - 2209}{4836}$$

$$= \frac{3156}{4836} = .6527$$

$$\alpha = 49° \ 15'.$$

Figure 5.23

Then

$$\frac{\sin \beta}{b} = \frac{\sin \alpha}{a}; \quad \sin \beta = \frac{b \sin \alpha}{a} = \frac{(39)(.7576)}{47} = .6286,$$

$$\beta = 38° \ 57'$$

$$\gamma = 180° - (\alpha + \beta) = 180° - (49°15' + 38°57') = 180° - (88°12') = 91°48'.$$

Exercises 5.4

Solve the following triangles. Assume the given information is exact.

1. $a = 38$ ft, $b = 27$ ft, $\gamma = 74°$.
2. $a = 123$ in., $b = 75$ in., $\gamma = 39°$.
3. $a = 56$ yd, $b = 83$ yd, $\gamma = 97°$.
4. $a = 23.8$ ft, $c = 29.1$ ft, $\beta = 31°20'$.
5. $a = 29.5$ in., $c = 28.4$ in., $\beta = 58°30'$.
6. $a = 94.6$ yd, $c = 29.2$ yd, $\beta = 17°10'$.
7. $b = 78.4$ ft, $c = 69.2$ ft, $\alpha = 131°50'$.
8. $b = 15$ in., $c = 8.66$ in., $\alpha = 48°20'$.
9. $b = 42.7$ yd, $c = 42.7$ yd, $\alpha = 95°40'$.
10. $a = 38.2$ in., $b = 54.1$ in., $c = 46.3$ in.
11. $b = 835$ ft, $c = 925$ ft, $a = 760$ ft.
12. $c = 500$ yds, $a = 375$ yds, $b = 600$ yds.
13. $a = 3$ yds, $b = 4$ yds, $c = 5$ yds.
14. $b = 73$ in., $c = 94$ in., $a = 128$ in.
15. Tom and Frank want to find the distance across the lake pictured here. They cannot measure across the water, but they did find the information indicated in the sketch. What is the distance across the lake?

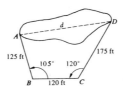

16. The quadrilateral $ABCD$ is such that $m(\overline{AB}) = 12$ feet, $m(\overline{BC}) = 15$ feet, $m(\overline{CD}) = 10$ feet, $m(\overline{DA}) = 9.0$ feet, and $m(\angle ABC) = 90°$. Find the measures of the remaining angles of the quadrilateral and the lengths of the two diagonals.

17. The circumference of a regular polygon inscribed in a circle can be found by considering one side of the polygon to be the base of an isosceles triangle which has its third vertex at the center of the circle and proceeding from there. Find the circumference of a regular decagon (10 sides) inscribed in a circle with radius 6.0 feet.

18. The quadrilateral $ABCD$ is such that $m(\overline{AB}) = 25$ feet, $m(\overline{BC}) = 60$ feet, $m(\overline{CD}) = 55$ feet, $m(\overline{DA}) = 20$ feet, and the measure of one of the diagonals is 50 feet. Find the measures of the four angles of the quadrilateral and the length of the other diagonal.

19. Find the circumference of a regular hexagon (6 sides) circumscribed about a circle with radius 8.0 feet.

20. Prove the law of cosines for an obtuse triangle.

5.6 Areas of triangular regions

We defined a triangle to be the union of the three line segments which join three noncollinear points. In Figure 5.24 the points A, B, and C are non-collinear. The three segments $\overline{AB}$, $\overline{BC}$, and $\overline{CA}$ form $\triangle ABC$. Since $\triangle ABC$ consists of just three line segments, $\triangle ABC$ cannot have an area. The region bounded by the segments $\overline{AB}$, $\overline{BC}$, and $\overline{CA}$ is called a **triangular region**, and it does have an area. In this book we shall speak of the *area of a triangle* to refer to the *area of the triangular region bounded by that triangle.*

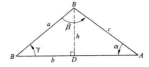

Figure 5.24

Most of us are familiar with one formula for finding the area of a triangle. If b is the measure of one side of the triangle and if h is the measure of the altitude from that side of the triangle, then the area,

$$\mathscr{A} = 1/2\ bh.$$

A question might arise, however, as to how to find the area of a triangle without the information needed above. Any time that we have enough information to solve a triangle, we can eventually find the area of the triangle by securing enough information to apply the above formula. In this section two additional formulas are given to find the area of a triangle.

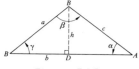

Figure 5.25

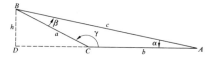

Figure 5.26

Although the two triangles pictured in Figures 5.25 and 5.26 look very different, the process of finding the area is the same in each case. Assume that we know b, c, and α. In either of these triangles, if we can find h, then the area $\mathscr{A}$ of $\triangle ABC$ is $1/2\, bh$. In each figure, we see that $h/c = \sin \alpha$, so that $h = c \sin \alpha$. Thus

$$\mathscr{A} = \frac{1}{2} bh = \frac{1}{2} b(c \sin \alpha) = \frac{1}{2} bc \sin \alpha.$$

If $\alpha = 90°$, as in Figure 5.27, it should be clear that $\sin \alpha = 1$, so that

$$\mathscr{A} = \frac{1}{2} bc \sin \alpha = \frac{1}{2} bc.$$

If A is an obtuse angle, as in Figure 5.28, we find that in $\triangle ACD$, $h/b =$

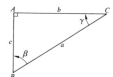

Figure 5.27

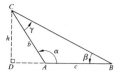

Figure 5.28

$\sin (180° - \alpha)$. But $\sin(180° - \alpha) \equiv \sin \alpha$, so $h/b = \sin \alpha$, and $h = b \sin \alpha$. Thus, $\mathscr{A} = 1/2\, bc \sin \alpha$ in this case also.

In a similar fashion, it can be shown that for any $\triangle ABC$,

$$\mathscr{A} = \frac{1}{2} ac \sin \beta \quad \text{or} \quad \mathscr{A} = \frac{1}{2} ab \sin \gamma.$$

Example 1

Find the area of $\triangle ABC$ if $a = 38$ ft, $c = 20$ ft, and $\beta = 30°$.

Solution

$$\mathscr{A} = \frac{1}{2} ac \sin \beta = \frac{1}{2} (38)(20)\left(\frac{1}{2}\right) = 190 \text{ square ft.}$$

A second formula for finding the area of a triangle is developed below. This development makes use of the law of cosines.

$$\cos \alpha = \frac{b^2 + c^2 - a^2}{2bc}, \tag{1}$$

$$1 + \cos \alpha = 1 + \frac{b^2 + c^2 - a^2}{2bc} \tag{2}$$

$$= \frac{2bc}{2bc} + \frac{b^2 + c^2 - a^2}{2bc} \tag{3}$$

$$= \frac{(b^2 + 2bc + c^2) - a^2}{2bc} \tag{4}$$

$$= \frac{(b + c)^2 - a^2}{2bc} \tag{5}$$

$$= \frac{(b + c + a)(b + c - a)}{2bc}. \tag{6}$$

$$1 - \cos \alpha = 1 - \frac{b^2 + c^2 - a^2}{2bc} \tag{7}$$

$$= \frac{2bc - b^2 - c^2 + a^2}{2bc} \tag{8}$$

$$= \frac{a^2 - (b^2 - 2bc + c^2)}{2bc} \tag{9}$$

$$= \frac{a^2 - (b - c)^2}{2bc} \tag{10}$$

$$= \frac{(a - b + c)(a + b - c)}{2bc}. \tag{11}$$

$$(1 + \cos \alpha)(1 - \cos \alpha)$$
$$= \frac{(b + c + a)(b + c - a)(a - b + c)(a + b - c)}{(2bc)^2}. \tag{12}$$

$$1 - \cos^2 \alpha = \frac{(b + c + a)(b + c - a)(a - b + c)(a + b - c)}{(2bc)^2}. \tag{13}$$

$$\sin^2 \alpha = \frac{(b + c + a)(b + c - a)(a - b + c)(a + b - c)}{(2bc)^2}. \tag{14}$$

$$(bc)^2 \sin^2 \alpha = \frac{(b + c + a)(b + c - a)(a - b + c)(a + b - c)}{4}. \tag{15}$$

$$\frac{(bc \sin \alpha)^2}{4} = \left(\frac{b + c + a}{2}\right)\left(\frac{b + c - a}{2}\right)\left(\frac{a - b + c}{2}\right)\left(\frac{a + b - c}{2}\right). \tag{16}$$

If $s = \frac{a + b + c}{2}$, we can express (16) as

$$\frac{(bc \sin \alpha)^2}{4} = s(s - a)(s - b)(s - c). \tag{17}$$

$$\left(\frac{bc \sin \alpha}{2}\right)^2 = s(s-a)(s-b)(s-c). \tag{18}$$

$$\frac{bc \sin \alpha}{2} = \sqrt{s(s-a)(s-b)(s-c)}. \tag{19}$$

Since for any $\triangle ABC$, we can express the area of $\triangle ABC$ as $\mathcal{A} = 1/2\, bc \sin \alpha$, we have that for any $\triangle ABC$, the area

$$\mathcal{A} = \sqrt{s(s-a)(s-b)(s-c)}. \tag{20}$$

The use of this formula is illustrated in the following example.

Example 2

Find the area of ABC if $a = 27$ in., $b = 35$ in., and $c = 28$ in.

Solution

$$s = \frac{27 + 35 + 28}{2} = \frac{90}{2} = 45,$$
$$\mathcal{A} = \sqrt{(45)(18)(10)(17)}$$
$$= \sqrt{137,700} = 371.1 \text{ sq in.}$$

Exercises 5.5

Find the area of $\triangle ABC$ if the following is known. (Assume the given information is exact.)

1. $a = 25$ ft, $b = 32$ ft, $\gamma = 29°$.
2. $b = 84$ in., $c = 73$ in., $\alpha = 42°$.
3. $c = 65$ yds, $a = 128$ yds, $\beta = 104°$.
4. $a = 30$ ft, $b = 15$ ft, $\gamma = 60°$.
5. $a = 32$ in., $b = 48$ in., $c = 29$ in.
6. $a = 53$ yds, $b = 53$ yds, $c = 53$ yds.
7. $a = 74$ ft, $b = 29$ ft, $c = 58$ ft.
8. $a = 86$ in., $b = 93$ in., $c = 47$ in.
9. $\alpha = 35°$, $\beta = 64°$, $a = 28$ ft.
10. $\gamma = 64°$, $\beta = 57°$, $c = 16$ yds.
11. $\gamma = 103°$, $\alpha = 47°$, $a = 29$ in.
12. $\alpha = 37°$, $\beta = 83°$, $c = 329$ ft.
13. $\beta = 75°$, $\gamma = 35°$, $a = 806$ yds.
14. $\gamma = 75°$, $\alpha = 83°$, $b = 3$ in.
15. $a = 16$ ft, $b = 32$ ft, $\alpha = 28°$.
16. $b = 63$ in., $c = 87$ in., $\gamma = 69°$.
17. $c = 45$ yds, $a = 55$ yds, $\gamma = 58°$.

18. Find the area of the quadrilateral described in Problem 16 of Exercises 5.4.
19. Find the area of the decagon described in Problem 17 of Exercises 5.4.
20. Find the area of the quadrilateral described in Problem 18 of Exercises 5.4.
21. Find the area of the hexagon described in Problem 19 of Exercises 5.4.
22. Find the area of the triangle which has its vertices at the points (2, 3), (10, 9), and (5, −3).

Review Exercises

Solve the following triangles, if possible. Assume that the given information is exact.

1. $\alpha = 47°$, $\gamma = 63°$, $b = 281$ in.
2. $a = 62.8$ ft, $b = 393.3$ ft, $\gamma = 64°20'$.
3. $\gamma = 90°$, $c = 25$ ft, $b = 19$ ft.
4. $a = 28$ ft, $c = 60$ ft, $\alpha = 30°$.
5. $c = 19.2$ ft, $b = 28.4$ ft, $\beta = 74°23'$.
6. $c = 29.4$ yds, $a = 49.2$ yds., $\beta = 49°20'$.

7. Convert each of the following radian measures to its corresponding degree measure.

    a. $\frac{\pi}{18}$ radians   b. $-\frac{3\pi}{10}$ radians

    c. $-\frac{23\pi}{5}$ radians   d. $\frac{41\pi}{6}$ radians

Find the areas of the triangles for which the given information is known. Assume that the given information is exact.

8. $a = 32$ in., $c = 25$ in., $\beta = 36°$.
9. $a = 28$ ft, $b = 35$ ft, $c = 31$ ft.
10. $\alpha = 49°$, $\beta = 72°$, $c = 16$ yds.
11. Convert each of the following degree measures to its corresponding radian measure.

    a. $40°$ b. $-630°$ c. $-162°$ d. $810°$

Solve the following triangles, if possible. Assume that the given information is exact.

12. $\gamma = 90°$, $a = 4$ ft, $b = 5$ ft.
13. $a = 28$ in., $b = 36$ in., $c = 48$ in.
14. $\alpha = 131°$, $a = 26$ yds, $b = 21$ yds.
15. $a = 28$ ft, $c = 60$ ft, $\alpha = 43°$.
16. $c = 25$ yds, $b = 40$ yds, $a = 30$ yds.
17. $a = 28$ yds, $c = 60$ yds, $\beta = 49°20'$.
18. $b = 42$ in., $a = 31$ in., $\beta = 54°30'$.

Complex numbers

6.1 The rectangular form of complex numbers

In Chapter 0 we indicated that the set C of complex numbers could be expressed as

$$C = \{x + yi \mid x \in R, y \in R, i = \sqrt{-1}\}.$$

We did not consider the complex numbers further at that point, but here we shall consider them in more detail.

Recall that in the set of real numbers we can always find the sum, the difference, the product, or the quotient of two real numbers, provided that we do not divide by zero. There is some difficulty with root extraction, since we cannot extract even roots of negative numbers. You will discover that in the set of complex numbers we can do all of the operations possible in the set of real numbers, and that root extraction is always possible in the set of complex numbers.

In the complex number $a + bi$, a is considered to be the **real part** of $a + bi$ and b is considered to be the **imaginary part** or, sometimes, the **coefficient of the imaginary part.**

The complex number $a + 0i = a$ is considered to be a **real number** and the complex number $0 + bi = bi$ is called a **pure imaginary number.**

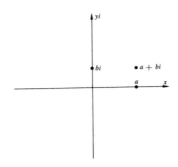

Figure 6.1

When we wish to represent complex numbers graphically, we often use what is called the **Argand plane**, in which we have a horizontal axis, called the **real axis**, and a vertical axis, called the **imaginary axis**. The plotting of the complex number $a + bi$, illustrated in Figure 6.1, is done in the same fashion as the plotting of the ordered pair (a, b) in R^2. Corresponding to the complex number $a + bi$ is a complex number called the **complex conjugate** of $a + bi$. The complex conjugate of $a + bi$ is $a - bi$. We can readily see that this complex conjugate is symmetric to the complex number $a + bi$ with respect to the real axis.

The complex conjugate of $3 + 4i$ is $3 - 4i$; the complex conjugate of $5 - 2i$ is $5 - (-2i) = 5 + 2i$. Figure 6.2 illustrates the symmetry of $3 + 4i$ and $3 - 4i$ with respect to the x-axis.

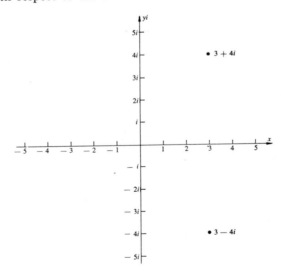

Figure 6.2

If $z = a + bi$, we often use $\bar{z}$ to refer to the complex conjugate of z. If $z = 4 + i$,

$$\bar{z} = 4 - i,$$

and if $w = 2 - 2i$,

$$\bar{w} = 2 + 2i.$$

Two complex numbers $a + bi$ and $c + di$ are considered to be equal if and only if $a = c$ and $b = d$. Thus, we can see that two complex numbers are equal if and only if their real parts are equal and their imaginary parts are equal.

The four standard operations, addition, subtraction, multiplication, and division, will be defined in this section. The operations of addition and subtraction are defined quite easily, as is shown below.

*The **sum** of $a + bi$ and $c + di$ is given by*
$$(a + bi) + (c + di) = (a + c) + (b + d)i.$$

*The **difference** of $a + bi$ and $c + di$ is given by*
$$(a + bi) - (c + di) = (a - c) + (b - d)i.$$

We can readily see that the sum (difference) of two complex numbers can be obtained by taking the sum (difference) of their real parts and of their imaginary parts, respectively. Examples of these two operations are shown below. Let

$$w = 3 - 4i, \quad z = 5 + 2i, \quad \text{and} \quad u = 4 + i.$$

Then

$$\begin{aligned}
w + z &= 8 - 2i, & z + u &= 9 + 3i, \\
\bar{w} &= 3 + 4i, & \bar{z} &= 5 - 2i, \\
\bar{w} + u &= 7 + 5i, & w - z &= -2 - 6i, \\
z - u &= 1 + i, & \text{and} \quad \bar{z} - w &= 2 + 2i.
\end{aligned}$$

*The **product** of $a + bi$ and $c + di$ is given by*
$$(a + bi)(c + di) = (ac - bd) + (ad + bc)i.$$

This definition might be developed if we assume that multiplication of complex numbers has the same properties as multiplication of real numbers—namely, that it is commutative and associative, and that it distributes over addition. This development is shown below.

$$\begin{aligned}
(a + bi)(c + di) &= a(c + di) + bi(c + di) \\
&= [ac + (ad)i] + [(bc)i + (bd)i^2] \\
&= [ac + (bd)i^2] + [ad + bc]i \\
&= (ac - bd) + (ad + bc)i \quad (\text{since } i^2 = -1).
\end{aligned}$$

Thus,

$$(2 + 3i)(5 - 7i) = [2 \cdot 5 - 3 \cdot (-7)] + [2 \cdot (-7) + 3 \cdot 5]i$$
$$= (10 + 21) + (-14 + 15)i$$
$$= 31 + i,$$

and

$$(3 + 4i)(3 - 4i) = [3 \cdot 3 - 4 \cdot (-4)] + [3 \cdot (-4) + 4 \cdot 3]i$$
$$= [9 + 16] + [-12 + 12]i$$
$$= 25 + 0i = 25.$$

The last example illustrated that the product of a complex number and its conjugate is a real number. This is shown in general below.

$$(a + bi) \cdot (a - bi) = a^2 - (bi)^2$$
$$= a^2 - b^2 i^2$$
$$= a^2 + b^2.$$

The last fact is helpful in developing the definition of **division** of one complex number by another. We would like $(a + bi)/(c + di)$ to be a complex number. This means that this quotient should have a real part and an imaginary part. If we multiply both the numerator and the denominator of $(a + bi)/(c + di)$ by the complex conjugate of $c + di$, we have the following development.

$$\frac{a + bi}{c + di} = \frac{(a + bi)(c - di)}{(c + di)(c - di)}$$
$$= \frac{(ac + bd) + (bc - ad)i}{c^2 + d^2}$$
$$= \frac{ac + bd}{c^2 + d^2} + \frac{bc - ad}{c^2 + d^2}i.$$

You may find it easier to remember the technique used in developing this definition than to remember the definition. Using the technique above, we find that

$$(7 - 2i) \div (2 + 5i) = \frac{(7 - 2i)(2 - 5i)}{(2 + 5i)(2 - 5i)}$$
$$= \frac{(14 - 10) + (-35 - 4)i}{4 + 25}$$
$$= \frac{4 - 39i}{29}$$
$$= \frac{4}{29} - \frac{39}{29}i.$$

Either of these last two forms would be considered appropriate as an answer.

Exercises 6.1

1. Identify the real part, the imaginary part, and the complex conjugate of each of the following. Plot each of the following complex numbers.

a. $7 - i$ b. $3 + 2i$ c. $2 + 5i$
d. $1 - 3i$ e. $-4i$ f. $4 + i$
g. $9 - 2i$ h. -5 i. $\sqrt{3} + \sqrt{2i}$
j. $e + \pi i$ k. 3 l. $3i$

Perform the indicated operations.

2. $(3 - 2i) + (17 + i)$ 3. $(\pi + 3i) + (-3\pi - 4i)$
4. $3i + (4 - 3i)$ 5. $(-2 + 7i) + (2 - i)$
6. $(3 - 2i) - (17 + i)$ 7. $(\pi + 3i) - (-3\pi - 4i)$
8. $(6 - i) - (4 - 5i)$ 9. $(4 + 4i) - (3 + 2i)$
10. $(6 - 2i)(3 + i)$ 11. $(e + 13i)(3e - 2i)$
12. $i(4 - 3i)$ 13. $(2 - 3i)(3 - 4i)$
14. $(3 - 2i) \div (1 + i)$ 15. $(1 + i) \div (3 - 2i)$
16. $(4 - 3i) \div (3 - 9i)$ 17. $1 \div (c + di)$
18. $[(3 + i) + (2 - 3i)](4 + 5i)$ 19. $[(5 - 2i)(3 + 4i)] \div (4 + 6i)$
20. $[(3 - i) \div (2 + 2i)](5 - 6i)$ 21. $[(3 + 2i) - (-3 + i)](6 - 3i)$
22. $(1 + i)^4$ 23. $(3 + 2i)^2 \div (1 + 2i)^3$
24. $(-5 + 2i)^3 - (4 - i)^2$ 25. $(1 + i)^4 \div (4 - i)^2$

6.2   The polar form of complex numbers

     In Section 6.1 we explored the method known as the rectangular form of representing complex numbers. In this section we shall examine the **polar form** of representing complex numbers.

     First, we shall consider the *distance* that the point representing a complex number is from the origin. Through the use of the Pythagorean theorem we can easily see in Figure 6.3 that the distance of the point $x + yi$ from the origin is given by $\sqrt{x^2 + y^2}$. This distance is usually referred to as the **modulus** of the complex number, and it is denoted by r.

     Second, we shall consider the *angle* that the segment connecting the point $x + yi$ to the origin makes with the positive half of the x-axis. This angle is denoted by θ in Figure 6.3, and it is called the **argument** or the **amplitude** of the complex number $x + yi$. *The argument of a complex number will be given in radians, not degrees, in this book.*

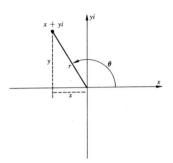

Figure 6.3

We can note that $\tan \theta = y/x$, but we cannot go further to state that $\theta = \text{Tan}^{-1} y/x$, the reason being that y/x has the same value for two points which are symmetric with respect to the origin even though they are on opposite half-lines emanating from the origin. It is important to notice the quadrant in which a complex number lies when determining the argument of the complex number. If we consider the complex numbers $-2 + 2i$ and $2 - 2i$, we note that $-2 + 2i$ lies in the second quadrant and $3\pi/4$ is an appropriate selection for the argument of $-2 + 2i$. The complex number $2 - 2i$ lies in the fourth quadrant and $-\pi/4$ is an appropriate selection for the argument of $2 - 2i$. These two complex numbers are graphed in Figure 6.4.

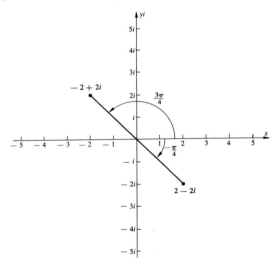

Figure 6.4

For the complex number $-2 + 2i$,

$$\frac{y}{x} = \frac{2}{-2} = -1,$$

and for the complex number $2 - 2i$,

$$\frac{y}{x} = \frac{-2}{2} = -1.$$

Since $\tan \theta = -1$ for each of these complex numbers, it is necessary to see which quadrant the complex number is in before we choose the argument of the complex number.

You may ask why pick $-\pi/4$ instead of $7\pi/4$ for the argument of $2 - 2i$. Remember that if the measures of two angles differ by an integral multiple of 2π radians, the two angles have the same terminal side. This means that if θ is an argument for the complex number $a + bi$, then any number of the form $\theta + 2n\pi$, where $n \in J$, is also an argument for the complex number $a + bi$. To achieve uniformity in the determination of the argument of a complex number, we shall agree that the **principal argument** of a complex number will be in the interval $(-\pi, \pi]$.

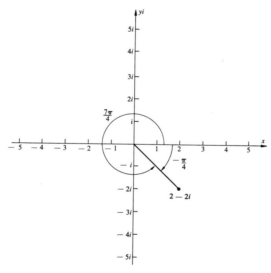

Figure 6.5

When writing a complex number in polar form, we usually consider the origin to be the **pole**, and the ray which corresponds to the positive half of the x-axis is called the **polar axis**. The complex number is written as $r(\cos \theta + i \sin \theta)$ where r and θ are as described above.

Two complex numbers

$$r_1(\cos \theta_1 + i \sin \theta_1) \quad \text{and} \quad r_2(\cos \theta_2 + i \sin \theta_2)$$

are the same complex number if $r_1 = r_2$ and $\boldsymbol{\theta_1 = \theta_2 + 2n\pi}$ for some $n \in J$. Although we do not customarily write complex numbers with negative moduli,

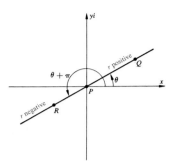

Figure 6.6

this is occasionally done. If r is negative, we first determine the ray emanating from the origin which makes an angle of θ radians with the polar axis. The other half of the line determined by this ray makes an angle of $\theta + \pi$ radians with the polar axis. We might consider that if the modulus r in the complex number $r(\cos \theta + i \sin \theta)$ is *positive*, we moved r units along the ray $(\overrightarrow{PQ})$, making an angle of θ radians with the polar axis. If r is *negative*, we might consider the ray $(\overrightarrow{PR})$, making an angle of $\theta + \pi$ radians with the polar axis, to be the "negative half" of the ray $(\overrightarrow{PQ})$ for the purposes of graphing.

We have included a sufficient amount of material to see that if we wish to convert a complex number $x + yi$ from rectangular form to polar form, we can do it by letting $r = \sqrt{x^2 + y^2}$ and $\tan \theta = y/x$.

Example 1

Convert $-3 - 3\sqrt{3}i$ to polar form.

Solution

$$r = \sqrt{(-3)^2 + (-3\sqrt{3})^2} = \sqrt{9 + 27} = \sqrt{36} = 6.$$

$-3 - 3\sqrt{3}i$ is in the third quadrant.

$\tan \theta = \dfrac{-3\sqrt{3}}{-3} = \sqrt{3}$, so $\theta = \dfrac{-2\pi}{3}$ and

$$-3 - 3\sqrt{3}i = 6\left[\cos\left(-\frac{2\pi}{3}\right) + i \sin\left(-\frac{2\pi}{3}\right)\right].$$

To convert the complex number $r(\cos \theta + i \sin \theta)$ to rectangular form, we let

$$x = r \cos \theta \quad \text{and} \quad y = r \sin \theta.$$

This should be easy to see, since

$$r(\cos \theta + i \sin \theta) = (r \cos \theta) + (r \sin \theta)i.$$

Example 2

Convert $2\left[\cos\left(-\frac{\pi}{4}\right) + i\sin\left(-\frac{\pi}{4}\right)\right]$ to rectangular form.

Solution

$$x = 2\cos\left(-\frac{\pi}{4}\right) = 2\left(\frac{\sqrt{2}}{2}\right) = \sqrt{2}.$$
$$y = 2\sin\left(-\frac{\pi}{4}\right) = 2\left(-\frac{\sqrt{2}}{2}\right) = -\sqrt{2}.$$
$$2\left[\cos\left(-\frac{\pi}{4}\right) + i\sin\left(-\frac{\pi}{4}\right)\right] = \sqrt{2} - \sqrt{2}i.$$

Exercises 6.2

Convert the following complex numbers from rectangular form to polar form.

1. $-1 + i$ 2. $1 - \sqrt{3}i$
3. $-4i$ 4. $3 + \sqrt{3}i$
5. $6 - 2\sqrt{3}i$ 6. $4 - 4i$
7. $-1 + \sqrt{3}i$ 8. -9

Graph each of the following complex numbers. Then convert the complex number from polar form to rectangular form.

9. $5\left(\cos\frac{3\pi}{4} + i\sin\frac{3\pi}{4}\right)$

10. $3\left(\cos\frac{5\pi}{3} + i\sin\frac{5\pi}{3}\right)$

11. $4\left[\cos\left(-\frac{\pi}{3}\right) + i\sin\left(-\frac{\pi}{3}\right)\right]$

12. $10\left(\cos\frac{5\pi}{6} + i\sin\frac{5\pi}{6}\right)$

13. $8\left(\cos\frac{5\pi}{4} + i\sin\frac{5\pi}{4}\right)$

14. $6\left(\cos\frac{3\pi}{2} + i\sin\frac{3\pi}{2}\right)$

15. $-6\left[\cos\left(-\frac{\pi}{6}\right) + i\sin\left(-\frac{\pi}{6}\right)\right]$

16. $4[\cos(-\pi) + i\sin(-\pi)]$

6.3   De Moivre's theorem

The representation of complex numbers in polar form has some distinct advantages. One is that it is much easier to multiply or divide complex numbers in polar form than in rectangular form. If we let two complex numbers z_1 and z_2 be represented by

$$r_1(\cos\theta + i\sin\theta) \quad \text{and} \quad r_2(\cos\phi + i\sin\phi),$$

respectively, we have the following development for their product.

$$z_1 \cdot z_2 = [r_1(\cos \theta + i \sin \theta)] \cdot [r_2(\cos \phi + i \sin \phi)]$$
$$= [r_1 \cos \theta + (r_1 \sin \theta)i] \cdot [r_2 \cos \phi + (r_2 \sin \phi)i]$$
$$= (r_1 r_2 \cos \theta \cos \phi - r_1 r_2 \sin \theta \sin \phi)$$
$$+ (r_1 r_2 \cos \theta \sin \phi + r_1 r_2 \sin \theta \cos \phi)i$$
$$= r_1 r_2 (\cos \theta \cos \phi - \sin \theta \sin \phi)$$
$$+ r_1 r_2 (\cos \theta \sin \phi + \sin \theta \cos \phi)i$$
$$= r_1 r_2 \cos (\theta + \phi) + r_1 r_2 \sin (\theta + \phi)i$$
$$= r_1 r_2 [\cos (\theta + \phi) + i \sin (\theta + \phi)].$$
$$\therefore \quad z_1 \cdot z_2 = r_1 r_2 [\cos (\boldsymbol{\theta} + \boldsymbol{\phi}) + i \sin (\boldsymbol{\theta} + \boldsymbol{\phi})].$$

Thus, we see that when we take the product of two complex numbers, the modulus of the product is the product of the moduli of the two factors, and the argument of the product is the sum of the arguments of the factors. This result can be generalized in the following way.

If $z = r(\cos \theta + i \sin \theta)$, and $n \in N$, then

$$z^n = r^n (\cos n\theta + i \sin n\theta).$$

This result, known as **De Moivre's theorem,** can be proved by mathematical induction, as follows:

(i) $z^1 = z = r (\cos \theta + i \sin \theta) = r^1 (\cos 1 \cdot \theta + i \sin 1 \cdot \theta).$

(ii) Assume that $z^k = r^k (\cos k\theta + i \sin k\theta)$ for some $k \in J$. Using this as the induction hypothesis, we wish to prove that

$$z^{k+1} = r^{k+1}[\cos (k + 1)\theta + i \sin (k + 1)\theta].$$
$$z^{k+1} = z^k \cdot z$$
$$= [r^k(\cos k\theta + i \sin k\theta)] \cdot [r(\cos \theta + i \sin \theta)] \quad \text{(by the induction hypothesis)}$$
$$= r^k \cdot r[\cos (k\theta + \theta) + i \sin (k\theta + \theta)] \quad \text{(by the previous result about the product)}$$
$$= r^{k+1}[\cos (k + 1)\theta + i \sin (k + 1)\theta] \quad \text{(by properties of algebra)}.$$
$$\therefore \quad z^{k+1} = r^{k+1} [\cos (k + 1) \theta + i \sin (k + 1)\theta].$$
$$\therefore \quad \textbf{If } z = r(\cos \boldsymbol{\theta} + i \sin \boldsymbol{\theta}) \textbf{ and } n \in N, \textbf{ then } z^n = r^n(\cos n\boldsymbol{\theta} + i \sin n\boldsymbol{\theta}).$$

Examples using these results are given below.

Example 1

$$\left[3\left(\cos \frac{\pi}{4} + i \sin \frac{\pi}{4}\right)\right] \cdot \left[\frac{2}{3}\left(\cos \frac{\pi}{3} + \sin \frac{\pi}{3}\right)\right]$$

Solution

$$\left(3 \cdot \frac{2}{3}\right)\left[\cos \left(\frac{\pi}{4} + \frac{\pi}{3}\right) + i \sin \left(\frac{\pi}{4} + \frac{\pi}{3}\right)\right] = 2\left[\cos \frac{7\pi}{12} = i \sin \frac{7\pi}{12}\right].$$

Example 2

Evaluate $(1 + i)^6$

Solution

$$(1 + i)^6 = \left[\sqrt{2} \left(\cos \frac{\pi}{4} + i \sin \frac{\pi}{4} \right) \right]^6$$

$$= (\sqrt{2})^6 \left[\cos \left(6 \cdot \frac{\pi}{4} \right) + i \sin \left(6 \cdot \frac{\pi}{4} \right) \right]$$

$$= 8 \left(\cos \frac{3\pi}{2} + i \sin \frac{3\pi}{2} \right)$$

$$= 8(0 - i)$$

$$= -8i.$$

$\tan 0 = \dfrac{\sin 0}{\cos 0} = \dfrac{0}{1} = 0$

$\tan \pi = \dfrac{\sin \pi}{\cos \pi} = \dfrac{0}{-1} = 0$

$\tan \dfrac{\pi}{6} = \dfrac{\sin \dfrac{\pi}{6}}{\cos \dfrac{\pi}{6}} = \dfrac{\dfrac{1}{2}}{\dfrac{\sqrt{3}}{2}} = \dfrac{1}{\sqrt{3}}$

We have seen that finding products and powers is quite easy using polar coordinates. Finding quotients is also quite easy. We first express $1/z$ in polar coordinates. Using this result, we then find a way of expressing z_1/z_2. If

$$z = r(\cos \theta + i \sin \theta),$$

then

$$\frac{1}{z} = \frac{1}{r(\cos \theta + i \sin \theta)}$$

$$= \frac{1}{r(\cos \theta + i \sin \theta)} \cdot \frac{r(\cos \theta - i \sin \theta)}{r(\cos \theta - i \sin \theta)}$$

$$= \frac{r(\cos \theta - i \sin \theta)}{r^2 (\cos^2 \theta - i^2 \sin^2 \theta)}$$

$$= \frac{\cos \theta - i \sin \theta}{r(\cos^2 \theta + \sin^2 \theta)}$$

$$= \frac{1}{r} (\cos \theta - i \sin \theta)$$

$$= \frac{1}{r} [\cos (-\theta) + i \sin (-\theta)]$$

$\tan \dfrac{\pi}{4} = \dfrac{\sin \dfrac{\pi}{4}}{\cos \dfrac{\pi}{4}} = \dfrac{\dfrac{1}{\sqrt{2}}}{\dfrac{1}{\sqrt{2}}} = 1$

$\tan \dfrac{\pi}{3} = \dfrac{\sin \dfrac{\pi}{3}}{\cos \dfrac{\pi}{3}} = \dfrac{\dfrac{\sqrt{3}}{2}}{\dfrac{1}{2}} = \sqrt{3}$

[since $\cos (-\theta) \equiv \cos \theta$ and $\sin (-\theta) \equiv -\sin \theta$]. Using this result, if

$$z_1 = r_1 (\cos \theta + i \sin \theta) \quad \text{and} \quad z_2 = r_2 (\cos \phi + i \sin \phi),$$

then

$$\frac{z_1}{z_2} = \left[r_1 (\cos \theta + i \sin \theta) \right] \cdot \left[\frac{1}{r_2} (\cos (-\phi) + i \sin (-\phi)) \right]$$

$$= \frac{r_1}{r_2} [\cos (\theta - \phi) + i \sin (\theta - \phi)],$$

using the rule for the product of two complex numbers in polar form. Thus, the modulus of the quotient is the quotient of the moduli, and the argument of the quotient is the difference of the arguments. Examples of this rule are shown below.

Example 3

$$\left[3\left(\cos\frac{\pi}{2}+i\sin\frac{\pi}{2}\right)\right]\div\left[6\left(\cos\frac{\pi}{3}+i\sin\frac{\pi}{3}\right)\right]$$

Solution

$$\frac{3}{6}\left[\cos\left(\frac{\pi}{2}-\frac{\pi}{3}\right)+i\sin\left(\frac{\pi}{2}-\frac{\pi}{3}\right)\right]=\frac{1}{2}\left(\cos\frac{\pi}{6}+i\sin\frac{\pi}{6}\right)$$

Example 4

$$\frac{12\left(\cos\frac{\pi}{4}+i\sin\frac{\pi}{4}\right)}{\left[2\left(\cos\frac{3\pi}{2}+i\sin\frac{3\pi}{2}\right)\right]^2}$$

Solution

$$\frac{12\left(\cos\frac{\pi}{4}+i\sin\frac{\pi}{4}\right)}{\left[2\left(\cos\frac{3\pi}{2}+i\sin\frac{3\pi}{3}\right)\right]^2}=\frac{12\left(\cos\frac{\pi}{4}+i\sin\frac{\pi}{4}\right)}{4\left(\cos3\pi+i\sin3\pi\right)}$$

$$=\frac{12}{4}\left[\cos\left(\frac{\pi}{4}-3\pi\right)+i\sin\left(\frac{\pi}{4}-3\pi\right)\right]$$

$$=3\left[\cos\left(\frac{-11\pi}{4}\right)+i\sin\left(\frac{-11\pi}{4}\right)\right]$$

Exercises 6.3

Find the indicated products, powers, and quotients.

1. $\left[5\left(\cos\frac{2\pi}{3}+i\sin\frac{2\pi}{3}\right)\right]\cdot\left[2\left(\cos\frac{3\pi}{2}+i\sin\frac{3\pi}{2}\right)\right]$

2. $\left[\sqrt{2}\left(\cos\frac{7\pi}{4}+i\sin\frac{7\pi}{4}\right)\right]\cdot\left[13\left(\cos\left(-\pi\right)+i\sin\left(-\pi\right)\right)\right]$

3. $\left[\sqrt{6}\left(\cos\frac{\pi}{9}+i\sin\frac{\pi}{9}\right)\right]\cdot\left[\sqrt{18}\left(\cos\frac{\pi}{5}+i\sin\frac{\pi}{5}\right)\right]$

4. $\left[3\left(\cos\left(\frac{-\pi}{2}\right)+i\sin\left(\frac{-\pi}{2}\right)\right)\right]\cdot\left[7\left(\cos\frac{\pi}{6}+i\sin\frac{\pi}{6}\right)\right]$

5. $\left[3\left(\cos\frac{2\pi}{5}+i\sin\frac{2\pi}{5}\right)\right]^3$

6. $\left[\sqrt{5}\left(\cos\frac{3\pi}{4}+i\sin\frac{3\pi}{4}\right)\right]^6$

7. $\left[\cos\frac{\pi}{4}+i\sin\frac{\pi}{4}\right]^8$

8. $\left[2\left(\cos\frac{4\pi}{3}+i\sin\frac{4\pi}{3}\right)\right]^{10}$

9. $\left[8\left(\cos\frac{3\pi}{4} + i\sin\frac{3\pi}{4}\right)\right] \div \left[4\left(\cos\frac{\pi}{2} + i\sin\frac{\pi}{2}\right)\right]$

10. $\left[35\left(\cos\frac{3\pi}{2} + i\sin\frac{3\pi}{2}\right)\right] \div \left[7\left(\cos\frac{2\pi}{3} + i\sin\frac{2\pi}{3}\right)\right]$

11. $\left[4\left(\cos\frac{\pi}{5} + i\sin\frac{\pi}{5}\right)\right] \div \left[16\left(\cos\frac{\pi}{3} + i\sin\frac{\pi}{3}\right)\right]$

12. $\left[3\left(\cos\frac{\pi}{7} + i\sin\frac{\pi}{7}\right)\right] \div \left[\sqrt{3}\left(\cos\frac{3\pi}{2} + i\sin\frac{3\pi}{2}\right)\right]$

13. $(1 - i)^8$

14. $\left(\frac{\sqrt{3}}{2} + \frac{i}{2}\right)^6$

15. $(3 - \sqrt{3}i)^4$

16. $(-2 - 2i)^8$

17. $(1 - i)^8 \div (3 - \sqrt{3}i)^4$

18. $\left(\frac{\sqrt{3}}{2} + \frac{i}{2}\right)^6 \div (-2 - 2i)^8$

6.4   Roots of complex numbers

We indicated earlier that the extraction of roots is always possible within the system of complex numbers. This process is accomplished fairly easily by using an application of De Moivre's theorem.

Let $z = r(\cos\theta + i\sin\theta)$. We wish to find the complex number(s) w such that $w^n = z$. Assume that $w = \rho(\sin\phi + i\sin\phi)$. Then, by De Moivre's theorem,

$$w^n = \rho^n(\cos n\phi + i\sin n\phi).$$

In order to have $w^n = z$, we must have

$$\rho^n(\sin n\phi + i\sin n\phi) = r(\cos\theta + i\sin\theta).$$

This means that $\rho^n = r$ and $n\phi = \theta$ or $n\phi = \theta + 2k\pi$, where $k \in J$. If $\rho^n = r$ then $\rho = \sqrt[n]{r}$, and if $n\phi = \theta + 2k\pi$, $k \in J$, then

$$\phi = \frac{\theta + 2k\pi}{n}, k \in J.$$

If k takes the different values $0, 1, 2, \ldots, n - 1$, then

$$\phi_1 = \frac{\theta}{n}, \quad \phi_2 = \frac{\theta + 2\pi}{n} \quad \phi_3 = \frac{\theta + 4\pi}{n}, \cdots, \quad \phi_n = \frac{\theta + (n - 1)2\pi}{n}$$

will be n *different* angles which are not coterminal. Since these angles are not coterminal,

$$w_1 = \sqrt[n]{r}\left(\cos\frac{\theta}{n} + i\sin\frac{\theta}{n}\right),$$

$$w_2 = \sqrt[n]{r}\left[\cos\left(\frac{\theta + 2\pi}{n}\right) + i\sin\left(\frac{\theta + 2\pi}{n}\right)\right],$$

. . .

$$w_n = \sqrt[n]{r}\left[\cos\frac{\theta + (n-1)2\pi}{n} + i\sin\frac{\theta + (n-1)2\pi}{n}\right]$$

are all different complex numbers, and z has n distinct nth roots.

Let us illustrate by finding the four fourth roots of -4.

$$-4 = 4(\cos\pi + i\sin\pi).$$

Let

$$w = \rho(\cos\phi + i\sin\phi).$$

If $w^4 = -4$, then

$$[\rho(\cos\phi + i\sin\phi)]^4 = 4(\cos\pi + i\sin\pi),$$

$$\rho^4(\cos 4\phi + i\sin 4\phi) = 4(\cos\pi + i\sin\pi).$$

$$\rho^4 = 4, \qquad 4\phi = \pi + 2k\pi, \quad k = 0, 1, 2, 3 \quad \text{(since } n = 4\text{)},$$

$$\rho^2 = 2, \qquad 4\phi = \pi \quad \text{or} \quad \pi + 2\pi \quad \text{or} \quad \pi + 4\pi \quad \text{or} \quad \pi + 6\pi,$$

$$\rho = \sqrt{2}, \qquad 4\phi = \pi \quad \text{or} \quad 3\pi \quad \text{or} \quad 5\pi \quad \text{or} \quad 7\pi,$$

$$\rho = \sqrt{2}, \qquad \phi_1 = \frac{\pi}{4}, \qquad \phi_2 = \frac{3\pi}{4}, \qquad \phi_3 = \frac{5\pi}{4}, \qquad \phi_4 = \frac{7\pi}{4}.$$

The four fourth roots of -4 are given by

$$w_1 = \sqrt{2}\left(\cos\frac{\pi}{4} + i\sin\frac{\pi}{4}\right) = \sqrt{2}\left(\frac{\sqrt{2}}{2} + \frac{\sqrt{2}}{2}i\right) = 1 + i,$$

$$w_2 = \sqrt{2}\left(\cos\frac{3\pi}{4} + i\sin\frac{3\pi}{4}\right) = \sqrt{2}\left(\frac{-\sqrt{2}}{2} + \frac{\sqrt{2}}{2}i\right) = -1 + i,$$

$$w_3 = \sqrt{2}\left(\cos\frac{5\pi}{4} + i\sin\frac{5\pi}{4}\right) = \sqrt{2}\left(\frac{-\sqrt{2}}{2} - \frac{\sqrt{2}}{2}i\right) = -1 - i,$$

$$w_4 = \sqrt{2}\left(\cos\frac{7\pi}{4} + i\sin\frac{7\pi}{4}\right) = \sqrt{2}\left(\frac{\sqrt{2}}{2} - \frac{\sqrt{2}}{2}i\right) = 1 - i.$$

Anyone who is not convinced that $1 + i$, $-1 + i$, $-1 - i$, and $1 - i$ are all fourth roots of -4, can check this by using multiplication of complex numbers in rectangular form.

The n nth roots of 1 can be found in a similar fashion. These are often called the n **nth roots of unity**. Let us find the five fifth roots of unity. We can express 1 in the form $1(\cos 0 + i\sin 0)$. Thus, if

$$w = \rho(\cos\phi + i\sin\phi),$$

$\rho^5 = 1$ and $5\phi = 0$, 2π, 4π, 6π, or 8π. Thus, $\rho = 1$, $\phi_1 = 0$, $\phi_2 = 2\pi/5$, $\phi_3 = 4\pi/5$, $\phi_4 = 6\pi/5$, and $\phi_5 = 8\pi/5$. The five fifth roots of unity are given by

$$w_1 = 1(\cos 0 + i\sin 0) = 1,$$

$$w_2 = 1\left(\cos\frac{2\pi}{5} + i\sin\frac{2\pi}{5}\right),$$

$$w_3 = 1\left(\cos\frac{4\pi}{5} + i\sin\frac{4\pi}{5}\right),$$

$$w_4 = 1\left(\cos\frac{6\pi}{5} + i\sin\frac{6\pi}{5}\right),$$

$$w_5 = 1\left(\cos\frac{8\pi}{5} + i\sin\frac{8\pi}{5}\right).$$

These could be expressed without writing the modulus of 1. If no modulus appears, then it is understood that the modulus is 1.

Exercises 6.4

1. Find the 3 third roots of unity. Express them in rectangular form.
2. Find the 8 eighth roots of unity. Express them in rectangular form.
3. Find the 7 seventh roots of unity.
4. Find the 10 tenth roots of unity.
5. Find the 3 cube roots of $2 - 2i$.
6. Find the 5 fifth roots of $-4 - 4i$.
7. Find the 7 seventh roots of $5\left(\cos\frac{\pi}{5} + i\sin\frac{\pi}{5}\right)$.
8. Find the 6 sixth roots of $13\left(\cos\frac{\pi}{4} + i\sin\frac{\pi}{4}\right)$.
9. Find the 6 sixth roots of $-64i$.
10. Find the 3 cube roots of $27i$. Express them in rectangular form.
11. Find the 3 cube roots of $-i$. Express them in rectangular form.
12. Find the 2 square roots of $-25i$. Express them in rectangular form.

Review Exercises

1. Convert $6\left(\cos\frac{13\pi}{6} + i\sin\frac{13\pi}{6}\right)$ to rectangular form.
2. Convert $12 - 12i$ to polar form.
3. Give the complex conjugate of

    a. $3 - 14i$,   b. $6i$,   c. -3,   d. $6 + 2i$.

4. Find the 2 square roots of $4i$.
5. Find the 3 cube roots of -8.

6. Perform the indicated operations.

    a. $(3 - 2i)(-5 + 7i)$ b. $(3 - 2i) - (-5 + 7i)$

    c. $(25 + 50i) \div (3 - 4i)$ d. $(-17 + 16i) + (3 - 8i)$

    e. $\left[3\left(\cos\frac{\pi}{4} + i\sin\frac{\pi}{4}\right)\right]^3$ f. $\left[2\left(\cos\frac{-\pi}{3} + i\sin\frac{-\pi}{3}\right)\right]^4$

    g. $\left[3\left(\cos\frac{\pi}{5} + i\sin\frac{\pi}{5}\right)\right] \cdot \left[\frac{1}{3}\left(\cos\frac{\pi}{3} + i\sin\frac{\pi}{3}\right)\right]$

    h. $\left[3\left(\cos\frac{\pi}{5} + i\sin\frac{\pi}{5}\right)\right] \div \left[\frac{1}{3}\left(\cos\frac{\pi}{3} + i\sin\frac{\pi}{3}\right)\right]$

7. Convert $-6 + 6\sqrt{3}i$ to polar form.

8. Convert $-4\left(\cos\frac{3\pi}{4} + i\sin\frac{3\pi}{4}\right)$ to rectangular form.

9. Perform the indicated operations.

    a. $\left[5\left(\cos\frac{3\pi}{4} + i\sin\frac{3\pi}{4}\right)\right] \div \left[2\left(\cos\frac{\pi}{6} + i\sin\frac{\pi}{6}\right)\right]$

    b. $\left[5\left(\cos\frac{3\pi}{4} + i\sin\frac{3\pi}{4}\right)\right] \cdot \left[2\left(\cos\frac{\pi}{6} + i\sin\frac{\pi}{6}\right)\right]$

    c. $(3 + 6i) + (-2 + 3i)$ d. $(3 + 6i) - (-2 + 3i)$

    e. $(3 + 6i) \cdot (-2 + 3i)$ f. $(3 + 6i) \div (-2 + 3i)$

    g. $(1 - i)^5$

Appendix

Using logarithms

A.1 Logarithms to the base 10

A function of the type

$$\log_b = \{(x, y) \mid x = b^y\}$$

is called a **logarithmic function.** Any positive number, other than one, can be used as the base for a function of this type. One of the most common logarithmic functions is

$$\log_{10} = \{(x, y) \mid x = 10^y\}.$$

This function is called the **logarithmic function to the base 10.** If $x = 10^y$, y *is called the logarithm to the base* 10 *of x.* This function is quite useful in making many numerical computations.

The *domain* of the logarithmic function to the base 10 is the set of *all positive real numbers* and the *range* of the logarithmic function to the base 10 is the set of *all real numbers.*

We notice that the ordered pair (x, y) belongs to the logarithmic function to the base 10 if and only if $x = 10^y$. We shall indicate this relationship in another way, by writing

$$y = \log x$$

to indicate that $x = 10^y$. Thus, $y = \log x$ and $x = 10^y$ are equivalent equations. Since $y = \log x$ if and only if $x = 10^y$, we have that $x = 10^{\log x}$. This is a basic identity for positive real numbers. We can summarize this fact with the following identity.

$$x = 10^{\log x} \quad \mathcal{D} = (0, \infty).$$

We can illustrate three logarithms to the base 10 quite easily, as is done below.

$$\log 100 = 2, \quad \text{since } 100 = 10^2,$$
$$\log 1{,}000{,}000 = 6, \quad \text{since } 1{,}000{,}000 = 10^6,$$

and

$$\log \frac{1}{1000} = -3, \quad \text{since } \frac{1}{1000} = 10^{-3}.$$

The laws of exponents which you learned in algebra help you to use logarithms. You should remember the following laws of exponents from your study of algebra.

If $a, b, x, y \in R$ and $a, b > 0$, then

1. $a^x a^y = a^{x+y}$,
2. $(ab)^x = a^x b^x$,
3. $(a^x)^y = a^{xy}$,
4. $\dfrac{a^x}{a^y} = a^{x-y}$,
5. $\left(\dfrac{a}{b}\right)^x = \dfrac{a^x}{b^x}$, and
6. if $a \neq 1$, then $a^x = a^y$ if and only if $x = y$.

These laws of real-number exponents can be used to prove the following properties of logarithms to the base 10. If $k, x, y \in R$ and $x, y > 0$, then

1. $\log (xy) = \log x + \log y$,
2. $\log x^k = k \log x$,
3. $\log\left(\dfrac{x}{y}\right) = \log x - \log y$, and
4. $\log x = \log y$ if and only if $x = y$.

We shall prove the first two of these four properties of logarithms to the base 10. The last two properties are included in the exercises at the end of this section.

To prove the second property, we assume that

$$y = \log x.$$

This tells us that $x = 10^y$. Then, $x^k = (10^y)^k = 10^{yk} = 10^{ky}$. Therefore,

$$\log x^k = ky = k \log x.$$

The proof of the property $\log(xy) = \log x + \log y$ can be given in the following fashion. Let

$$w = \log x \quad \text{and} \quad z = \log y.$$

Then

$$x = 10^w \text{ and } \quad y = 10^z.$$

Then

$$xy = (10^w)(10^z) = 10^{w+z}.$$

But $\log(xy) = w + z = \log x + \log y$, since $xy = 10^{w+z}$.

We said earlier that logarithms to the base 10 are quite useful in making many numerical computations. For these logarithms to make numerical computations easier, we need to use the four given properties of logarithms to express the logarithms of products, powers, quotients, and roots as the sums and/or differences of logarithms. This is demonstrated in the following examples.

Example 1

Express $\log[(29)(33)(472)]$ as a sum.

Solution

By property 1,

$$\log[(29)(33)(472)] = \log[(29)(33)] + \log 472$$
$$= \log 29 + \log 33 + \log 472.$$

Example 2

Express $\log \dfrac{928}{(13)(127)}$ as sums and/or differences.

Solution

By property 2,

$$\log \frac{928}{(13)(127)} = \log 928 - \log[(13)(127)].$$

By property 1,

$$\log[(13)(127)] = \log 13 + \log 127.$$

Therefore,

$$\log \frac{928}{(13)(127)} = \log 928 - (\log 13 + \log 127).$$
$$= \log 928 - \log 13 - \log 127.$$

Example 3

Express $\log \dfrac{(75)^3(2\sqrt[3]{2})}{\sqrt[4]{39}}$ as sums and/or differences.

Solution

It is helpful to begin by rewriting the expression $\dfrac{(75)^3(2\sqrt[3]{2})}{\sqrt[4]{39}}$ with fractional exponents where necessary.

$$\frac{(75)^3(2\sqrt[3]{2})}{\sqrt[4]{39}} = \frac{(75)^3(2)^{4/3}}{(39)^{1/4}} .$$

Thus,

$$\log \frac{(75)^3(2\sqrt[3]{2})}{\sqrt[4]{39}} = \log \frac{(75)^3(2)^{4/3}}{39^{1/4}}$$

$$= \log [(75)^3(2)^{4/3}] - \log (39)^{1/4}$$

$$= \log (75)^3 + \log (2)^{4/3} - \log (39)^{1/4}$$

$$= 3 \log 75 + \frac{4}{3} \log 2 - \frac{1}{4} \log 39.$$

Logarithms to the base 10 are often called **common logarithms,** since they are used by many people.

Exercises A.1

Evaluate each of the following.

1. $\log 1000$ 2. $\log \dfrac{1}{100}$ 3. $\log \sqrt{10}$

4. $\log 10$ 5. $\log 1$ 6. $\log \dfrac{100}{\sqrt{10}}$

Express the given logarithms as sums and /or differences.

7. $\log [(291)(143)]$ 8. $\log [(428)(1024)(13)]$

9. $\log \dfrac{291}{143}$ 10. $\log \dfrac{(927)(516)}{(413)(372)}$

11. $\log [\sqrt{31}\,(29)^3]$ 12. $\log \sqrt[10]{29}$

13. $\log \dfrac{\sqrt[3]{729}\,(281)^4}{927}$ 14. $\log \dfrac{29\sqrt{29}}{(138)(75)}$

15. $\log \left[\dfrac{(314)^2(475)}{627}\right]^4$ 16. $\log \sqrt{\dfrac{(29)^3(74)^4}{(281)^5}}$

Express the following numbers as products of numbers between 1 and 10 and powers of 10.

Example

246

Solution

$2.46 \cdot 10^2$

Example

0.1345

Solution

$1.345 \cdot 10^{-1}$

17. 1967   18. 64.291   19. .0842
20. .006175   21. .00009189   22. 2,576,000
23. Prove the third property of logarithms to the base 10.
24. Prove the fourth property of logarithms to the base 10.

A.2 Table of values for log₁₀

Table III gives the approximations, to four decimal places, of many numbers. The logarithms given in Table III are the logarithms of the given numbers rounded off to the nearest 1/10,000. Since these logarithms are not exact but only very good approximations, using them will occasionally introduce slight errors. However, we shall treat the logarithms we use as though they were exact, even though they are not.

In order to use Table III, it is necessary to be able to express a number in *scientific notation*. By expressing a number x in *scientific notation*, we mean expressing x as a product of a number between 1 and 10 and an integral power of 10. In problems 17–22 in Exercises A.1 we were actually expressing numbers in scientific notation. Two examples of scientific notation are

$$.006175 = 6.175 \cdot 10^{-3} \quad \text{and} \quad 2,576,000 = 2.576 \cdot 10^{6}.$$

Example 1

Find log 6.78.

Solution

The logarithms in Table III are the logarithms of numbers between 1 and 10. We can find log 6.78 on page 189 in the following fashion. Locate the row in the left-hand column which contains 6.7 and the column which has 8 at the top. The number in the intersection of the row containing 6.7 and the column with 8 at the top is the logarithm of 6.78. By referring to page 189, we find that

$$\log 6.78 = .8312.$$

Example 2

Find log 678.

Solution

$$678 = 6.78 \cdot 10^{2}$$
$$\log 678 = \log 6.78 + \log 10^{2}$$
$$= .8312 + 2$$
$$= 2.8312.$$

To find the logarithm of a number like 678, it is necessary to find two numbers. One of these numbers is the logarithm of a number between 1 and 10. This logarithm is a decimal fraction between 0 and 1, and it is called the *mantissa* of the logarithm. The second number is an integer which is the logarithm of a power of 10, and it is called the *characteristic* of the logarithm. When we expressed log 678 as 2.8312, we could have called .8312 the *mantissa* of the logarithm and the 2 the *characteristic* of the logarithm.

In general, if a is any positive real number, we can express a in the form $a = m \cdot 10^c$, where $1 \leq m < 10$ and c is an integer. Then

$$\log a = \log m + \log 10^c$$
$$= \log m + c.$$

If $c \geq 0$, we can express log a as we did log 6.78 without difficulty. If $c < 0$, then we can express c in the form $c = b - d$, where b and d are integers $0 < b < d$. Then

$$\log a = \log m + c$$
$$= \log m + (b - d)$$
$$= (b + \log m) - d.$$

Example 3

Find log .678.

Solution

Since $.678 = 6.78 \cdot 10^{-1}$, we can write

$$\log (.678) = \log 6.78 - 1$$
$$= .8312 + (9 - 10)$$
$$= (9 + .8312) - 10$$
$$= 9.8312 - 10.$$

We could have expressed -1 as $1 -2$, $2 -3$, $5 -6$, or any other pair of positive integers b and d such that $b - d = -1$. Although $9 - 10$ is the customary notation, it is possible to use another form.

Example 4

Find log 0.0591.

Solution

We see that $0.0591 = 5.91 \cdot 10^{-2}$, and from page 189, we see that the number in the intersection of the row with 5.9 on the left and the column with 1 at the top is .7716. Thus,

$$\log 5.91 = 0.7716.$$

Then,

$$\begin{aligned}
\log 0.0591 &= \log 5.91 + \log 10^{-2} \\
&= 0.7716 + (-2) \\
&= 0.7716 + (8 - 10) \\
&= 8.7716 - 10.
\end{aligned}$$

It is possible to find the logarithm of a four-digit number by using linear interpolation. For example, let us find $\log 3.584$. From the table on page 188, we see that $\log 3.58 = 0.5539$ and $\log 3.59 = 0.5551$.

$$0.5551 - 0.5539 = .0012.$$

$$\frac{4}{10}(.0012) = .00048.$$

We shall use $.0005$ as an approximation of $(4/10)(.0012)$, since our logarithms are only given to four decimal places. Since 3.584 is 4/10 of the way from 3.58 to 3.59, we add $.0005$ to 0.5539 to obtain $\log 3.584 = 0.5544$.

On the basis of the foregoing you should be able to use Table III to find the common logarithms of many numbers. The exercises at the end of this section will give you an opportunity to practice this skill.

Another skill in the use of logarithms which you need to develop is that of finding antilogarithms. If $y = \log x$, we frequently say that y is the common logarithm of x. We can also express this idea by saying that x is the antilogarithm of y.

Example 5

Find the antilogarithm of 0.3764.

Solution

We see from Table III that $\log 2.37 = 0.3747$ and $\log 2.38 = 0.3766$. This tells us that the antilogarithm of 0.3764 is between 2.37 and 2.38.

$$0.3766 - 0.3747 = .0019 \quad \text{and} \quad 0.3764 - 0.3747 = .0017.$$

$.0017/.0019 = 17/19$, which is approximately 9/10 to the nearest tenth. This tells us that the antilogarithm of 0.3764 is about 9/10 of the way from 2.37 to 2.38. Thus, the *antilogarithm of* 0.3764 *is* approximately 2.379.

Example 6

Find the antilogarithm of 2.8912.

Solution

Let x be the antilogarithm of 2.8912. Then

$$\log x = 2.8912 = 2 + (0.8912).$$

This tells us that x is the product of 10^2 (the antilogarithm of 2) and the antilogarithm of 0.8912. We find in Table III that

$$\log 7.78 = 0.8910 \quad \text{and} \quad \log 7.79 = 0.8915.$$

$$0.8915 - 0.8910 = .0005 \quad \text{and} \quad 0.8912 - 0.8910 = .0002$$

$.0002/.0005 = 2/5 = 4/10$. The antilogarithm of 0.8912 is 4/10 of the way from 7.78 to 7.79, so the *antilogarithm of* 0.8912 *is* 7.784. Thus, the *antilogarithm of* 2.8912 *is*

$$(10^2)(7.784) = 778.4.$$

Example 7

Find the antilogarithm of $8.6931 - 10$.

Solution

We can see that

$$8.6931 - 10 = 0.6931 + (8 - 10)$$
$$= 0.6931 + (-2).$$

The antilogarithm of 0.6928 *is* 4.93 and *the antilogarithm of* 0.6937 *is* 4.94. By using the methods of Examples 5 and 6, we determine that *the antilogarithm of* 0.6931 *is* 4.933. The antilogarithm of (-2) is 10^{-2}, so *the antilogarithm of* $8.6931 - 10$ *is*

$$(4.933)(10^{-2}) = .04933.$$

Exercises A.2

Use Table III to find the common logarithms of the following numbers.

1. 291
2. 37.8
3. 0.518
4. 0.00913
5. 25.43
6. 678.7
7. 0.04891
8. 0.9186
9. 1,049,000
10. 79,350
11. 0.00006183
12. 0.002914

Use Table III to find the antilogarithms of the following numbers.

13. 0.6955
14. 0.2967
15. 2.9142
16. 1.3694
17. $9.8137 - 10$
18. $8.6146 - 10$
19. 3.2908
20. 6.5931
21. $7.1233 - 10$

A.3   Using logarithms for computation

We can use the properties of logarithms developed in section A.1 to assist us in performing many different calculations. Some of the ways in which we can use logarithms are shown below.

Example 1

Find $\dfrac{(275)(931.8)}{(213)(74.2)}$.

Solution

Let $N = \dfrac{(275)(931.8)}{(213)(74.2)}$. Then $\log N = \log [(275)(931.8)] - \log [(213)(74.2)]$.

$$\begin{aligned} \log [(275)(931.8)] &= \log 275 + \log 931.8 \\ &= 2.4393 + 2.9693 \\ &= 5.4086. \end{aligned}$$

$$\begin{aligned} \log [(213)(74.2)] &= \log 213 + \log 74.2 \\ &= 2.3284 + 1.8704 \\ &= 4.1988. \end{aligned}$$

$$\log N = 5.4086 - 4.1988 = 1.2098,$$
$$N = \text{the antilogarithm of } 1.2098 = 16.21.$$

When we say that $N = 16.21$, this is the nearest approximation to the value of $[(275)(931.8)]/[(213)(74.2)]$ we can make using Table III. In all cases that we consider in this book, such approximations are close enough.

Example 2

Find $(35)^3(321)^4$.

Solution

Let $N = (35)^3(321)^4$.

$$\begin{aligned} \log N &= \log (35)^3 + \log (321)^4 \\ &= 3 \log 35 + 4 \log 321 \\ &= 3(1.5441) + 4(2.5065) \\ &= 4.6323 + 10.0260 \\ &= 14.6583. \end{aligned}$$

$$\begin{aligned} N &= \text{antilogarithm of } 14.6583 \\ &= (\text{antilogarithm of } 0.6583)(10^{14}) \\ &= 4.553 \cdot 10^{14}. \end{aligned}$$

Example 3

Find $(329.5)(.0461)$.

Solution

Let $N = (329.5)(.0461)$.

$$\begin{aligned} \log N &= \log (329.5) + \log (.0461) \\ &= 2.5178 + (8.6637 - 10) \\ &= 11.1815 - 10 \\ &= 1.1815. \end{aligned}$$

$$\begin{aligned} N &= (\text{antilogarithm of } 0.1815)(10) \\ &= (1.519)(10) = 15.19. \end{aligned}$$

Example 4

Find $\sqrt{31.46}$.

Solution

We see that $\sqrt{31.46} = (31.46)^{1/2}$.
Let $N = (31.46)^{1/2}$.
Then

$$\log N = \log (31.46)^{1/2}$$
$$= \frac{1}{2} \log (31.46)$$
$$= \frac{1}{2} (1.4977)$$
$$= 0.7489.$$
$$N = \text{antilogarithm of } 0.7489 = 5.609.$$

Exercises A.3

Use logarithms in performing the following calculations.

1. $(34)(472.1)(913)$
2. $(687)(56)(762.8)$
3. $\dfrac{(921)(0.645)}{(3.218)(0.043)}$
4. $\dfrac{(.0032)(19.67)}{(314.5)(0.693)}$
5. $\dfrac{(56)^2\sqrt{329}}{(19)}$
6. $\sqrt[3]{\dfrac{(24)^4(17)^2}{(56)}}$
7. $\dfrac{(5.621)^2(16.34)^3}{(.04375)^4}$
8. $\dfrac{\sqrt{192}\sqrt[3]{291}}{\sqrt[4]{675}}$
9. $\sqrt[4]{\dfrac{(5.46)^3\sqrt[3]{167}}{(19.5)^2}}$
10. $\dfrac{43}{6.19}\sqrt{\dfrac{(21)^3(34)^5}{(41)^3}}$

A.4   Common logarithms of trigonometric functions of angles

The process of solving triangles numerically usually involves making several different computations. Many people use logarithms for these computations, since this is easier and faster than actually performing the calculations.

If you need to use tan 23°37′ in a problem, you begin by using Table II to find tan 23°37′ = .4372. Turning to Table III, we find that

$$\log .4372 = 9.6407 - 10.$$

, Thus,

$$\log (\tan 23°37') = 9.6407 - 10.$$

This process would involve using two different tables to find log (tan 23°37'). However, tables have been developed which enable us to find log (tan 23°37') by using only one table instead of two. *Table IV* is such a table. There, the logarithms given are 10 larger than the actual logarithms of the numbers involved. For example, on page 192, we see that log (tan 23°37') comes out 9.6407. Since this is 10 larger than the actual value of log (tan 23°37'), we subtract 10 from the value obtained from Table IV, obtaining

$$\log (\tan 23°37') = 9.6407 - 10,$$

which agrees with our earlier result.

You will notice that Table IV includes only the logarithms of the function values of four trigonometric functions, the sine, cosine, tangent, and cotangent functions—which should be sufficient for any problem you encounter while trying to solve triangles.

The logarithms of function values of angles between 0° and 45° are obtained by using the angle measures in the left-hand column and the column headings at the *top* of the page. The logarithms of function values of angles between 45° and 90° are obtained by using the angle measures in the right-hand column and the column headings at the bottom of the page.

Exercises A.4

Use Table IV to find the indicated logarithms:

1. log (sin 49°40′)
2. log (tan 17°50′)
3. log (cos 37°20′)
4. log (cot 83°10′)
5. log (tan 59°32′)
6. log (sin 23°19′)
7. log (cot 41°24′)
8. log (cos 81°14′)
9. log (sin 74°27′)
10. log (tan 56°53′)
11. log (cos 67°35′)
12. log (cot 32°58′)

Use Table IV to find α in problems 13–24.

13. log (sin α) = 9.6546 − 10
14. log (tan α) = 10.0659 − 10
15. log (cot α) = 9.9494 − 10
16. log (cos α) = 8.8946 − 10
17. log (tan α) = 8.9163 − 10
18. log (sin α) = 9.9842 − 10
19. log (cot α) = 10.6413 − 10
20. log (cos α) = 9.9084 − 10
21. log (sin α) = 9.6082 − 10
22. log (tan α) = 11.1891 − 10
23. log (cos α) = 9.9019 − 10
24. log (cot α) = 9.4872 − 10

A.5 Using logarithms of trigonometric functions to solve triangles

We indicated in Section A.4 that Table IV could help us to solve triangles more quickly. The examples below illustrate how.

Example 1

Solve triangle ABC if

$\gamma = 90°$,

$a = 35.3$ in.,

$c = 46.1$ in.

Figure A.1

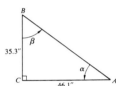

Solution

We can see from Figure A.1 that $\sin\alpha = \dfrac{35.3}{46.1}$. Thus,

$$\begin{aligned}\log(\sin\alpha) &= \log 35.3 - \log 46.1\\ &= 1.5478 - 1.6637\\ &= (11.5478 - 10) - (1.6637)\\ &= 9.8841 - 10.\end{aligned}$$

Using Table IV, we determine that $\alpha = 49°58'$.

$$\beta = 90° - \alpha = 90° - 49°58' = 40°2'.$$

$\sin\beta = \dfrac{b}{c}$,

$$\begin{aligned}\text{so } b &= c\sin\beta\\ &= (46.1)(\sin 40°2'),\\ \log b &= \log 46.1 + \log(\sin 40°2')\\ &= (1.6637) + (9.8084 - 10)\\ &= 1.4721,\\ b &= 29.65 \text{ in.}\end{aligned}$$

Thus, $\alpha = 49°58'$, $\beta = 40°2'$, $b = 29.65$ in.

Example 2

Solve $\triangle ABC$ if

$\alpha = 48°30'$,

$\beta = 71°40'$,

$c = 31.3$ ft.

Figure A.2

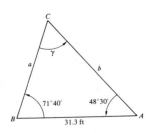

Solution

$\gamma = 180° - (\alpha + \beta) = 180° - (120°10') = 59°50'.$

$$\frac{\sin\alpha}{a} = \frac{\sin\gamma}{c};\quad a = \frac{c\sin\alpha}{\sin\gamma} = \frac{(31.3)(\sin 48°30')}{\sin 59°50'}.$$

$$\log a = \log (31.3) + \log (\sin 48°30') - \log (\sin 59°50')$$
$$= 1.4955 + (9.8745 - 10) - (9.9368 - 10)$$
$$= 1.4332,$$
$$a = 27.11 \text{ ft.}$$
$$\frac{\sin \beta}{b} = \frac{\sin \gamma}{c}; \ b = \frac{c \sin \beta}{\sin \gamma} = \frac{(31.3)(\sin 71°40')}{\sin 59°50'} \ .$$
$$\log b = \log 31.3 + \log (\sin 71°40') - \log \sin 59°50'$$
$$= 1.4955 + (9.9774 - 10) - (9.9368 - 10)$$
$$= 1.5361,$$
$$b = 34.36 \text{ ft.}$$

Common logarithms can also be used in finding the area of a triangle.

Table I

VALUES OF CIRCULAR FUNCTIONS

Real Number x or θ radians	θ degrees	sin x or sin θ	csc x or csc θ	tan x or tan θ	cot x or cot θ	sec x or sec θ	cos x or cos θ
0.00	0° 00′	0.0000	No value	0.0000	No value	1.000	1.000
.01	0° 34′	.0100	100.0	.0100	100.0	1.000	1.000
.02	1° 09′	.0200	50.00	.0200	49.99	1.000	0.9998
.03	1° 43′	.0300	33.34	.0300	33.32	1.000	0.9996
.04	2° 18′	.0400	25.01	.0400	24.99	1.001	0.9992
0.05	2° 52′	0.0500	20.01	0.0500	19.98	1.001	0.9988
.06	3° 26′	.0600	16.68	.0601	16.65	1.002	.9982
.07	4° 01′	.0699	14.30	.0701	14.26	1.002	.9976
.08	4° 35′	.0799	12.51	.0802	12.47	1.003	.9968
.09	5° 09′	.0899	11.13	.0902	11.08	1.004	.9960
0.10	5° 44′	0.0998	10.02	0.1003	9.967	1.005	0.9950
.11	6° 18′	.1098	9.109	.1104	9.054	1.006	.9940
.12	6° 53′	.1197	8.353	.1206	8.293	1.007	.9928
.13	7° 27′	.1296	7.714	.1307	7.649	1.009	.9916
.14	8° 01′	.1395	7.166	.1409	7.096	1.010	.9902
0.15	8° 36′	0.1494	6.692	0.1511	6.617	1.011	0.9888
.16	9° 10′	.1593	6.277	.1614	6.197	1.013	.9872
.17	9° 44′	.1692	5.911	.1717	5.826	1.015	.9856
.18	10° 19′	.1790	5.586	.1820	5.495	1.016	.9838
.19	10° 53′	.1889	5.295	.1923	5.200	1.018	.9820
0.20	11° 28′	0.1987	5.033	0.2027	4.933	1.020	0.9801
.21	12° 02′	.2085	4.797	.2131	4.692	1.022	.9780
.22	12° 36′	.2182	4.582	.2236	4.472	1.025	.9759
.23	13° 11′	.2280	4.386	.2341	4.271	1.027	.9737
.24	13° 45′	.2377	4.207	.2447	4.086	1.030	.9713
0.25	14° 19′	0.2474	4.042	0.2553	3.916	1.032	0.9689
.26	14° 54′	.2571	3.890	.2660	3.759	1.035	.9664
.27	15° 28′	.2667	3.749	.2768	3.613	1.038	.9638
.28	16° 03′	.2764	3.619	.2876	3.478	1.041	.9611
.29	16° 37′	.2860	3.497	.2984	3.351	1.044	.9582
0.30	17° 11′	0.2955	3.384	0.3093	3.233	1.047	0.9553
.31	17° 46′	.3051	3.278	.3203	3.122	1.050	.9523
.32	18° 20′	.3146	3.179	.3314	3.018	1.053	.9492
.33	18° 54′	.3240	3.086	.3425	2.920	1.057	.9460
.34	19° 29′	.3335	2.999	.3537	2.827	1.061	.9428
0.35	20° 03′	0.3429	2.916	0.3650	2.740	1.065	0.9394
.36	20° 38′	.3523	2.839	.3764	2.657	1.068	.9359
.37	21° 12′	.3616	2.765	.3879	2.578	1.073	.9323
.38	21° 46′	.3709	2.696	.3994	2.504	1.077	.9287
.39	22° 21′	.3802	2.630	.4111	2.433	1.081	.9249
0.40	22° 55′	0.3894	2.568	0.4228	2.365	1.086	0.9211
.41	23° 29′	.3986	2.509	.4346	2.301	1.090	.9171
.42	24° 04′	.4078	2.452	.4466	2.239	1.095	.9131
.43	24° 38′	.4169	2.399	.4586	2.180	1.100	.9090
.44	25° 13′	.4259	2.348	.4708	2.124	1.105	.9048
0.45	25° 47′	0.4350	2.299	0.4831	2.070	1.111	0.9004

Table I (continued)

Real Number x or θ radians	θ degrees	$\sin x$ or $\sin \theta$	$\csc x$ or $\csc \theta$	$\tan x$ or $\tan \theta$	$\cot x$ or $\cot \theta$	$\sec x$ or $\sec \theta$	$\cos x$ or $\cos \theta$
0.45	25° 47′	0.4350	2.299	0.4831	2.070	1.111	0.9004
.46	26° 21′	.4439	2.253	.4954	2.018	1.116	.8961
.47	26° 56′	.4529	2.208	.5080	1.969	1.122	.8916
.48	27° 30′	.4618	2.166	.5206	1.921	1.127	.8870
.49	28° 04′	.4706	2.125	.5334	1.875	1.133	.8823
0.50	28° 39′	0.4794	2.086	0.5463	1.830	1.139	0.8776
.51	29° 13′	.4882	2.048	.5594	1.788	1.146	.8727
.52	29° 48′	.4969	2.013	.5726	1.747	1.152	.8678
.53	30° 22′	.5055	1.978	.5859	1.707	1.159	.8628
.54	30° 56′	.5141	1.945	.5994	1.668	1.166	.8577
0.55	31° 31′	0.5227	1.913	0.6131	1.631	1.173	0.8525
.56	32° 05′	.5312	1.883	.6269	1.595	1.180	.8473
.57	32° 40′	.5396	1.853	.6410	1.560	1.188	.8419
.58	33° 14′	.5480	1.825	.6552	1.526	1.196	.8365
.59	33° 48′	.5564	1.797	.6696	1.494	1.203	.8309
0.60	34° 23′	0.5646	1.771	0.6841	1.462	1.212	0.8253
.61	34° 57′	.5729	1.746	.6989	1.431	1.220	.8196
.62	35° 31′	.5810	1.721	.7139	1.401	1.229	.8139
.63	36° 06′	.5891	1.697	.7291	1.372	1.238	.8080
.64	36° 40′	.5972	1.674	.7445	1.343	1.247	.8021
0.65	37° 15′	0.6052	1.652	0.7602	1.315	1.256	0.7961
.66	37° 49′	.6131	1.631	.7761	1.288	1.266	.7900
.67	38° 23′	.6210	1.610	.7923	1.262	1.276	.7838
.68	38° 58′	.6288	1.590	.8087	1.237	1.286	.7776
.69	39° 32′	.6365	1.571	.8253	1.212	1.297	.7712
0.70	40° 06′	0.6442	1.552	0.8423	1.187	1.307	0.7648
.71	40° 41′	.6518	1.534	.8595	1.163	1.319	.7584
.72	41° 15′	.6594	1.517	.8771	1.140	1.330	.7518
.73	41° 50′	.6669	1.500	.8949	1.117	1.342	.7452
.74	42° 24′	.6743	1.483	.9131	1.095	1.354	.7385
0.75	42° 58′	0.6816	1.467	0.9316	1.073	1.367	0.7317
.76	43° 33′	.6889	1.452	.9505	1.052	1.380	.7248
.77	44° 07′	.6961	1.436	.9697	1.031	1.393	.7179
.78	44° 41′	.7033	1.422	.9893	1.011	1.407	.7109
.79	45° 16′	.7104	1.408	1.009	.9908	1.421	.7038
0.80	45° 50′	0.7174	1.394	1.030	0.9712	1.435	0.6967
.81	46° 25′	.7243	1.381	1.050	.9520	1.450	.6895
.82	46° 59′	.7311	1.368	1.072	.9331	1.466	.6822
.83	47° 33′	.7379	1.355	1.093	.9146	1.482	.6749
.84	48° 08′	.7446	1.343	1.116	.8964	1.498	.6675
0.85	48° 42′	0.7513	1.331	1.138	0.8785	1.515	0.6600
.86	49° 16′	.7578	1.320	1.162	.8609	1.533	.6524
.87	49° 51′	.7643	1.308	1.185	.8437	1.551	.6448
.88	50° 25′	.7707	1.297	1.210	.8267	1.569	.6372
.89	51° 00′	.7771	1.287	1.235	.8100	1.589	.6294
0.90	51° 34′	0.7833	1.277	1.260	0.7936	1.609	0.6216
.91	52° 08′	.7895	1.267	1.286	.7774	1.629	.6137
.92	52° 43′	.7956	1.257	1.313	.7615	1.651	.6058
.93	53° 17′	.8016	1.247	1.341	.7458	1.673	.5978
.94	53° 51′	.8076	1.238	1.369	.7303	1.696	.5898
0.95	54° 26′	0.8134	1.229	1.398	0.7151	1.719	0.5817

Table I (continued)

Real Number x or θ radians	θ degrees	$\sin x$ or $\sin \theta$	$\csc x$ or $\csc \theta$	$\tan x$ or $\tan \theta$	$\cot x$ or $\cot \theta$	$\sec x$ or $\sec \theta$	$\cos x$ or $\cos \theta$
0.95	54° 26′	0.8134	1.229	1.398	0.7151	1.719	0.5817
.96	55° 00′	.8192	1.221	1.428	.7001	1.744	.5735
.97	55° 35′	.8249	1.212	1.459	.6853	1.769	.5653
.98	56° 09′	.8305	1.204	1.491	.6707	1.795	.5570
.99	56° 43′	.8360	1.196	1.524	.6563	1.823	.5487
1.00	57° 18′	0.8415	1.188	1.557	0.6421	1.851	0.5403
1.01	57° 52′	.8468	1.181	1.592	.6281	1.880	.5319
1.02	58° 27′	.8521	1.174	1.628	.6142	1.911	.5234
1.03	59° 01′	.8573	1.166	1.665	.6005	1.942	.5148
1.04	59° 35′	.8624	1.160	1.704	.5870	1.975	.5062
1.05	60° 10′	0.8674	1.153	1.743	0.5736	2.010	0.4976
1.06	60° 44′	.8724	1.146	1.784	.5604	2.046	.4889
1.07	61° 18′	.8772	1.140	1.827	.5473	2.083	.4801
1.08	61° 53′	.8820	1.134	1.871	.5344	2.122	.4713
1.09	62° 27′	.8866	1.128	1.917	.5216	2.162	.4625
1.10	63° 02′	0.8912	1.122	1.965	0.5090	2.205	0.4536
1.11	63° 36′	.8957	1.116	2.014	.4964	2.249	.4447
1.12	64° 10′	.9001	1.111	2.066	.4840	2.295	.4357
1.13	64° 45′	.9044	1.106	2.120	.4718	2.344	.4267
1.14	65° 19′	.9086	1.101	2.176	.4596	2.395	.4176
1.15	65° 53′	0.9128	1.096	2.234	0.4475	2.448	0.4085
1.16	66° 28′	.9168	1.091	2.296	.4356	2.504	.3993
1.17	67° 02′	.9208	1.086	2.360	.4237	2.563	.3902
1.18	67° 37′	.9246	1.082	2.427	.4120	2.625	.3809
1.19	68° 11′	.9284	1.077	2.498	.4003	2.691	.3717
1.20	68° 45′	0.9320	1.073	2.572	0.3888	2.760	0.3624
1.21	69° 20′	.9356	1.069	2.650	.3773	2.833	.3530
1.22	69° 54′	.9391	1.065	2.733	.3659	2.910	.3436
1.23	70° 28′	.9425	1.061	2.820	.3546	2.992	.3342
1.24	71° 03′	.9458	1.057	2.912	.3434	3.079	.3248
1.25	71° 37′	0.9490	1.054	3.010	0.3323	3.171	0.3153
1.26	72° 12′	.9521	1.050	3.113	.3212	3.270	.3058
1.27	72° 46′	.9551	1.047	3.224	.3102	3.375	.2963
1.28	72° 20′	.9580	1.044	3.341	.2993	3.488	.2867
1.29	73° 55′	.9608	1.041	3.467	.2884	3.609	.2771
1.30	74° 29′	0.9636	1.038	3.602	0.2776	3.738	0.2675
1.31	75° 03′	.9662	1.035	3.747	.2669	3.878	.2579
1.32	75° 38′	.9687	1.032	3.903	.2562	4.029	.2482
1.33	76° 12′	.9711	1.030	4.072	.2456	4.193	.2385
1.34	76° 47′	.9735	1.027	4.256	.2350	4.372	.2288
1.35	77° 21′	0.9757	1.025	4.455	0.2245	4.566	0.2190
1.36	77° 55′	.9779	1.023	4.673	.2140	4.779	.2092
1.37	78° 30′	.9799	1.021	4.913	.2035	5.014	.1994
1.38	79° 04′	.9819	1.018	5.177	.1931	5.273	.1896
1.39	79° 38′	.9837	1.017	5.471	.1828	5.561	.1798
1.40	80° 13′	0.9854	1.015	5.798	0.1725	5.883	0.1700
1.41	80° 47′	.9871	1.013	6.165	.1622	6.246	.1601
1.42	81° 22′	.9887	1.011	6.581	.1519	6.657	.1502
1.43	81° 56′	.9901	1.010	7.055	.1417	7.126	.1403
1.44	82° 30′	.9915	1.009	7.602	.1315	7.667	.1304
1.45	83° 05′	0.9927	1.007	8.238	0.1214	8.299	0.1205

Table I (continued)

Real Number x or θ radians	θ degrees	sin x or sin θ	csc x or csc θ	tan x or tan θ	cot x or cot θ	sec x or sec θ	cos x or cos θ
1.45	83° 05′	0.9927	1.007	8.238	0.1214	8.299	0.1205
1.46	83° 39′	.9939	1.006	8.989	.1113	9.044	.1106
1.47	84° 13′	.9949	1.005	9.887	.1011	9.938	.1006
1.48	84° 48′	.9959	1.004	10.98	.0910	11.03	.0907
1.49	85° 22′	.9967	1.003	12.35	.0810	12.39	.0807
1.50	85° 57′	0.9975	1.003	14.10	0.0709	14.14	0.0707
1.51	86° 31′	.9982	1.002	16.43	.0609	16.46	.0608
1.52	87° 05′	.9987	1.001	19.67	.0508	19.69	.0508
1.53	87° 40′	.9992	1.001	24.50	.0408	24.52	.0408
1.54	88° 14′	.9995	1.000	32.46	.0308	32.48	.0308
1.55	88° 49′	0.9998	1.000	48.08	0.0208	48.09	0.0208
1.56	89° 23′	.9999	1.000	92.62	.0108	92.63	.0108
1.57	89° 57′	1.000	1.000	1256	.0008	1256	.0008

Table II

VALUES OF TRIGONOMETRIC FUNCTIONS

Angle θ Degrees	Radians	sin θ	csc θ	tan θ	cot θ	sec θ	cos θ		
0° 00′	.0000	.0000	No value	.0000	No value	1.000	1.0000	1.5708	90° 00′
10	029	029	343.8	029	343.8	000	000	679	50
20	058	058	171.9	058	171.9	000	000	650	40
30	087	087	114.6	087	114.6	000	1.0000	621	30
40	116	116	85.95	116	85.94	000	.9999	592	20
50	145	145	68.76	145	68.75	000	999	563	10
1° 00′	.0175	.0175	57.30	.0175	57.29	1.000	.9998	1.5533	89° 00′
10	204	204	49.11	204	49.10	000	998	504	50
20	233	233	42.98	233	42.96	000	997	475	40
30	262	262	38.20	262	38.19	000	997	446	30
40	291	291	34.38	291	34.37	000	996	417	20
50	320	320	31.26	320	31.24	001	995	388	10
2° 00′	.0349	.0349	28.65	.0349	28.64	1.001	.9994	1.5359	88° 00′
10	378	378	26.45	378	26.43	001	993	330	50
20	407	407	24.56	407	24.54	001	992	301	40
30	436	436	22.93	437	22.90	001	990	272	30
40	465	465	21.49	466	21.47	001	989	243	20
50	495	494	20.23	495	20.21	001	988	213	10
3° 00′	.0524	.0523	19.11	.0524	19.08	1.001	.9986	1.5184	87° 00′
10	553	552	18.10	553	18.07	002	985	155	50
20	582	581	17.20	582	17.17	002	983	126	40
30	611	610	16.38	612	16.35	002	981	097	30
40	640	640	15.64	641	15.60	002	980	068	20
50	669	669	14.96	670	14.92	002	978	039	10
4° 00′	.0698	.0698	14.34	.0699	14.30	1.002	.9976	1.5010	86° 00′
10	727	727	13.76	729	13.73	003	974	981	50
20	756	765	13.23	758	13.20	003	971	952	40
30	785	785	12.75	787	12.71	003	969	923	30
40	814	814	12.29	816	12.25	003	967	893	20
50	844	843	11.87	846	11.83	004	964	864	10
5° 00′	.0873	.0872	11.47	0.875	11.43	1.004	.9962	1.4835	85° 00′
10	902	901	11.10	904	11.06	004	959	806	50
20	931	929	10.76	934	10.71	004	957	777	40
30	960	958	10.43	963	10.39	005	954	748	30
40	.0989	.0987	10.13	.0992	10.08	005	951	719	20
50	.1018	.1016	9.839	.1022	9.788	005	948	690	10
6° 00′	.1047	.1045	9.567	.1051	9.514	1.006	.9945	1.4661	84° 00′
10	076	074	9.309	080	9.255	006	942	632	50
20	105	103	9.065	110	9.010	006	939	603	40
30	134	132	8.834	139	8.777	006	936	573	30
40	164	161	8.614	169	8.556	007	932	544	20
50	193	190	8.405	198	8.345	007	929	515	10
7° 00′	.1222	.1219	8.206	.1228	8.144	1.008	.9925	1.4486	83° 00′
10	251	248	8.016	257	7.953	008	922	457	50
20	280	276	7.834	287	7.770	008	918	428	40
30	309	305	7.661	317	7.596	009	914	399	30
40	338	334	7.496	346	7.429	009	911	370	20
50	367	363	7.337	376	7.269	009	907	341	10
8° 00′	.1396	.1392	7.185	.1405	7.115	1.010	.9903	1.4312	82° 00′
		cos θ	sec θ	cot θ	tan θ	csc θ	sin θ	Radians	Degrees
								Angle θ	

Table II (continued)

Angle θ									
Degrees	Radians	sin θ	csc θ	tan θ	cot θ	sec θ	cos θ		
8° 00′	.1396	.1392	7.185	.1405	7.115	1.010	.9903	1.4312	82° 00′
10	425	421	7.040	435	6.968	010	899	283	50
20	454	449	6.900	465	827	011	894	254	40
30	484	478	765	495	691	011	890	224	30
40	513	507	636	524	561	012	886	195	20
50	542	536	512	554	435	012	881	166	10
9° 00′	.1571	.1564	6.392	.1584	6.314	1.012	.9877	1.4137	81° 00′
10	600	593	277	614	197	013	872	108	50
20	629	622	166	644	6.084	013	868	079	40
30	658	650	6.059	673	5.976	014	863	050	30
40	687	679	5.955	703	871	014	858	1.4021	20
50	716	708	855	733	769	015	853	1.3992	10
10° 00′	.1745	.1736	5.759	.1763	5.671	1.015	.9848	1.3963	80° 00′
10	774	765	665	793	576	016	843	934	50
20	804	794	575	823	485	016	838	904	40
30	833	822	487	853	396	017	833	875	30
40	862	851	403	883	309	018	827	846	20
50	891	880	320	914	226	018	822	817	10
11° 00′	.1920	.1908	5.241	.1944	5.145	1.019	.9816	1.3788	79° 00′
10	949	937	164	.1974	5.066	019	811	759	50
20	.1978	965	089	.2004	4.989	020	805	730	40
30	.2007	.1994	5.016	035	915	020	799	701	30
40	036	.2022	4.945	065	843	021	793	672	20
50	065	051	876	095	773	022	787	643	10
12° 00′	.2094	.2079	4.810	.2126	4.705	1.022	.9781	1.3614	78° 00′
10	123	108	745	156	638	023	775	584	50
20	153	136	682	186	574	024	769	555	40
30	182	164	620	217	511	024	763	526	30
40	211	193	560	247	449	025	757	497	20
50	240	221	502	278	390	026	750	468	10
13° 00′	.2269	.2250	4.445	.2309	4.331	1.026	.9744	1.3439	77° 00′
10	298	278	390	339	275	027	737	410	50
20	327	306	336	370	219	028	730	381	40
30	356	334	284	401	165	028	724	352	30
40	385	363	232	432	113	029	717	323	20
50	414	391	.182	462	061	030	710	294	10
14° 00′	.2443	.2419	4.134	.2493	4.011	1.031	.9703	1.3265	76° 00′
10	473	447	086	524	3.962	031	696	235	50
20	502	476	4.039	555	914	032	689	206	40
30	531	504	3.994	586	867	033	681	177	30
40	560	532	950	617	821	034	674	148	20
50	589	560	906	648	776	034	667	119	10
15° 00′	.2618	.2588	3.864	.2679	3.732	1.035	.9659	1.3090	75° 00′
10	647	616	822	711	689	036	652	061	50
20	676	644	782	742	647	037	644	032	40
30	705	672	742	773	606	038	636	1.3003	30
40	734	700	703	805	566	039	628	1.2974	20
50	763	728	665	836	526	039	621	945	10
16° 00′	.2793	.2756	3.628	.2867	3.487	1.040	.9613	1.2915	74° 00′
		cos θ	sec θ	cot θ	tan θ	csc θ	sin θ	Radians	Degrees
								Angle θ	

Table II (continued)

Degrees	Radians	sin θ	csc θ	tan θ	cot θ	sec θ	cos θ		
16° 00′	.2793	.2756	3.628	.2867	3.487	1.040	.9613	1.2915	74° 00′
10	822	784	592	899	450	041	605	886	50
20	851	812	556	931	412	042	596	857	40
30	880	840	521	962	376	043	588	828	30
40	909	868	487	.2944	340	044	580	799	20
50	938	896	453	.3026	305	045	572	770	10
17° 00′	.2967	.2924	3.420	.3057	3.271	1.046	.9563	1.2741	73° 00′
10	.2996	952	388	089	237	047	555	712	50
20	.3025	.2979	357	121	204	048	546	683	40
30	054	.3007	326	153	172	048	537	654	30
40	083	035	295	185	140	049	528	625	20
50	113	062	265	217	108	050	520	595	10
18° 00′	.3142	.3090	3.236	.3249	3.078	1.051	.9511	1.2566	72° 00′
10	171	118	207	281	047	052	502	537	50
20	200	145	179	314	3.018	053	492	508	40
30	229	173	152	346	2.989	054	483	479	30
40	258	201	124	378	960	056	474	450	20
50	287	228	098	411	932	057	465	421	10
19° 00′	.3316	.3256	3.072	.3443	2.904	1.058	.9455	1.2392	71° 00′
10	345	283	046	476	877	059	446	363	50
20	374	311	3.021	508	850	060	436	334	40
30	403	338	2.996	541	824	061	426	305	30
40	432	365	971	574	798	062	417	275	20
50	462	393	947	607	773	063	407	246	10
20° 00′	.3491	.3420	2.924	.3640	2.747	1.064	.9397	1.2217	70° 00′
10	520	448	901	673	723	065	387	188	50
20	549	475	878	706	699	066	377	159	40
30	578	502	855	739	675	068	367	130	30
40	607	529	833	772	651	069	356	101	20
50	636	557	812	805	628	070	346	072	10
21° 00′	.3665	.3584	2.790	.3839	2.605	1.071	.9336	1.2043	69° 00′
10	694	611	769	872	583	072	325	1.2014	50
20	723	638	749	906	560	074	315	985	40
30	752	665	729	939	539	075	304	956	30
40	782	692	709	.3973	517	076	293	926	20
50	811	719	689	.4006	496	077	283	897	10
22° 00′	.3840	.3746	2.669	.4040	2.475	1.079	.9272	1.1868	68° 00′
10	869	773	650	074	455	080	261	839	50
20	898	800	632	108	434	081	250	810	40
30	927	827	613	142	414	082	239	781	30
40	956	854	595	176	394	084	228	752	20
50	985	881	577	210	375	085	216	723	10
23° 00′	.4014	.3907	2.559	.4245	2.356	1.086	.9205	1.1694	67° 00′
10	043	934	542	279	337	088	194	665	50
20	072	961	525	314	318	089	182	636	40
30	102	.3987	508	348	300	090	171	606	30
40	131	.4014	491	383	282	092	159	577	20
50	160	041	475	417	264	093	147	548	10
24° 00′	.4189	.4067	2.459	.4452	2.246	1.095	.9135	1.1519	66° 00′
		cos θ	sec θ	cot θ	tan θ	csc θ	sin θ	Radians	Degrees

Angle θ

Table II (continued)

Degrees	Radians	sin θ	csc θ	tan θ	cot θ	sec θ	cos θ		
24° 00'	.4189	.4067	2.459	.4452	2.246	1.095	.9135	1.1519	66° 00'
10	218	094	443	487	229	096	124	490	50
20	247	120	427	522	211	097	112	461	40
30	276	147	411	557	194	099	100	432	30
40	305	173	396	592	177	100	088	403	20
50	334	200	381	628	161	102	075	374	10
25° 00'	.4363	.4226	2.366	.4663	2.145	1.103	.9063	1.1345	65° 00'
10	392	253	352	699	128	105	051	316	50
20	422	279	337	734	112	106	038	286	40
30	451	305	323	770	097	108	026	257	30
40	480	331	309	806	081	109	013	228	20
50	509	358	295	841	066	111	.9001	199	10
26° 00'	.4538	.4384	2.281	.4877	2.050	1.113	.8988	1.1170	64° 00'
10	567	410	268	913	035	114	975	141	50
20	596	436	254	950	020	116	962	112	40
30	625	462	241	.4986	2.006	117	949	083	30
40	654	488	228	.5022	1.991	119	936	054	20
50	683	514	215	059	977	121	923	1.1025	10
27° 00'	.4712	.4540	2.203	.5095	1.963	1.122	.8910	1.0996	63° 00'
10	741	566	190	132	949	124	897	966	50
20	771	592	178	169	935	126	884	937	40
30	800	617	166	206	921	127	870	908	30
40	829	643	154	243	907	129	857	879	20
50	858	669	142	280	894	131	843	850	10
28° 00'	.4887	.4695	2.130	.5317	1.881	1.133	.8829	1.0821	62° 00'
10	916	720	118	354	868	134	816	792	50
20	945	746	107	392	855	136	802	763	40
30	.4974	772	096	430	842	138	788	734	30
40	.5003	797	085	467	829	140	774	705	20
50	032	823	074	505	816	142	760	676	10
29° 00'	.5061	.4848	2.063	.5543	1.804	1.143	.8746	1.0647	61° 00'
10	091	874	052	581	792	145	732	617	50
20	120	899	041	619	780	147	718	588	40
30	149	924	031	658	767	149	704	559	30
40	178	950	020	696	756	151	689	530	20
50	207	.4975	010	735	744	153	675	501	10
30° 00'	.5236	.5000	2.000	.5774	1.732	1.155	.8660	1.0472	60° 00'
10	265	025	1.990	812	720	157	646	443	50
20	294	050	980	851	709	159	631	414	40
30	323	075	970	890	698	161	616	385	30
40	352	100	961	930	686	163	601	356	20
50	381	125	951	.5969	675	165	587	327	10
31° 00'	.5411	.5150	1.942	.6009	1.664	1.167	.8572	1.0297	59° 00'
10	440	175	932	048	653	169	557	268	50
20	469	200	923	088	643	171	542	239	40
30	498	225	914	128	632	173	526	210	30
40	527	250	905	168	621	175	51•1	181	20
50	556	275	896	208	611	177	496	152	10
32° 00'	.5585	.5299	1.887	.6249	1.600	1.179	.8480	1.0123	58° 00'
		cos θ	sec θ	cot θ	tan θ	csc θ	sin θ	Radians	Degrees

Angle θ

Table II (continued)

Angle θ									
Degrees	Radians	sin θ	csc θ	tan θ	cot θ	sec θ	cos θ		
32° 00′	.5585	.5299	1.887	.6249	1.600	1.179	.8480	1.0123	58° 00′
10	614	324	878	289	590	181	465	094	50
20	643	348	870	330	580	184	450	065	40
30	672	373	861	371	570	186	434	036	30
40	701	398	853	412	560	188	418	1.0007	20
50	730	422	844	453	550	190	403	.9977	10
33° 00′	.5760	.5446	1.836	.6494	1.540	1.192	.8387	.9948	57° 00′
10	789	471	828	536	530	195	371	919	50
20	818	495	820	577	520	197	355	890	40
30	847	519	812	619	511	199	339	861	30
40	876	544	804	661	501	202	323	832	20
50	905	568	796	703	492	204	307	803	10
34° 00′	.5934	.5592	1.788	.6745	1.483	1.206	.8290	.9774	56° 00′
10	963	616	781	787	473	209	274	745	50
20	.5992	640	773	830	464	211	258	716	40
30	.6021	664	766	873	455	213	241	687	30
40	050	688	758	916	446	216	225	657	20
50	080	712	751	.6959	437	218	208	628	10
35° 00′	.6109	.5736	1.743	.7002	1.428	1.221	.8192	.9599	55° 00′
10	138	760	736	046	419	223	175	570	50
20	167	783	729	089	411	226	158	541	40
30	196	807	722	133	402	228	141	512	30
40	225	831	715	177	393	231	124	483	20
50	254	854	708	221	385	233	107	454	10
36° 00′	.6283	.5878	1.701	.7265	1.376	1.236	.8090	.9425	54° 00′
10	312	901	695	310	368	239	073	396	50
20	341	925	688	355	360	241	056	367	40
30	370	948	681	400	351	244	039	338	30
40	400	972	675	445	343	247	021	308	20
50	429	.5995	668	490	335	249	.8004	279	10
37° 00′	.6458	.6018	1.662	.7536	1.327	1.252	.7986	.9250	53° 00′
10	487	041	655	581	319	255	696	221	50
20	516	065	649	627	311	258	951	192	40
30	545	088	643	673	303	260	934	163	30
40	574	111	636	720	295	263	916	134	20
50	603	134	630	766	288	266	898	105	10
38° 00′	.6632	.6157	1.624	.7813	1.280	1.269	.7880	.9076	52° 00′
10	661	180	618	860	272	272	862	047	50
20	690	202	612	907	265	275	844	.9018	40
30	720	225	606	.7954	257	278	826	.8988	30
40	749	248	601	.8002	250	281	808	959	20
50	778	271	595	050	242	284	790	930	10
39° 00′	.6807	.6293	1.589	.8098	1.235	1.287	.7771	.8901	51° 00′
10	836	316	583	146	228	290	753	872	50
20	865	338	578	195	220	293	735	843	40
30	894	361	572	243	213	296	716	814	30
40	923	383	567	292	206	299	698	785	20
50	952	406	561	342	199	302	679	756	10
40° 00′	.6981	.6428	1.556	.8391	1.192	1.305	.7660	.8727	50° 00′
		cos θ	sec θ	cot θ	tan θ	csc θ	sin θ	Radians	Degrees
								Angle θ	

Table II (continued)

Angle θ									
Degrees	Radians	sin θ	csc θ	tan θ	cot θ	sec θ	cos θ		
40° 00′	.6981	.6428	1.556	.8391	1.192	1.305	.7660	.8727	50° 00′
10	.7010	450	550	441	185	309	642	698	50
20	039	472	545	491	178	312	623	668	40
30	069	494	540	541	171	315	604	639	30
40	098	517	535	591	164	318	585	610	20
50	127	539	529	642	157	322	566	581	10
41° 00′	.7156	.6561	1.524	.8693	1.150	1.325	.7547	.8552	49° 00′
10	185	583	519	744	144	328	528	523	50
20	214	604	514	796	137	332	509	494	40
30	243	626	509	847	130	335	490	465	30
40	272	648	504	899	124	339	470	436	20
50	301	670	499	.8952	117	342	451	407	10
42° 00′	.7330	.6691	1.494	.9004	1.111	1.346	.7431	.8378	48° 00′
10	359	713	490	057	104	349	412	348	50
20	389	734	485	110	098	353	392	319	40
30	418	756	480	163	091	356	373	290	30
40	447	777	476	217	085	360	353	261	20
50	476	799	471	271	079	364	333	232	10
43° 00′	.7505	.6820	1.466	.9325	1.072	1.367	.7314	.8203	47° 00′
10	534	841	462	380	066	371	294	174	50
20	563	862	457	435	060	375	274	145	40
30	592	884	453	490	054	379	254	116	30
40	621	905	448	545	048	382	234	087	20
50	650	926	444	601	042	386	214	058	10
44° 00′	.7679	.6947	1.440	.9657	1.036	1.390	.7193	.8029	46° 00′
10	709	967	435	713	030	394	173	.7999	50
20	738	.6988	431	770	024	398	153	970	40
30	767	.7009	427	827	018	402	133	941	30
40	796	030	423	884	012	406	112	912	20
50	825	050	418	.9942	006	410	092	883	10
45° 00′	.7854	.7071	1.414	1.000	1.000	1.414	.7071	.7854	45° 00′
		cos θ	sec θ	cot θ	tan θ	csc θ	sin θ	Radians	Degrees
								Angle θ	

Table III

COMMON LOGARITHMS

x	0	1	2	3	4	5	6	7	8	9
1.0	.0000	.0043	.0086	.0128	.0170	.0212	.0253	.0294	.0334	.0374
1.1	.0414	.0453	.0492	.0531	.0569	.0607	.0645	.0682	.0719	.0755
1.2	.0792	.0828	.0864	.0899	.0934	.0969	.1004	.1038	.1072	.1106
1.3	.1139	.1173	.1206	.1239	.1271	.1303	.1335	.1367	.1399	.1430
1.4	.1461	.1492	.1523	.1553	.1584	.1614	.1644	.1673	.1703	.1732
1.5	.1761	.1790	.1818	.1847	.1875	.1903	.1931	.1959	.1987	.2014
1.6	.2041	.2068	.2095	.2122	.2148	.2175	.2201	.2227	.2253	.2279
1.7	.2304	.2330	.2355	.2380	.2405	.2430	.2455	.2480	.2504	.2529
1.8	.2553	.2577	.2601	.2625	.2648	.2672	.2695	.2718	.2742	.2765
1.9	.2788	.2810	.2833	.2856	.2878	.2900	.2923	.2945	.2967	.2989
2.0	.3010	.3032	.3054	.3075	.3096	.3118	.3139	.3160	.3181	.3201
2.1	.3222	.3243	.3263	.3284	.3304	.3324	.3345	.3365	.3385	.3404
2.2	.3424	.3444	.3464	.3483	.3502	.3522	.3541	.3560	.3579	.3598
2.3	.3617	.3636	.3655	.3674	.3692	.3711	.3729	.3747	.3766	.3784
2.4	.3802	.3820	.3838	.3856	.3874	.3892	.3909	.3927	.3945	.3962
2.5	.3979	.3997	.4014	.4031	.4048	.4065	.4082	.4099	.4116	.4133
2.6	.4150	.4166	.4183	.4200	.4216	.4232	.4249	.4265	.4281	.4298
2.7	.4314	.4330	.4346	.4362	.4378	.4393	.4409	.4425	.4440	.4456
2.8	.4472	.4487	.4502	.4518	.4533	.4548	.4564	.4579	.4594	.4609
2.9	.4624	.4639	.4654	.4669	.4683	.4698	.4713	.4728	.4742	.4757
3.0	.4771	.4786	.4800	.4814	.4829	.4843	.4857	.4871	.4886	.4900
3.1	.4914	.4928	.4942	.4955	.4969	.4983	.4997	.5011	.5024	.5038
3.2	.5051	.5065	.5079	.5092	.5105	.5119	.5132	.5145	.5159	.5172
3.3	.5185	.5198	.5211	.5224	.5237	.5250	.5263	.5276	.5289	.5302
3.4	.5315	.5328	.5340	.5353	.5366	.5378	.5391	.5403	.5416	.5428
3.5	.5441	.5453	.5465	.5478	.5490	.5502	.5514	.5527	.5539	.5551
3.6	.5563	.5575	.5587	.5599	.5611	.5623	.5635	.5647	.5658	.5670
3.7	.5682	.5694	.5705	.5717	.5729	.5740	.5752	.5763	.5775	.5786
3.8	.5798	.5809	.5821	.5832	.5843	.5855	.5866	.5877	.5888	.5899
3.9	.5911	.5922	.5933	.5944	.5955	.5966	.5977	.5988	.5999	.6010
4.0	.6021	.6031	.6042	.6053	.6064	.6075	.6085	.6096	.6107	.6117
4.1	.6128	.6138	.6149	.6160	.6170	.6180	.6191	.6201	.6212	.6222
4.2	.6232	.6243	.6253	.6263	.6274	.6284	.6294	.6304	.6314	.6325
4.3	.6335	.6345	.6355	.6365	.6375	.6385	.6395	.6405	.6415	.6425
4.4	.6435	.6444	.6454	.6464	.6474	.6484	.6493	.6503	.6513	.6522
4.5	.6532	.6542	.6551	.6561	.6571	.6580	.6590	.6599	.6609	.6618
4.6	.6628	.6637	.6646	.6656	.6665	.6675	.6684	.6693	.6702	.6712
4.7	.6721	.6730	.6739	.6749	.6758	.6767	.6776	.6785	.6794	.6803
4.8	.6812	.6821	.6830	.6839	.6848	.6857	.6866	.6875	.6884	.6893
4.9	.6902	.6911	.6920	.6928	.6937	.6946	.6955	.6964	.6972	.6981
5.0	.6990	.6998	.7007	.7016	.7024	.7033	.7042	.7050	.7059	.7067
5.1	.7076	.7084	.7093	.7101	.7110	.7118	.7126	.7135	.7143	.7152
5.2	.7160	.7168	.7177	.7185	.7193	.7202	.7210	.7218	.7226	.7235
5.3	.7243	.7251	.7259	.7267	.7275	.7284	.7292	.7300	.7308	.7316
5.4	.7324	.7332	.7340	.7348	.7356	.7364	.7372	.7380	.7388	.7396
x	0	1	2	3	4	5	6	7	8	9

Table III (continued)

x	0	1	2	3	4	5	6	7	8	9
5.5	.7404	.7412	.7419	.7427	.7435	.7443	.7451	.7459	.7466	.7474
5.6	.7482	.7490	.7497	.7505	.7513	.7520	.7528	.7536	.7543	.7551
5.7	.7559	.7566	.7574	.7582	.7589	.7597	.7604	.7612	.7619	.7627
5.8	.7634	.7642	.7649	.7657	.7664	.7672	.7679	.7686	.7694	.7701
5.9	.7709	.7716	.7723	.7731	.7738	.7745	.7752	.7760	.7767	.7774
6.0	.7782	.7789	.7796	.7803	.7810	.7818	.7825	.7832	.7839	.7846
6.1	.7853	.7860	.7868	.7875	.7882	.7889	.7896	.7903	.7910	.7917
6.2	.7924	.7931	.7938	.7945	.7952	.7959	.7966	.7973	.7980	.7987
6.3	.7993	.8000	.8007	.8014	.8021	.8028	.8035	.8041	.8048	.8055
6.4	.8062	.8069	.8075	.8082	.8089	.8096	.8102	.8109	.8116	.8122
6.5	.8129	.8136	.8142	.8149	.8156	.8162	.8169	.8176	.8182	.8189
6.6	.8195	.8202	.8209	.8215	.8222	.8228	.8235	.8241	.8248	.8254
6.7	.8261	.8267	.8274	.8280	.8287	.8293	.8299	.8306	.8312	.8319
6.8	.8325	.8331	.8338	.8344	.8351	.8357	.8363	.8370	.8376	.8382
6.9	.8388	.8395	.8401	.8407	.8414	.8420	.8426	.8432	.8439	.8445
7.0	.8451	.8457	.8463	.8470	.8476	.8482	.8488	.8494	.8500	.8506
7.1	.8513	.8519	.8525	.8531	.8537	.8543	.8549	.8555	.8561	.8567
7.2	.8573	.8579	.8585	.8591	.8597	.8603	.8609	.8615	.8621	.8627
7.3	.8633	.8639	.8645	.8651	.8657	.8663	.8669	.8675	.8681	.8686
7.4	.8692	.8698	.8704	.8710	.8716	.8722	.8727	.8733	.8739	.8745
7.5	.8751	.8756	.8762	.8768	.8774	.8779	.8785	.8791	.8797	.8802
7.6	.8808	.8814	.8820	.8825	.8831	.8837	.8842	.8848	.8854	.8859
7.7	.8865	.8871	.8876	.8882	.8887	.8893	.8899	.8904	.8910	.8915
7.8	.8921	.8927	.8932	.8938	.8943	.8949	.8954	.8960	.8965	.8971
7.9	.8976	.8982	.8987	.8993	.8998	.9004	.9009	.9015	.9020	.9025
8.0	.9031	.9036	.9042	.9047	.9053	.9058	.9063	.9069	.9074	.9079
8.1	.9085	.9090	.9096	.9101	.9106	.9112	.9117	.9122	.9128	.9133
8.2	.9138	.9143	.9149	.9154	.9159	.9165	.9170	.9175	.9180	.9186
8.3	.9191	.9196	.9201	.9206	.9212	.9217	.9222	.9227	.9232	.9238
8.4	.9243	.9248	.9253	.9258	.9263	.9269	.9274	.9279	.9284	.9289
8.5	.9294	.9299	.9304	.9309	.9315	.9320	.9325	.9330	.9335	.9340
8.6	.9345	.9350	.9355	.9360	.9365	.9370	.9375	.9380	.9385	.9390
8.7	.9395	.9400	.9405	.9410	.9415	.9420	.9425	.9430	.9435	.9440
8.8	.9445	.9450	.9455	.9460	.9465	.9469	.9474	.9479	.9484	.9489
8.9	.9494	.9499	.9504	.9509	.9513	.9518	.9523	.9528	.9533	.9538
9.0	.9542	.9547	.9552	.9557	.9562	.9566	.9571	.9576	.9581	.9586
9.1	.9590	.9595	.9600	.9605	.9609	.9614	.9619	.9624	.9628	.9633
9.2	.9638	.9643	.9647	.9652	.9657	.9661	.9666	.9671	.9675	.9680
9.3	.9685	.9689	.9694	.9699	.9703	.9708	.9713	.9717	.9722	.9727
9.4	.9731	.9736	.9741	.9745	.9750	.9754	.9759	.9763	.9768	.9773
9.5	.9777	.9782	.9786	.9791	.9795	.9800	.9805	.9809	.9814	.9818
9.6	.9823	.9827	.9832	.9836	.9841	.9845	.9850	.9854	.9859	.9863
9.7	.9868	.9872	.9877	.9881	.9886	.9890	.9894	.9899	.9903	.9908
9.8	.9912	.9917	.9921	.9926	.9930	.9934	.9939	.9943	.9948	.9952
9.9	.9956	.9961	.9965	.9969	.9974	.9978	.9983	.9987	.9991	.9996
x	0	1	2	3	4	5	6	7	8	9

Table IV

LOGARITHMS OF VALUES OF TRIGONOMETRIC FUNCTIONS

Angle	L Sin	d	L Tan	cd	L Cot	d	L Cos	
0° 0′	——		——		——	0	10.0000	90° 0′
10′	7.4637	3011	7.4637	3011	12.5363	0	10.0000	50′
20′	7.7648	1760	7.7648	1761	12.2352	0	10.0000	40′
30′	7.9408	1250	7.9409	1249	12.0591	0	10.0000	30′
40′	8.0658	969	8.0658	969	11.9342	0	10.0000	20′
50′	8.1627	792	8.1627	792	11.8373	1	10.0000	10′
1° 0′	8.2419	669	8.2419	670	11.7581	0	9.9999	89° 0′
10′	8.3088	580	8.3089	580	11.6911	0	9.9999	50′
20′	8.3668	511	8.3669	512	11.6331	0	9.9999	40′
30′	8.4179	458	8.4181	457	11.5819	1	9.9999	30′
40′	8.4637	413	8.4638	415	11.5362	0	9.9998	20′
50′	8.5050	378	8.5053	378	11.4947	1	9.9998	10′
2° 0′	8.5428	348	8.5431	348	11.4569	0	9.9997	88° 0′
10′	8.5776	321	8.5779	322	11.4221	1	9.9997	50′
20′	8.6097	300	8.6101	300	11.3899	0	9.9996	40′
30′	8.6397	280	8.6401	281	11.3599	1	9.9996	30′
40′	8.6677	263	8.6682	263	11.3318	0	9.9995	20′
50′	8.6940	248	8.6945	249	11.3055	1	9.9995	10′
3° 0′	8.7188	235	8.7194	235	11.2806	1	9.9994	87° 0′
10′	8.7423	222	8.7429	223	11.2571	0	9.9993	50′
20′	8.7645	212	8.7652	213	11.2348	1	9.9993	40′
30′	8.7857	202	8.7865	202	11.2135	1	9.9992	30′
40′	8.8059	192	8.8067	194	11.1933	1	9.9991	20′
50′	8.8251	185	8.8261	185	11.1739	1	9.9990	10′
4° 0′	8.8436	177	8.8446	178	11.1554	0	9.9989	86° 0′
10′	8.8613	170	8.8624	171	11.1376	1	9.9989	50′
20′	8.8783	163	8.8795	165	11.1205	1	9.9988	40′
30′	8.8946	158	8.8960	158	11.1040	1	9.9987	30′
40′	8.9104	152	8.9118	154	11.0882	1	9.9986	20′
50′	8.9256	147	8.9272	148	11.0728	2	9.9985	10′
5° 0′	8.9403	142	8.9420	143	11.0580	1	9.9983	85° 0′
10′	8.9545	137	8.9563	138	11.0437	1	9.9982	50′
20′	8.9682	134	8.9701	135	11.0299	1	9.9981	40′
30′	8.9816	129	8.9836	130	11.0164	1	9.9980	30′
40′	8.9945	125	8.9966	127	11.0034	2	9.9979	20′
50′	9.0070	122	9.0093	123	10.9907	1	9.9977	10′
6° 0′	9.0192	119	9.0216	120	10.9784	1	9.9976	84° 0′
10′	9.0311	115	9.0336	117	10.9664	2	9.9975	50′
20′	9.0426	113	9.0453	114	10.9547	1	9.9973	40′
30′	9.0539	109	9.0567	111	10.9433	1	9.9972	30′
40′	9.0648	107	9.0678	108	10.9322	2	9.9971	20′
50′	9.0755	104	9.0786	105	10.9214	1	9.9969	10′
7° 0′	9.0859	102	9.0891	104	10.9109	2	9.9968	83° 0′
10′	9.0961	99	9.0995	101	10.9005	2	9.9966	50′
20′	9.1060	97	9.1096	98	10.8904	2	9.9964	40′
30′	9.1157	95	9.1194	97	10.8806	1	9.9963	30′
40′	9.1252	93	9.1291	94	10.8709	2	9.9961	20′
50′	9.1345	91	9.1385	93	10.8615	2	9.9959	10′
8° 0′	9.1436	89	9.1478	91	10.8522	1	9.9958	82° 0′
10′	9.1525	87	9.1569	89	10.8431	2	9.9956	50′
20′	9.1612	85	9.1658	87	10.8342	2	9.9954	40′
30′	9.1697	84	9.1745	86	10.8255	2	9.9952	30′
40′	9.1781	82	9.1831	84	10.8169	2	9.9950	20′
50′	9.1863	80	9.1915	82	10.8085	2	9.9948	10′
9° 0′	9.1943		9.1997		10.8003		9.9946	81° 0′
	L Cos	d	L Cot	cd	L Tan	d	L Sin	Angle

These tables give the logarithms increased by 10. Hence in each case 10 should be subtracted.

Table IV (continued)

Angle	L Sin	d	L Tan	cd	L Cot	d	L Cos	
9 ° 0′	9.1943		9.1997		10.8003		9.9946	81° 0′
		79		81		2		
10′	9.2022		9.2078		10.7922		9.9944	50′
		78		80		2		
20′	9.2100		9.2158		10.7842		9.9942	40′
		76		78		2		
30′	9.2176		9.2236		10.7764		9.9940	30′
		75		77		2		
40′	9.2251		9.2313		10.7687		9.9938	20′
		73		76		2		
50′	9.2324		9.2389		10.7611		9.9936	10′
		73		74		2		
10° 0′	9.2397		9.2463		10.7537		9.9934	80° 0′
		71		73		3		
10′	9.2468		9.2536		10.7464		9.9931	50′
		70		73		2		
20′	9.2538		9.2609		10.7391		9.9929	40′
		68		71		2		
30′	9.2606		9.2680		10.7320		9.9927	30′
		68		70		3		
40′	9.2674		9.2750		10.7250		9.9924	20′
		66		69		2		
50′	9.2740		9.2819		10.7181		9.9922	10′
		66		68		3		
11° 0′	9.2806		9.2887		10.7113		9.9919	79° 0′
		64		66		2		
10′	9.2870		9.2953		10.7047		9.9917	50′
		64		67		3		
20′	9.2934		9.3020		10.6980		9.9914	40′
		63		65		2		
30′	9.2997		9.3085		10.6915		9.9912	30′
		61		64		3		
40′	9.3058		9.3149		10.6851		9.9909	20′
		61		63		2		
50′	9.3119		9.3212		10.6788		9.9907	10′
		60		63		3		
12° 0′	9.3179		9.3275		10.6725		9.9904	78° 0′
		59		61		3		
10′	9.3238		9.3336		10.6664		9.9901	50′
		58		61		2		
20′	9.3296		9.3397		10.6603		9.9899	40′
		57		61		3		
30′	9.3353		9.3458		10.6542		9.9896	30′
		57		59		3		
40′	9.3410		9.3517		10.6483		9.9893	20′
		56		59		3		
50′	9.3466		9.3576		10.6424		9.9890	10′
		55		58		3		
13° 0′	9.3521		9.3634		10.6366		9.9887	77° 0′
		54		57		3		
10′	9.3575		9.3691		10.6309		9.9884	50′
		54		57		3		
20′	9.3629		9.3748		10.6252		9.9881	40′
		53		56		3		
30′	9.3682		9.3804		10.6196		9.9878	30′
		52		55		3		
40′	9.3734		9.3859		10.6141		9.9875	20′
		52		55		3		
50′	9.3786		9.3914		10.6086		9.9872	10′
		51		54		3		
14° 0′	9.3837		9.3968		10.6032		9.9869	76° 0′
		50		53		3		
10′	9.3887		9.4021		10.5979		9.9866	50′
		50		53		3		
20′	9.3937		9.4074		10.5926		9.9863	40′
		49		53		4		
30′	9.3986		9.4127		10.5873		9.9859	30′
		49		51		3		
40′	9.4035		9.4178		10.5822		9.9856	20′
		48		52		3		
50′	9.4083		9.4230		10.5770		9.9853	10′
		47		51		4		
15° 0′	9.4130		9.4281		10.5719		9.9849	75° 0′
		47		50		3		
10′	9.4177		9.4331		10.5669		9.9846	50′
		46		50		3		
20′	9.4223		9.4381		10.5619		9.9843	40′
		46		49		4		
30′	9.4269		9.4430		10.5570		9.9839	30′
		45		49		3		
40′	9.4314		9.4479		10.5521		9.9836	20′
		45		48		4		
50′	9.4359		9.4527		10.5473		9.9832	10′
		44		48		4		
16° 0′	9.4403		9.4575		10.5425		9.9828	74° 0′
		44		47		3		
10′	9.4447		9.4622		10.5378		9.9825	50′
		44		47		4		
20′	9.4491		9.4669		10.5331		9.9821	40′
		42		47		4		
30′	9.4533		9.4716		10.5284		9.9817	30′
		43		46		3		
40′	9.4576		9.4762		10.5238		9.9814	20′
		42		46		4		
50′	9.4618		9.4808		10.5192		9.9810	10′
		41		45		4		
17° 0′	9.4659		9.4853		10.5147		9.9806	73° 0′
		41		45		4		
10′	9.4700		9.4898		10.5102		9.9802	50′
		41		45		4		
20′	9.4741		9.4943		10.5057		9.9798	40′
		40		44		4		
30′	9.4781		9.4987		10.5013		9.9794	30′
		40		44		4		
40′	9.4821		9.5031		10.4969		9.9790	20′
		40		44		4		
50′	9.4861		9.5075		10.4925		9.9786	10′
		39		43		4		
18° 0′	9.4900		9.5118		10.4882		9.9782	72° 0′
	L Cos	d	L Cot	cd	L Tan	d	L Sin	Angle

Table IV (continued)

Angle	L Sin	d	L Tan	cd	L Cot	d	L Cos	
18° 0′	9.4900		9.5118		10.4882		9.9782	72° 0′
10′	9.4939	39	9.5161	43	10.4839	4	9.9778	50′
20′	9.4977	38	9.5203	42	10.4797	4	9.9774	40′
30′	9.5015	38	9.5245	42	10.4755	4	9.9770	30′
40′	9.5052	37	9.5287	42	10.4713	5	9.9765	20′
50′	9.5090	38	9.5329	42	10.4671	4	9.9761	10′
		36		41		4		
19° 0′	9.5126		9.5370		10.4630		9.9757	71° 0′
10′	9.5163	37	9.5411	41	10.4589	5	9.9752	50′
20′	9.5199	36	9.5451	40	10.4549	4	9.9748	40′
30′	9.5235	36	9.5491	40	10.4509	5	9.9743	30′
40′	9.5270	35	9.5531	40	10.4469	4	9.9739	20′
50′	9.5306	36	9.5571	40	10.4429	5	9.9734	10′
		35		40		4		
20° 0′	9.5341		9.5611		10.4389		9.9730	70° 0′
10′	9.5375	34	9.5650	39	10.4350	5	9.9725	50′
20′	9.5409	34	9.5689	39	10.4311	4	9.9721	40′
30′	9.5443	34	9.5727	38	10.4273	5	9.9716	30′
40′	9.5477	34	9.5766	39	10.4234	5	9.9711	20′
50′	9.5510	33	9.5804	38	10.4196	5	9.9706	10′
		33		38		4		
21° 0′	9.5543		9.5842		10.4158		9.9702	69° 0′
10′	9.5576	33	9.5879	37	10.4121	5	9.9697	50′
20′	9.5609	33	9.5917	38	10.4083	5	9.9692	40′
30′	9.5641	32	9.5954	37	10.4046	5	9.9687	30′
40′	9.5673	32	9.5991	37	10.4009	5	9.9682	20′
50′	9.5704	31	9.6028	37	10.3972	5	9.9677	10′
		32		36		5		
22° 0′	9.5736		9.6064		10.3936		9.9672	68° 0′
10′	9.5767	31	9.6100	36	10.3900	5	9.9667	50′
20′	9.5798	31	9.6136	36	10.3864	6	9.9661	40′
30′	9.5828	30	9.6172	36	10.3828	5	9.9656	30′
40′	9.5859	31	9.6208	36	10.3792	5	9.9651	20′
50′	9.5889	30	9.6243	35	10.3757	5	9.9646	10′
		30		36		6		
23° 0′	9.5919		9.6279		10.3721		9.9640	67° 0′
10′	9.5948	29	9.6314	35	10.3686	5	9.9635	50′
20′	9.5978	30	9.6348	34	10.3652	6	9.9629	40′
30′	9.6007	29	9.6383	35	10.3617	5	9.9624	30′
40′	9.6036	29	9.6417	34	10.3583	6	9.9618	20′
50′	9.6065	29	9.6452	35	10.3548	5	9.9613	10′
		28		34		6		
24° 0′	9.6093		9.6486		10.3514		9.9607	66° 0′
10′	9.6121	28	9.6520	34	10.3480	5	9.9602	50′
20′	9.6149	28	9.6553	33	10.3447	6	9.9596	40′
30′	9.6177	28	9.6587	34	10.3413	6	9.9590	30′
40′	9.6205	28	9.6620	33	10.3380	6	9.9584	20′
50′	9.6232	27	9.6654	34	10.3346	5	9.9579	10′
		27		33		6		
25° 0′	9.6259		9.6687		10.3313		9.9573	65° 0′
10′	9.6286	27	9.6720	33	10.3280	6	9.9567	50′
20′	9.6313	27	9.6752	32	10.3248	6	9.9561	40′
30′	9.6340	27	9.6785	33	10.3215	6	9.9555	30′
40′	9.6366	26	9.6817	32	10.3183	6	9.9549	20′
50′	9.6392	26	9.6850	33	10.3150	6	9.9543	10′
		26		32		6		
26° 0′	9.6418		9.6882		10.3118		9.9537	64° 0′
10′	9.6444	26	9.6914	32	10.3086	7	9.9530	50′
20′	9.6470	26	9.6946	32	10.3054	6	9.9524	40′
30′	9.6495	25	9.6977	31	10.3023	6	9.9518	30′
40′	9.6521	26	9.7009	32	10.2991	6	9.9512	20′
50′	9.6546	25	9.7040	31	10.2960	7	9.9505	10′
		24		32		6		
27° 0′	9.6570		9.7072		10.2928		9.9499	63° 0′
	L Cos	d	L Cot	cd	L Tan	d	L Sin	Angle

Table IV (continued)

Angle	L Sin	d	L Tan	cd	L Cot	d	L Cos	Angle
27° 0'	9.6570		9.7072		10.2928		9.9499	63° 0'
10'	9.6595	25	9.7103	31	10.2897	7	9.9492	50'
20'	9.6620	25	9.7134	31	10.2866	6	9.9486	40'
30'	9.6644	24	9.7165	31	10.2835	7	9.9479	30'
40'	9.6668	24	9.7196	31	10.2804	6	9.9473	20'
50'	9.6692	24	9.7226	30	10.2774	7	9.9466	10'
		24		31		7		
28° 0'	9.6716		9.7257		10.2743		9.9459	62° 0'
10'	9.6740	24	9.7287	30	10.2713	6	9.9453	50'
20'	9.6763	23	9.7317	30	10.2683	7	9.9446	40'
30'	9.6787	24	9.7348	31	10.2652	7	9.9439	30'
40'	9.6810	23	9.7378	30	10.2622	7	9.9432	20'
50'	9.6833	23	9.7408	30	10.2592	7	9.9425	10'
		23		30		7		
29° 0'	9.6856		9.7438		10.2562		9.9418	61° 0'
10'	9.6878	22	9.7467	29	10.2533	7	9.9411	50'
20'	9.6901	23	9.7497	30	10.2503	7	9.9404	40'
30'	9.6923	22	9.7526	29	10.2474	7	9.9397	30'
40'	9.6946	23	9.7556	30	10.2444	7	9.9390	20'
50'	9.6968	22	9.7585	29	10.2415	7	9.9383	10'
		22		29		8		
30° 0'	9.6990		9.7614		10.2386		9.9375	60° 0'
10'	9.7012	22	9.7644	30	10.2356	7	9.9368	50'
20'	9.7033	21	9.7673	29	10.2327	7	9.9361	40'
30'	9.7055	22	9.7701	28	10.2299	8	9.9353	30'
40'	9.7076	21	9.7730	29	10.2270	7	9.9346	20'
50'	9.7097	21	9.7759	29	10.2241	8	9.9338	10'
		21		29		7		
31° 0'	9.7118		9.7788		10.2212		9.9331	59° 0'
10'	9.7139	21	9.7816	28	10.2184	8	9.9323	50'
20'	9.7160	21	9.7845	29	10.2155	8	9.9315	40'
30'	9.7181	21	9.7873	28	10.2127	7	9.9308	30'
40'	9.7201	20	9.7902	29	10.2098	8	9.9300	20'
50'	9.7222	21	9.7930	28	10.2070	8	9.9292	10'
		20		28		8		
32° 0'	9.7242		9.7958		10.2042		9.9284	58° 0'
10'	9.7262	20	9.7986	28	10.2014	8	9.9276	50'
20'	9.7282	20	9.8014	28	10.1986	8	9.9268	40'
30'	9.7302	20	9.8042	28	10.1958	8	9.9260	30'
40'	9.7322	20	9.8070	28	10.1930	8	9.9252	20'
50'	9.7342	20	9.8097	27	10.1903	8	9.9244	10'
		19		28		8		
33° 0'	9.7361		9.8125		10.1875		9.9236	57° 0'
10'	9.7380	19	9.8153	28	10.1847	8	9.9228	50'
20'	9.7400	20	9.8180	27	10.1820	9	9.9219	40'
30'	9.7419	19	9.8208	28	10.1792	8	9.9211	30'
40'	9.7438	19	9.8235	27	10.1765	8	9.9203	20'
50'	9.7457	19	9.8263	28	10.1737	9	9.9194	10'
		19		27		8		
34° 0'	9.7476		9.8290		10.1710		9.9186	56° 0'
10'	9.7494	18	9.8317	27	10.1683	9	9.9177	50'
20'	9.7513	19	9.8344	27	10.1656	8	9.9169	40'
30'	9.7531	18	9.8371	27	10.1629	9	9.9160	30'
40'	9.7550	19	9.8398	27	10.1602	9	9.9151	20'
50'	9.7568	18	9.8425	27	10.1575	9	9.9142	10'
		18		27		8		
35° 0'	9.7586		9.8452		10.1548		9.9134	55° 0'
10'	9.7604	18	9.8479	27	10.1521	9	9.9125	50'
20'	9.7622	18	9.8506	27	10.1494	9	9.9116	40'
30'	9.7640	18	9.8533	27	10.1467	9	9.9107	30'
40'	9.7657	17	9.8559	26	10.1441	9	9.9098	20'
50'	9.7675	18	9.8586	27	10.1414	9	9.9089	10'
		17		27		9		
36° 0'	9.7692		9.8613		10.1387		9.9080	54° 0'
	L Cos	d	L Cot	cd	L Tan	d	L Sin	Angle

Table IV (continued)

Angle	L Sin	d	L Tan	cd	L Cot	d	L Cos	Angle
36° 0′	9.7692	18	9.8613	26	10.1387	10	9.9080	54° 0′
10′	9.7710	17	9.8639	27	10.1361	9	9.9070	50′
20′	9.7727	17	9.8666	26	10.1334	9	9.9061	40′
30′	9.7744	17	9.8692	26	10.1308	10	9.9052	30′
40′	9.7761	17	9.8718	27	10.1282	9	9.9042	20′
50′	9.7778	17	9.8745	26	10.1255	10	9.9033	10′
37° 0′	9.7795	16	9.8771	26	10.1229	9	9.9023	53° 0′
10′	9.7811	17	9.8797	27	10.1203	10	9.9014	50′
20′	9.7828	16	9.8824	26	10.1176	9	9.9004	40′
30′	9.7844	17	9.8850	26	10.1150	10	9.8995	30′
40′	9.7861	16	9.8876	26	10.1124	10	9.8985	20′
50′	9.7877	16	9.8902	26	10.1098	10	9.8975	10′
38° 0′	9.7893	17	9.8928	26	10.1072	10	9.8965	52° 0′
10′	9.7910	16	9.8954	26	10.1046	10	9.8955	50′
20′	9.7926	15	9.8980	26	10.1020	10	9.8945	40′
30′	9.7941	16	9.9006	26	10.0994	10	9.8935	30′
40′	9.7957	16	9.9032	26	10.0968	10	9.8925	20′
50′	9.7973	16	9.9058	26	10.0942	10	9.8915	10′
39° 0′	9.7989	15	9.9084	26	10.0916	10	9.8905	51° 0′
10′	9.8004	16	9.9110	25	10.0890	11	9.8895	50′
20′	9.8020	15	9.9135	26	10.0865	10	9.8884	40′
30′	9.8035	15	9.9161	26	10.0839	10	9.8874	30′
40′	9.8050	16	9.9187	25	10.0813	11	9.8864	20′
50′	9.8066	15	9.9212	26	10.0788	10	9.8853	10′
40° 0′	9.8081	15	9.9238	26	10.0762	11	9.8843	50° 0′
10′	9.8096	15	9.9264	25	10.0736	11	9.8832	50′
20′	9.8111	14	9.9289	26	10.0711	11	9.8821	40′
30′	9.8125	15	9.9315	26	10.0685	10	9.8810	30′
40′	9.8140	15	9.9341	25	10.0659	11	9.8800	20′
50′	9.8155	14	9.9366	26	10.0634	11	9.8789	10′
41° 0′	9.8169	15	9.9392	25	10.0608	11	9.8778	49° 0′
10′	9.8184	14	9.9417	26	10.0583	11	9.8767	50′
20′	9.8198	15	9.9443	25	10.0557	11	9.8756	40′
30′	9.8213	14	9.9468	26	10.0532	12	9.8745	30′
40′	9.8227	14	9.9494	25	10.0506	11	9.8733	20′
50′	9.8241	14	9.9519	25	10.0481	11	9.8722	10′
42° 0′	9.8255	14	9.9544	26	10.0456	12	9.8711	48° 0′
10′	9.8269	14	9.9570	25	10.0430	11	9.8699	50′
20′	9.8283	14	9.9595	26	10.0405	12	9.8688	40′
30′	9.8297	14	9.9621	25	10.0379	11	9.8676	30′
40′	9.8311	13	9.9646	25	10.0354	12	9.8665	20′
50′	9.8324	14	9.9671	26	10.0329	12	9.8653	10′
43° 0′	9.8338	13	9.9697	25	10.0303	12	9.8641	47° 0′
10′	9.8351	14	9.9722	25	10.0278	11	9.8629	50′
20′	9.8365	13	9.9747	25	10.0253	12	9.8618	40′
30′	9.8378	13	9.9772	26	10.0228	12	9.8606	30′
40′	9.8391	14	9.9798	25	10.0202	12	9.8594	20′
50′	9.8405	13	9.9823	25	10.0177	13	9.8582	10′
44° 0′	9.8418	13	9.9848	26	10.0152	12	9.8569	46° 0′
10′	9.8431	13	9.9874	25	10.0126	12	9.8557	50′
20′	9.8444	13	9.9899	25	10.0101	13	9.8545	40′
30′	9.8457	12	9.9924	25	10.0076	12	9.8532	30′
40′	9.8469	13	9.9949	26	10.0051	13	9.8520	20′
50′	9.8482	13	9.9975	25	10.0025	12	9.8507	10′
45° 0′	9.8495		10.0000		10.0000		9.8495	45° 0′
	L Cos	d	L Cot	cd	L Tan	d	L Sin	Angle

Selected answers

Chapter 0

Exercises 0.1

1. a. $\emptyset$ b. $\{1\}, \{2\}$ c. $\{1, 2\}$ d. 4 e. $\emptyset, \{1\}, \{2\}$
3. a. $\emptyset$
   b. $\{4\}, \{5\}, \{6\}, \{7\}$
   c. $\{4, 5\}, \{4, 6\}, \{4, 7\}, \{5, 6\}, \{5, 7\}, \{6, 7\}$
   d. $\{4, 5, 6\}, \{4, 5, 7\}, \{4, 6, 7\}, \{5, 6, 7\}$
   e. $\{4, 5, 6, 7\}$
   f. 16
   g. $\emptyset, \{4\}, \{5\}, \{6\}, \{7\}, \{4, 5\}, \{4, 6\}, \{4, 7\}, \{5, 6\}, \{5, 7\}, \{6, 7\}, \{4, 5, 6\}, \{4, 5, 7\}, \{4, 6, 7\}, \{5, 6, 7\}$
5. a. $A \subseteq A, B \subseteq A, B \subseteq B, C \subseteq C, \emptyset \subseteq A, \emptyset \subseteq B, \emptyset \subseteq C, \emptyset \subseteq \emptyset$
   b. $B \subset A, \emptyset \subset A, \emptyset \subset B, \emptyset \subset C$
   c. $A \nsubseteq B, A \nsubseteq C, A \nsubseteq \emptyset, B \nsubseteq C, B \nsubseteq \emptyset, C \nsubseteq A, C \nsubseteq B, C \nsubseteq \emptyset$
7. $A = B$ 9. $\{0\} \neq \emptyset$ 11. no   13. no
15. $\{7\} \nsubseteq \{4, 5, 6, 7\}$ 17. $5 \in \{x \mid x$ is an odd natural number$\}$
19. $\{16, 17, 18, 19, 20\}$
21. {January, February, March, April, May, June, July, August, September, October, November, December}.
23. $\{1, 2, 3, 4, 5, 6\}$
25. $\{x \mid x$ is a natural number between 4 and 11$\}$
27. $\{x \mid x$ is a month with exactly 30 days$\}$

Exercises 0.2

1. {2, 4, 6, 8}
3. {3, 5, 6, 7}
5. {1, 2, 3, 4, 5, 6, 7}
7. {1, 3, 5, 7}
9. U
11. {8}
13. {1}
15. {2, 4, 8}
17. {1, 8}
19. Ø
21. Ø
23. {5, 6, 7}
25. {2, 4, 8}
27. {1, 2, 3}
29. {1, 2, 4, 8}
31. {1, 2, 4, 8}
33. {1, 2}
35. {2, 4, 5, 6, 7, 8}
37. Yes. In either case an element must belong to at least one of the two sets A and B.
39. No. An element in $A - B$ must be in A but not in B while an element in $B - A$ must be in B and not in A.
41. Yes. In either case an element must belong to at least one of the three sets A, B, and C.

Exercises 0.3

1. .2
3. $.66\overline{6}$
5. $.27\overline{27}$
7. $.\overline{714285}$
9. $2.63\overline{63}$
11. $\frac{47}{200}$
13. $\frac{161}{10}$
15. $\frac{5}{11}$
17. $\frac{896}{999}$
19. $\frac{433}{99}$
21. $\frac{6376}{999}$

Exercises 0.4

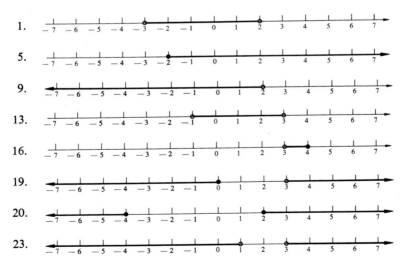

Exercises 0.5

1. {($, 3), ($, 6), (&, 6), (&, 3)}
3. {($, $), ($, &), (&, $), (&, &)}
5. {(7, 7), (7, 8), (7, 9), (8, 7), (8, 8), (8, 9), (9, 7), (9, 8), (9, 9)}

7. {(7, $), (7, &), (8, $), (8, &), (9, $), (9, &)}
9. {(7, 3), (7, 6), (8, 3), (8, 6), (9, 3), (9, 6)}
11. a. 6, 6   b. 8, 8   c. 15, 15   d. 54, 54
     e. *mn, mn*   f. Yes

Exercises 0.6

2. a. II   c. Not in a quadrant
    e. IV   g. I
5. a. 10, (−1, −2), 5, 5   c. 5, $\left(\frac{9}{2}, -1\right), \frac{5}{2}, \frac{5}{2}$
7. a. (x, 0)   c. (0, 0)
9. a. (14, −123)   b. (−14, 123)   c. (−14, −123)
11. An isosceles right triangle
13. An isosceles triangle
15. None of the three

Exercises 0.7

1. No   3. Yes   5. Yes   7. Yes
9. Yes   11. No   13. 5   15. 11
17. $-2\sqrt{2} + 5$ 19. $2a + 5$ 21. 11   23. $k^2 - 6k + 11$
25. 3   27. 3   29. −1   31. $2x - 1$
33. Yes   35. No   37. Yes   39. No
41. No

Exercises 0.8

1. a. 2   c. 2   e. 2   g. 2
    i. 0   k. 2
3. Yes
5.

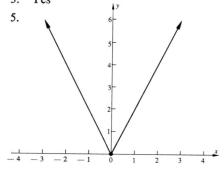

8.

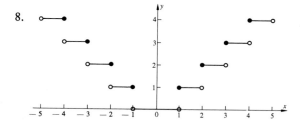

9.

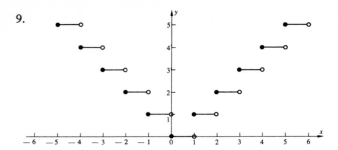

Exercises 0.9

1. a. 10   c. 5   e. 50

3. the interval [0, 3)   5. a. 1   c. $\dfrac{17}{2}$

Review Exercises

1. a. {1, 5, 6, 7, 8}   c. {1}   e. Ø   g. {1, 5, 6}
    i. {2, 3, 4, 7, 8}   2. a. −3   c. 2   e. 2
4. c, d, and e are functions,
7. a. 1   c. 4   e. −1

Chapter 1

Exercises 1.1

1. a. II   c. IV   e. I   g. IV
2. a. $\dfrac{7\pi}{3}\ \dfrac{13\pi}{3}\ -\dfrac{5\pi}{3}\ -\dfrac{11\pi}{3}$ c. $\dfrac{11\pi}{4}\ \dfrac{19\pi}{4}\ -\dfrac{5\pi}{4}\ -\dfrac{13\pi}{4}$
    e. $\dfrac{7\pi}{6}\ \dfrac{19\pi}{6}\ -\dfrac{17\pi}{6}\ -\dfrac{29\pi}{6}$
3. a. $-\dfrac{\pi}{6}$ b. $\dfrac{5\pi}{6}$ c. $\dfrac{7\pi}{6}$
5. a. $-\dfrac{3\pi}{4}$ b. $\dfrac{\pi}{4}$ c. $\dfrac{7\pi}{4}$
7. a. $-\dfrac{3\pi}{7}$ b. $\dfrac{4\pi}{7}$ c. $\dfrac{10\pi}{7}$
9. a. $\dfrac{\pi}{12}$ b. $-\dfrac{11\pi}{12}$ c. $\dfrac{11\pi}{12}$

Exercises 1.2

1. a. $(u, -v)$ b. u c. $-v$
2. a. $\dfrac{1}{2}$ c. $\dfrac{\sqrt{3}}{2}$ e. $-\dfrac{\sqrt{2}}{2}$
3. a. $(-u, -v)$ b. $-u$ c. $-v$
4. a. $-\dfrac{\sqrt{3}}{2}$ c. $-\dfrac{1}{2}$ e. $-\dfrac{\sqrt{2}}{2}$
5. a. $(-u, v)$ b. $-u$ c. v
6. a. $-\dfrac{\sqrt{2}}{2}$ c. $-\dfrac{\sqrt{3}}{2}$ e. $\dfrac{\sqrt{3}}{2}$

9. $\dfrac{8}{17}$ 11. $\dfrac{2\sqrt{2}}{3}$ 13. $\dfrac{15}{17}$ 15. $-\dfrac{\sqrt{21}}{5}$ 17. $\dfrac{\sqrt{5}}{3}$

Exercises 1.3

3. 6π

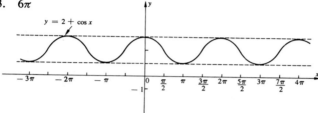

$y = 2 + \cos x$

5.

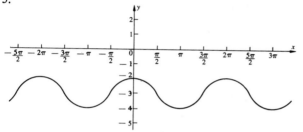

9. a. $\dfrac{2\pi}{3}$ c. 4π e. 6π

11.

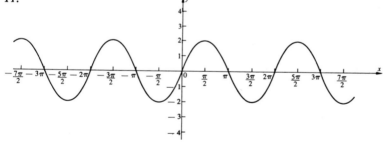

Exercises 1.4

1. a. $\dfrac{1}{3}$ c. 2 e. $\dfrac{4}{3}$ g. $\dfrac{9}{5}$ i. 6

3.

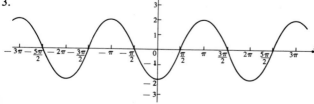

9.

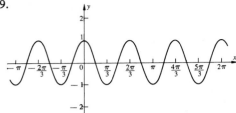

Exercises 1.5

1. $1, -\dfrac{\pi}{2}, 2\pi$

3. $1, -\dfrac{\pi}{2}, \pi$

5. $2, -\pi, 2\pi$

7. $3, \dfrac{\pi}{4}, \pi$

9.

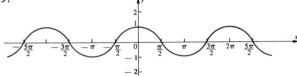

13.

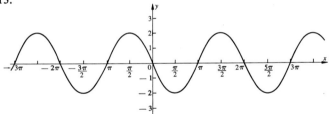

Exercises 1.6

1. a. $\tan(-x) = -\tan x.$ b. $\sec(-x) = \sec x.$
   c. $\cot(-x) = -\cot x.$ d. $\csc(-x) = -\csc x.$

2. a. -1 c. $\dfrac{-2}{\sqrt{3}}$ or $\dfrac{-2\sqrt{3}}{3}$

   e. 2 g. $-\dfrac{1}{\sqrt{3}}$

   i. $-\sqrt{3}$ k. $-\sqrt{3}$

3. a. $\tan(\pi - x) = -\tan x.$ b. $\cot(\pi - x) = -\cot x.$
   c. $\sec(\pi - x) = -\sec x.$ d. $\csc(\pi - x) = \csc x.$

4. a. -1 c. $\dfrac{2}{\sqrt{3}}$ or $\dfrac{2\sqrt{3}}{3}$

   e. -2 g. $-\dfrac{1}{\sqrt{3}}$

i. $-\sqrt{3}$ k. 2
5. a. $\tan(x+\pi) = \tan x.$ b. $\cot(x+\pi) = \cot x.$
   c. $\sec(x+\pi) = -\sec x.$ d. $\csc(x+\pi) = -\csc x.$
6. a. $-\sqrt{2}$ c. $\sqrt{3}$
   e. $-\sqrt{2}$ g. $\dfrac{1}{\sqrt{3}}$
   i. 1   k. $-\dfrac{2}{\sqrt{3}}$ or $-\dfrac{2\sqrt{3}}{3}$

7. $\sin x = -\dfrac{12}{13}$, $\cos x = -\dfrac{5}{13}$, $\tan x = \dfrac{12}{5}$, $\cot x = \dfrac{5}{12}$, $\csc x = -\dfrac{13}{12}$.

9. $\sin x = \dfrac{1}{\sqrt{5}}$, $\cos x = \dfrac{2}{\sqrt{5}}$, $\cot x = 2$, $\sec x = \dfrac{\sqrt{5}}{2}$, $\csc x = \sqrt{5}$.

11. $\sin x = -\dfrac{3}{\sqrt{13}}$, $\tan x = -\dfrac{3}{2}$, $\cot x = -\dfrac{2}{3}$, $\sec x = \dfrac{\sqrt{13}}{2}$, $\csc x = -\dfrac{\sqrt{13}}{3}$

13. $\sin x = -\dfrac{3}{\sqrt{10}}$, $\cos x = -\dfrac{1}{\sqrt{10}}$, $\tan x = 3$, $\sec x = -\sqrt{10}$, $\csc x = -\dfrac{\sqrt{10}}{3}$.

Review Exercises

1. a. $\dfrac{\sqrt{2}}{2}$ c. $\dfrac{1}{\sqrt{3}}$ e. 1   g. $\dfrac{1}{2}$ i. $\dfrac{1}{\sqrt{3}}$ k. $-\dfrac{2}{\sqrt{3}}$

12. a. $-\dfrac{\sqrt{2}}{2}$ c. 1   e. 1   g. $-\dfrac{\sqrt{3}}{2}$ i. 2

Chapter 2

Exercises 2.1

1. $\dfrac{\pi}{6} \in \mathscr{D}$; $\cos\dfrac{\pi}{6} - \sin\dfrac{\pi}{6} = \dfrac{\sqrt{3}}{2} - \dfrac{1}{2} = \dfrac{\sqrt{3}-1}{2} \neq 1.$

5. $0 \in \mathscr{D}$; $\cos(2\cdot 0) = \cos 0 = 1$; $2\cos 0 = 2(1) = 2 \neq 1.$

9. $\pi \in \mathscr{D}$; $\sin\dfrac{\pi}{2} = 1$; $\dfrac{1}{2}\sin\pi = \dfrac{1}{2}(0) = 0 \neq 1.$

13. $\dfrac{\pi}{6} \in \mathscr{D}$; $\dfrac{\tan\dfrac{\pi}{6}+1}{\sin\dfrac{\pi}{6}} = \dfrac{\dfrac{1}{\sqrt{3}}+1}{\dfrac{1}{2}}$

$$= 2\left(\dfrac{1}{\sqrt{3}}+1\right) = \dfrac{2}{\sqrt{3}} + 2; \ \sec\dfrac{\pi}{6} = \dfrac{2}{\sqrt{3}} \neq \dfrac{2}{\sqrt{3}} + 2.$$

Exercises 2.2

The equations in exercises 9, 22, and 23 are conditional equations.
10. $\cos\theta\cos(-\theta) - \sin\theta\sin(-\theta) = (\cos\theta)(\cos\theta) - (\sin\theta)(-\sin\theta)$
$$= \cos^2\theta + \sin^2\theta$$
$$= 1.$$

11. $\tan^2 \theta \csc^2 \theta - \sec^2 \theta \sin^2 \theta = \left(\dfrac{\sin^2 \theta}{\cos^2 \theta}\right)\left(\dfrac{1}{\sin^2 \theta}\right) - \left(\dfrac{1}{\cos^2 \theta}\right)\sin^2 \theta$

$$= \frac{1}{\cos^2 \theta} - \frac{\sin^2 \theta}{\cos^2 \theta}$$
$$= \sec^2 \theta - \tan^2 \theta$$
$$= 1.$$

15. $\sec^4 x - \tan^4 x = (\sec^2 x - \tan^2 x)(\sec^2 x + \tan^2 x)$
$$= (1)(\sec^2 x + \tan^2 x)$$
$$= \sec^2 x + \tan^2 x.$$

20. $\cot^3 \beta + 1 = (\cot \beta + 1)(\cot^2 \beta - \cot \beta + 1)$
$$= (\cot \beta + 1)[(\cot^2 \beta + 1) - \cot \beta]$$
$$= (\cot \beta + 1)(\csc^2 \beta - \cot \beta).$$

31. $(\cos \beta + \sin \beta)^4 = \cos^4 \beta + 4 \cos^3 \beta \sin \beta + 6 \cos^2 \beta \sin^2 \beta$
$$+ 4 \cos \beta \sin^3 \beta + \sin^4 \beta$$
$$= \cos^4 \beta + 6 \cos^2 \beta \sin^2 \beta + \sin^4 \beta + 4 \cos^3 \beta \sin\beta$$
$$+ 4 \cos \beta \sin^3 \beta$$
$$= (\cos^4 \beta + \cos^2 \beta \sin^2 \beta) + 4 \cos^2 \beta \sin^2 \beta$$
$$+ (\cos^2 \beta \sin^2 \beta + \sin^4 \beta) + 4 \cos \beta \sin \beta (\cos^2 \beta + \sin^2 \beta)$$
$$= \cos^2 \beta(\cos^2 \beta + \sin^2 \beta) + 4 \cos^2 \beta \sin^2 \beta$$
$$+ (\cos^2 \beta + \sin^2 \beta) \sin^2 \beta + 4 \cos \beta \sin \beta (1)$$
$$= \cos^2 \beta (1) + 4 \cos^2 \beta \sin^2 \beta + (1) \sin^2 \beta + 4 \cos \beta \sin \beta$$
$$= \cos^2 \beta + 4 \cos^2 \beta \sin^2 \beta + \sin^2 \beta + 4 \cos \beta \sin \beta.$$

42. $\tan^2 z + \cot^2 z = \dfrac{\sin^2 z}{\cos^2 z} + \dfrac{\cos^2 z}{\sin^2 z}$

$$= \frac{(\sin^2 z)(\sin^2 z) + (\cos^2 z)(\cos^2 z)}{(\cos^2 z)(\sin^2 z)}$$
$$= \frac{\sin^4 z + (1 - \sin^2 z)(1 - \sin^2 z)}{\sin^2 z \cos^2 z}$$
$$= \frac{\sin^4 z + 1 - 2 \sin^2 z + \sin^4 z}{\sin^2 z \cos^2 z}$$
$$= \frac{2 \sin^4 z - 2 \sin^2 z + 1}{\sin^2 z \cos^2 z}.$$

Exercises 2.3

1. $\dfrac{\sqrt{6} - \sqrt{2}}{4}$

3. $\dfrac{\sqrt{6} - \sqrt{2}}{4}$

5. $-\dfrac{\sqrt{2} + \sqrt{6}}{4}$

7. $\dfrac{\sqrt{2} + \sqrt{6}}{4}$

16. $\sin 3\phi = \sin (5\phi - 2\phi)$
$$= \sin 5\phi \cos 2\phi - \cos 5\phi \sin 2\phi.$$

20. $\dfrac{\cos (\theta + \phi)}{\cos \theta \cos \phi} = \dfrac{\cos \theta \cos \phi - \sin \theta \sin \phi}{\cos \theta \cos \phi}$

$$= \frac{\cos \theta \cos \phi}{\cos \theta \cos \phi} - \frac{\sin \theta \sin \phi}{\cos \theta \cos \phi}$$
$$= 1 - \left(\frac{\sin \theta}{\cos \theta}\right)\left(\frac{\sin \phi}{\cos \phi}\right)$$
$$= 1 - \tan \theta \tan \phi.$$

5. $S = \{\alpha \mid \alpha = \pi - 1.369 + 2n\pi, n \in J\} \cup \{\alpha \mid \alpha = \pi + 1.369 + 2n\pi, n \in J\}.$

7. $S = \emptyset, \dfrac{5}{2}$ is not in the range of the sine function.

9. $S = \{\theta \mid \theta = 1.166 + n\pi, n \in J\}.$ 11. $S = \emptyset.$

13. $S = \{z \mid z = .985 + 2n\pi, n \in J\} \cup \{z \mid z = \pi - .985 + 2n\pi, n \in J\}.$

15. $S = \{\alpha \mid \alpha = .464 + n\pi, n \in J\}.$ 17. $S = \emptyset.$

19. $S = \{\theta \mid \theta = 2n\pi, n \in J\}.$

21. $S = \{\beta \mid \beta = .896 + n\pi, n \in J\}.$

23. $S = \{y \mid y = 2n\pi, n \in J\} \cup \{y \mid y = 1.231 + 2n\pi, n \in J\} \cup$
$\{y \mid y = -1.231 + 2n\pi, n \in J\}.$

25. $S = \left\{\alpha \mid \alpha = \dfrac{3\pi}{2} + 2n\pi, n \in J\right\} \cup \{\alpha \mid \alpha = .167 + 2n\pi, n \in J\} \cup$
$\{\alpha \mid \alpha = \pi - .167 + 2n\pi, n \in J\}.$

27. $S = \{\beta \mid \beta = 1.249 + n\pi, n \in J\} \cup \{\beta \mid \beta = -1.249 + n\pi, n \in J\}.$

29. $S = \{t \mid t = .955 + 2n\pi, n \in J\} \cup \{t \mid t = \pi - .955 + 2n\pi, n \in J\} \cup$
$\{t \mid t = \pi + .955 + 2n\pi, n \in J\} \cup \{t \mid t = -.955 + 2n\pi, n \in J\}.$

Exercises 3.2

1. $S = \left\{x \mid x = \dfrac{\pi}{2} + \dfrac{2n\pi}{3}, n \in J\right\}.$

3. $S = \left\{\beta \mid \beta = \dfrac{\pi}{8} + \dfrac{n\pi}{2}, n \in J\right\}.$ 5. $S = \emptyset.$

7. $S = \left\{y \mid y = \dfrac{\pi}{12} + \dfrac{n\pi}{2}, n \in J\right\} \cup \left\{y \mid y = -\dfrac{\pi}{12} + \dfrac{n\pi}{2}, n \in J\right\}.$

9. $S = \left\{\beta \mid \beta = \dfrac{\pi}{20} + \dfrac{n\pi}{5}, n \in J\right\}.$

11. $S = \left\{x \mid x = \dfrac{\pi}{4} + \dfrac{n\pi}{2}, n \in J\right\}.$

13. $S = \{\alpha \mid \alpha = -.101 + n\pi, n \in J\} \cup \left\{\alpha \mid \alpha = \dfrac{\pi}{2} + .101 + n\pi, n \in J\right\}.$

15. $S = \{z \mid z = 3\pi + 4n\pi, n \in J\}.$

17. $S = \{y \mid y = \pi + 2n\pi, n \in J\}.$

19. $S = \{\beta \mid \beta = 2n\pi, n \in J\}.$

21. $S = \{x \mid x = .616 + n\pi, n \in J\} \cup \{x \mid x = -.616 + n\pi, n \in J\}.$

23. $S = \emptyset.$

25. $S = \{z \mid z = 2n\pi, n \in J\} \cup \{z \mid z = .927 + 2n\pi, n \in J\}.$

27. $S = \{y \mid y = \pi - 1.176 + 2n\pi, n \in J\}.$

29. $S = \left\{\beta \mid \beta = \dfrac{3\pi}{4} + n\pi, n \in J\right\} \cup \{\beta \mid \beta = 1.107 + n\pi, n \in J\}.$

31. $S = \{\alpha \mid \alpha = \pi + 2n\pi, n \in J\}.$

33. $S = \left\{x \mid x = \dfrac{\pi}{12} + \dfrac{n\pi}{3}, n \in J\right\} \cup \left\{x \mid x = .369 + \dfrac{n\pi}{3}, n \in J\right\}.$

Exercises 3.3

1. $S = \left\{\theta \mid \theta = \dfrac{2n\pi}{7}, n \in J\right\} \cup \{\theta \mid \theta = \pi + 2n\pi, n \in J\}.$

3. $S = \left\{x \mid x = \dfrac{n\pi}{4}, n \in J, n \neq 4k + 2, k \in J\right\}.$

5. $S = \left\{\beta \mid \beta = \dfrac{\pi}{7} + \dfrac{2n\pi}{7}, n \in J\right\} \cup \{\beta \mid \beta = \pi + 2n\pi, n \in J\}.$

7. $S = \left\{ y \mid y = \frac{2n\pi}{3}, n \in J \right\}.$

9. $S = \left\{ \alpha \mid \alpha = \frac{n\pi}{3}, n \in J, n \neq 3k, k \in J \right\}.$

11. $S = \left\{ z \mid z = -\frac{\pi}{2} + 2n\pi, n \in J \right\} \cup \left\{ z \mid z = \frac{3\pi}{14} + \frac{2n\pi}{7}, n \in J \right\}.$

13. $S = \left\{ x \mid x = \frac{\pi}{10} + \frac{2n\pi}{5}, n \in J \right\}.$

15. $S = \left\{ \theta \mid \theta = \frac{\pi}{4} + \frac{n\pi}{3}, n \in J \right\}.$

Review Exercises

1. $S = \{ x \mid x = \pi + .412 + 2n\pi, n \in J \} \cup \{ x \mid x = -.412 + 2n\pi, n \in J \}.$

3. $S = \left\{ \alpha \mid \alpha = \frac{\pi}{2} + 2n\pi, n \in J \right\} \cup \{ \alpha \mid \alpha = .730 + 2n\pi, n \in J \} \cup$
   $\{ \alpha \mid \alpha = \pi - .730 + 2n\pi, n \in J \}.$

5. $S = \{ x \mid x = 2n\pi, n \in J \} \cup \left\{ x \mid x = \frac{\pi}{5} + \frac{2n\pi}{5}, n \in J \right\}.$

7. $S = \left\{ \beta \mid \beta = \frac{\pi}{2} + .616 + n\pi, n \in J \right\} \cup \left\{ \beta \mid \beta = \frac{\pi}{2} - .616 + n\pi, n \in J \right\}.$

9. $S = \{ \alpha \mid \alpha = 1.107 + n\pi, n \in J \}.$

11. $S = \left\{ y \mid y = -\frac{\pi}{2} + 2n\pi, n \in J \right\}.$

13. $S = \left\{ \gamma \mid \gamma = \frac{\pi}{18} + \frac{n\pi}{3}, n \in J \right\}.$

15. $S = \{ x \mid x = 1.326 + n\pi, n \in J \} \cup \{ x \mid x = 1.249 + n\pi, n \in J \}.$

17. $S = \left\{ \theta \mid \theta = -\frac{\pi}{12} + \frac{n\pi}{3}, n \in J \right\}.$

19. $S = \left\{ z \mid z = \frac{2\pi}{3} + 2n\pi, n \in J \right\} \cup \left\{ z \mid z = \frac{4\pi}{3} + 2n\pi, n \in J \right\}.$

21. $S = \{ x \mid x = 2n\pi, n \in J \}.$

23. $S = \left\{ \theta \mid \theta = \frac{2n\pi}{5}, n \in J \right\} \cup \left\{ \theta \mid \theta = \frac{2n\pi}{9}, n \in J \right\}.$

25. $S = \left\{ x \mid x = .464 - \frac{\pi}{3} + n\pi, n \in J \right\} \cup \left\{ x \mid x = \frac{\pi}{6} - .464 + n\pi, n \in J \right\}.$

Chapter 4

Exercises 4.1

1. No.
3. Yes. $h^{-1} = \{ (5, 1), (3, -1), (9, 3), (1, -3), (13, 5), (-1, -5) \}.$
5. Yes. $g^{-1} = \left\{ (x, y) \mid y = \frac{x + 13}{4} \right\}.$ 7. No.
9. Yes. $h^{-1} = \left\{ (x, y) \mid y = \frac{1 - x}{3} \right\}.$ 11. Yes. $g^{-1} = \left\{ (w, z) \mid z = \frac{w - 2}{3} \right\}.$
13. Let $f_1 = \{ (x, y) \mid y = x^2 - 1, x \geq 0 \}.$ $f_1^{-1} = \{ (x, y) \mid y = \sqrt{x + 1} \}.$

15. Let $h_1 = \{(w, z) \mid z = w^2 + 6w + 9, w \geq -3\}$. $h_1^{-1} = \{(w, z) \mid z = \sqrt{w} - 3\}$.
17. Let $j_1 = \{(u, v) \mid v = u^2 + 4u + 1, u \geq -2\}$. $j_1^{-1} = \{(u, v) \mid v = \sqrt{u + 3} - 2\}$.
19. Let $g_1 = \left\{(x, z) \mid z = \dfrac{1}{x^2 - 2x - 2}, x \geq 1\right\}$. $g_1^{-1} = \left\{(x, z) \mid z = 1 + \sqrt{\dfrac{1 - x}{x}}\right\}$.

Exercises 4.2

1. a. $-\dfrac{\pi}{2}$ c. $-\dfrac{\pi}{4}$ e. $-\dfrac{\pi}{3}$ 2. a. π c. $\dfrac{2\pi}{3}$ e. $\dfrac{\pi}{2}$

3. a. $\dfrac{\pi}{6}$ c. $-\dfrac{\pi}{3}$ e. $-\dfrac{\pi}{4}$ 4. a. 0 c. $\dfrac{7\pi}{6}$ e. $\dfrac{\pi}{3}$

5. $\dfrac{\pi}{6}$ 7. $-\dfrac{1}{2}$ 9. $\dfrac{5\pi}{6}$ 11. $-\dfrac{\sqrt{2}}{2}$

13. $\dfrac{\pi}{2}$ 15. $\dfrac{\pi}{4}$ 17. $\dfrac{\sqrt{2}}{2}$ 19. $\dfrac{1}{2}$

Exercises 4.3

3. $\{0\}$ 5. $\left\{\dfrac{\sqrt{2}}{2}\right\}$ 7. $\{0.8776\}$ 9. 0.3240
11. $\{-0.1987\}$

Review Exercises

1. 0 3. $\dfrac{1}{\sqrt{3}}$ 5. $-\sqrt{2}$ 7. $-\dfrac{\pi}{2}$

9. $\{0\}$ 11. $\left\{-\dfrac{\sqrt{2}}{2}\right\}$
13. Yes. $f^{-1} = \{(x, y) \mid y = \sqrt[3]{x + 1}\}$.   15. No.

Chapter 5

Exercises 5.1

1. $75°38'$ 3. $-62°27'$ 5. $71°37'$
7. $450°$ 9. $-810°$ 11. $.2327$ radians
13. $.5061$ radians   15. $-.5992$ radians   17. $-\dfrac{3\pi}{2}$ radians
19. $\dfrac{13\pi}{6}$ radians

21.

$0°$	$30°$	$45°$	$60°$
0 radians	$\dfrac{\pi}{6}$ radians	$\dfrac{\pi}{4}$ radians	$\dfrac{\pi}{3}$ radians

$90°$	$180°$	$270°$	$360°$
$\dfrac{\pi}{2}$ radians	π radians	$\dfrac{3\pi}{2}$ radians	2π radians

23. II	25. I	27. II
29. I	31. quadrantal angle	33. IV
35. I		

37. 381°, 741°, −339°, −699°

39. 455°, 815°, −265°, −625°

41. −553°, −913°, 167°, 527°

43. $-\dfrac{13\pi}{6}$ radians, $-\dfrac{25\pi}{6}$ radians, $\dfrac{11\pi}{6}$ radians, $\dfrac{23\pi}{6}$ radians

45. $\dfrac{7\pi}{3}$ radians, $\dfrac{\pi}{3}$ radians, $-\dfrac{5\pi}{3}$ radians, $-\dfrac{11\pi}{3}$ radians

Exercises 5.2

Use Figure 5.13 for 1 and 3.

1. $\tan \alpha = \dfrac{a}{b} = \left(\dfrac{a}{c}\right) \div \left(\dfrac{b}{c}\right) = \dfrac{\sin \alpha}{\cos \alpha} = \dfrac{\sin x}{\cos x} = \tan x.$

3. $\csc \alpha = \dfrac{c}{a} = 1 \div \left(\dfrac{a}{c}\right) = \dfrac{1}{\sin \alpha} = \dfrac{1}{\sin x} = \csc x$

5. $\sin \alpha = \dfrac{15}{17} = .882 = \cos \beta.$ $\cos \alpha = \dfrac{8}{17} = .471 = \sin \beta.$

   $\tan \alpha = \dfrac{15}{8} = 1.875 = \cot \beta.$ $\cot \alpha = \dfrac{8}{15} = .5333 = \tan \beta.$

   $\sec \alpha = \dfrac{17}{8} = 2.125 = \csc \beta.$ $\csc \alpha = \dfrac{17}{15} = 1.133 = \sec \beta.$

7. $\sin \alpha = \dfrac{5}{13} = .385 = \cos \beta.$ $\cos \alpha = \dfrac{12}{13} = .923 = \sin \beta.$

   $\tan \alpha = \dfrac{5}{12} = .417 = \cot \beta.$ $\cot \alpha = \dfrac{12}{5} = 2.4 = \tan \beta.$

   $\sec \alpha = \dfrac{13}{12} = 1.083 = \csc \beta.$ $\csc \alpha = \dfrac{13}{5} = 2.6 = \sec \beta.$

9. $\sin \alpha = \dfrac{40}{41} = .976 = \cos \beta.$ $\cos \alpha = \dfrac{9}{41} = .220 = \sin \beta.$

   $\tan \alpha = \dfrac{40}{9} = 4.444 = \cot \beta.$ $\cot \alpha = \dfrac{9}{40} = .225 = \tan \beta.$

   $\sec \alpha = \dfrac{41}{9} = 4.556 = \csc \beta.$ $\csc \alpha = \dfrac{41}{40} = 1.025 = \sec \alpha.$

11. $\alpha = 45°, \beta = 45°, c = 3\sqrt{2}$ ft.

13. $\alpha = 30°, \beta = 60°, b = 3\sqrt{3}$ yds.

15. $\alpha = 45°34', \beta = 44°26', a = 7.142$ in.

17. $\beta = 63°, b = 9.815$ ft, $c = 11.015$ ft.

19. $\alpha = 51°17', a = 18.63$ yds, $c = 23.985$ yds.

21. $\alpha = 63°, b = 2.548$ in., $c = 5.610$ in.

23. $\beta = 27°33', a = 28.76$ ft, $c = 32.43$ ft.

25. 36.1 ft

27. 94.3 ft, 58°, 32°

29. 7.48 ft, 29°56'   31. 355 ft

Exercises 5.3

3. $\gamma = 64°, a = 20.37$ ft, $c = 25.03$ ft.

5. $\alpha = 86°43', a = 3.282$ ft, $b = 1.223$ ft.

7. $\beta = 28°3', \gamma = 115°57', c = 53.57$ in.

9. $\alpha = 43°18'$, $\beta = 104°14'$, $b = 32.51$ yds or $\alpha = 136°42'$, $\beta = 10°40'$, $b = 6.207$ yds.
11.   No solution
13. $\alpha = 130°22'$, $\gamma = 11°48'$, $a = 41.0$ in .
15.   a.   210 ft   b.   703 ft   17.   110 ft   19.   180 ft

Exercises 5.4

1. $\alpha = 65°40'$, $\beta = 40°20'$, $c = 40.09$ ft.
3. $\alpha = 31°45'$, $\beta = 51°15'$, $c = 105.6$ yds.
5. $\alpha = 62°42'$, $\gamma = 58°48'$, $b = 28.31$ in.
7. $\beta = 25°41'$, $\gamma = 22°29'$, $a = 134.8$ ft.
9. $\beta = 42°10'$, $\gamma = 42°10'$, $a = 63.30$ yds.
11. $\alpha = 50°51'$, $\gamma = 70°43'$, $\beta = 58°26'$.
13. $\alpha = 36°52'$, $\beta = 53°8'$, $\gamma = 90°$.
15.   240 ft   17.   37 ft   19. $32\sqrt{3}$ ft

Exercises 5.5

1.   193.9 sq ft   3.   4036 sq yds   5.   450.8 sq in.
7.   778.6 sq ft   9.   606.7 sq ft   11.   280.2 sq in.
13.   191,500 sq yds   15.   170.9 sq ft or 253.6 sq ft
17.   No solution   19.   105.8 sq ft   21. $128\sqrt{3}$ sq ft

Review Exercises

1. $\beta = 70°$, $a = 218.7$ in., $c = 266.4$ in.
3. $\alpha = 40°32'$, $\beta = 49°28'$, $a = 2\sqrt{66}$ ft $= 16.25$ ft.
5. $\alpha = 64°59'$, $\gamma = 40°38'$, $a = 26.92$ ft.
7.   a. $10°$ c. $-828°$ 9.   414.1 ft
11.   a. $\frac{2\pi}{9}$ radians   c. $-\frac{9\pi}{10}$ radians
13. $\alpha = 35°26'$, $\beta = 48°11'$, $\gamma = 96°23'$ 15.   No solution
17. $b = 46.84$ yds, $\alpha = 26°58'$, $\gamma = 103°42'$.

Chapter 6

Exercises 6.1

1.   a. $7, -1, 7 + i$ c. $2, 5, 2 - 5i$ e. $0, -4, 4i$
     g. $9, -2, 9 + 2i$ i. $\sqrt{3}, \sqrt{2}, \sqrt{3} - \sqrt{2}\,i$ k. $3, 0, 3$
3. $-2\pi - i$ 5. $6i$ 7. $4\pi + 7i$
9. $1 + 2i$ 11. $(3e^2 + 2b) + 37$ 13. $-6 - 17i$
15. $\frac{1}{13} + \frac{5}{13}i$ 17. $\frac{c}{c^2 + d^2} - \frac{d}{c^2 + d^2}$ 19. $\frac{88}{26} - \frac{41}{26}i$
21. $39 - 21i$ 23. $-\frac{79}{125} - \frac{122}{125}i$ 25. $-\frac{60}{289} - \frac{32}{289}i$

Exercises 6.2

1. $\sqrt{2}\left(\cos\frac{3\pi}{4} + i\sin\frac{3\pi}{4}\right)$

3. $4\left[\cos\left(-\frac{\pi}{2}\right) + i\sin\left(-\frac{\pi}{2}\right)\right]$

5. $4\sqrt{3}\left[\cos\left(-\frac{\pi}{6}\right) + i\sin\left(-\frac{\pi}{6}\right)\right]$

7. $2\left(\cos\frac{2\pi}{3} + i\sin\frac{2\pi}{3}\right)$

9. $-\dfrac{5}{\sqrt{2}} + \dfrac{5}{\sqrt{2}}i$

11. $2 - 2\sqrt{3}\,i$

13. $-4\sqrt{2} - 4\sqrt{2}\,i$

15. $-3\sqrt{3} + 3i$

Exercises 6.3

1. $10\left(\cos\frac{13\pi}{6} + i\sin\frac{13\pi}{6}\right)$

3. $6\sqrt{3}\left(\cos\frac{14\pi}{45} + i\sin\frac{14\pi}{45}\right)$

5. $27\left(\cos\frac{6\pi}{5} + i\sin\frac{6\pi}{5}\right)$

7. 1

9. $2\left(\cos\frac{\pi}{4} + i\sin\frac{\pi}{4}\right)$

11. $\frac{1}{4}\left[\cos\left(-\frac{2\pi}{15}\right) + i\sin\left(-\frac{2\pi}{15}\right)\right]$

13. 16

15. $144\left[\cos\left(-\frac{2\pi}{3}\right) + i\sin\left(-\frac{2\pi}{3}\right)\right]$

17. $\frac{1}{9}\left(\cos\frac{2\pi}{3} + i\sin\frac{2\pi}{3}\right)$

Exercises 6.4

1. $1,\ -\dfrac{1}{2} + \dfrac{\sqrt{3}}{2}i,\ -\dfrac{1}{2} - \dfrac{\sqrt{3}}{2}i$

3. $1,\ \cos\frac{2\pi}{7} + i\sin\frac{2\pi}{7},\ \cos\frac{4\pi}{7} + i\sin\frac{4\pi}{7},\ \cos\frac{6\pi}{7} + i\sin\frac{6\pi}{7},$
$\cos\frac{8\pi}{7} + i\sin\frac{8\pi}{7},\ \cos\frac{10\pi}{7} + i\sin\frac{10\pi}{7},\ \cos\frac{12\pi}{7} + i\sin\frac{12\pi}{7}$

5. $\sqrt{2}\left[\cos\left(-\frac{\pi}{12}\right) + i\sin\left(-\frac{\pi}{12}\right)\right],\ \sqrt{2}\left(\cos\frac{7\pi}{12} + i\sin\frac{7\pi}{12}\right),$
$\sqrt{2}\left(\cos\frac{5\pi}{4} + i\sin\frac{5\pi}{4}\right)$

7. $\sqrt[7]{5}\left(\cos\frac{\pi}{35} + i\sin\frac{\pi}{35}\right),\ \sqrt[7]{5}\left(\cos\frac{11\pi}{35} + i\sin\frac{11\pi}{35}\right),$
$\sqrt[7]{5}\left(\cos\frac{21\pi}{35} + i\sin\frac{21\pi}{35}\right),\ \sqrt[7]{5}\left(\cos\frac{31\pi}{35} + i\sin\frac{31\pi}{35}\right),$
$\sqrt[7]{5}\left(\cos\frac{41\pi}{35} + i\sin\frac{41\pi}{35}\right),\ \sqrt[7]{5}\left(\cos\frac{51\pi}{35} + i\sin\frac{51\pi}{35}\right),$
$\sqrt[7]{5}\left(\cos\frac{61\pi}{35} + i\sin\frac{61\pi}{35}\right)$

9. $\sqrt{2}\left[\cos\left(-\frac{\pi}{12}\right) + i\sin\left(-\frac{\pi}{12}\right)\right],\ \sqrt{2}\left(\cos\frac{\pi}{4} + i\sin\frac{\pi}{4}\right),$
$\sqrt{2}\left(\cos\frac{7\pi}{12} + i\sin\frac{7\pi}{12}\right),\ \sqrt{2}\left(\cos\frac{11\pi}{12} + i\sin\frac{11\pi}{12}\right),$
$\sqrt{2}\left(\cos\frac{5\pi}{4} + i\sin\frac{5\pi}{4}\right),\ \sqrt{2}\left(\cos\frac{19\pi}{12} + i\sin\frac{19\pi}{12}\right)$

11. $\dfrac{\sqrt{3}}{2} - \dfrac{i}{2},\ i,\ -\dfrac{\sqrt{3}}{2} - \dfrac{i}{2}$

Review Exercises

1. $3\sqrt{3} + 3i$
3. a. $3 + 14i$ c. -3
5. $1 + \sqrt{3}\,i, -2, 1 - \sqrt{3}\,i$
6. a. $-1 + 31i$ c. $-5 + 10i$ e. $27\left(\cos\dfrac{3\pi}{4} + i\sin\dfrac{3\pi}{4}\right)$
   g. $\cos\dfrac{8\pi}{15} + i\sin\dfrac{8\pi}{15}$
7. $12\left(\cos\dfrac{2\pi}{3} + i\sin\dfrac{2\pi}{3}\right)$
9. a. $\dfrac{5}{2}\left(\cos\dfrac{7\pi}{12} + i\sin\dfrac{7\pi}{12}\right)$ c. $1 + 9i$
   e. $-24 - 3i$ g. $-4 + 4i$

Appendix

Exercises A.1

1. 3   3. $\dfrac{1}{2}$ 5. 0
7. $\log 291 + \log 243$
9. $\log 291 - \log 243$
11. $\dfrac{1}{2}\log 31 + 3\log 29$
13. $\dfrac{1}{3}\log 729 + 4\log 281 - \log 927$
15. $4[2\log 314 + \log 475 - \log 627]$
17. $1.967 \cdot 10^3$ 19. $8.42 \cdot 10^{-2}$ 21. $9.189 \cdot 10^{-5}$

Exercises A.2

1. 2.4639   3. $9.7143 - 10$ 5. 1.4053
7. $8.6894 - 10$ 9. 6.0208   11. $5.7912 - 10$
13. 4.96   15. 820.8   17. 0.6512
19. 1953   21. 0.001328

Exercises A.3

1. $1.466 \cdot 10^7$ 3. 4291   5. 2994
7. $3.760 \cdot 10^{10}$ 9. 1.239

Exercises A.4

1. $9.8821 - 10$ 3. $9.9004 - 10$ 5. $10.2307 - 10$
7. $10.0547 - 10$ 9. $9.9838 - 10$ 11. $9.5813 - 10$
13. $26°50'$ 15. $48°20'$ 17. $4°43'$
19. $12°52'$ 21. $23°56'$ 23. $37°4'$

Index